COLLECTING, PRESERVING
AND STUDYING INSECTS

Collecting, Preserving and Studying Insects

HAROLD OLDROYD
M.A., F.R.E.S.

THE MACMILLAN COMPANY
NEW YORK

First published 1958

53069

CONTENTS

Introduction   9

COLLECTING INSECTS

 i Where to look for insects   15
 ii Catching and trapping   26
 iii Keeping, breeding and rearing   65
 iv Killing and temporarily preserving   75

PRESERVING AND EXAMINING INSECTS

 v Preparing and mounting for permanent
     preservation   95
 vi Examining insects in a collection   145
 vii Photographing insects   175

STUDYING INSECTS

 viii The principles of zoological classifica-
     tion and nomenclature   197
 ix What are the insects and their allies?   209
 x How an insect is identified   263
 xi Further reading   285
 xii Recording new facts, and describing
     new species   294

APPENDICES

Some useful formulae reagents and   303
Glossary of terms as used in entomology   305
References   314
Useful addresses   320
Index   321

LIST OF PLATES

I   Using a short-handled net   *Facing page* 32

II   The finish of a stroke with a net   33

III   Removing an insect from a net   48

IV   Selecting small insects inside the net   48

V   Removing a middle-sized insect from a net   49

VI   Using an aspirator   80

VII   A muslin cage for transporting live insects   81

VIII   Equipment for collecting   96

IX   How to carry killed specimens   96

X   General equipment and apparatus   97

XI   Materials for pinning   160

XII   Containers for pinned insects   160

XIII   Methods of pinning insects   161

XIV   A binocular microscope and a spotlight   176

XV   A monocular microscope with a camera lucida   177

INTRODUCTION

Once, when I was collecting insects, a local official stopped and asked what I was doing. When I had explained, and shown him what I had caught, he made two comments: 'It's a strange occupation for a grown man', and, 'Surely all those things are known already'. If either of these were true, this book would not be necessary.

Collecting insects may be either an end or a beginning. Taken at its simplest level, just to build up and arrange a collection appeals to an instinct that is present in all of us. Compared with, say, stamp-collecting, it has the advantage of taking the collector out of doors, to spend sunny days in the country. Like photography and painting, with which it may compete in interest, it develops keen and accurate observation, which adds enormously to anyone's pleasure in the countryside. Whether these are suitable activities for an adult depends on whether we bring an adult mind to bear on them.

But there is more to collecting insects than just catching and arranging them. We are all used to gardening books and nurserymen's catalogues, which seem to know all the plants that exist and everything about their habits and their cultivation. Not surprisingly, the average person thinks that all this sort of knowledge was discovered long ago. By the same reasoning, it is assumed that there are people who know all about insects, too.

Nothing could be further from the truth. No one knows how many different kinds there are in the British Isles, and the figures for the world, given in Chapter IX, are a pure guess. What is more, the great majority of insects are little more than names even to specialist professional entomologists. Take a volume of the *Handbooks for the Identification of British Insects*, or the *Faune de France*, and you will be astonished to see how little information is given there about the life-history, or even the habits, of most of the insects listed. Some are vaguely said to be found 'on vegetation in wet places', and so on, but about the majority of species the authority is silent. Think how many words have been written about the honey-bee; then imagine how long it will be before the twenty thousand British insects, or the million that may exist in the world, have been studied to the same extent.

9

The real value of an insect collection, therefore, is not to admire it, but to use it to study living insects. There is no need for me to explain the attraction of such a study, since many lucid and persuasive writers, led by Fabre, have shown something of the diversity of insect-life, and the beautiful mechanisms of adaptation by which they fit themselves into their surroundings. But none of this can be understood until we can identify the insects, and separate one from another.

It was for this reason that I felt that a book on collecting alone would be to stop half-way, and that I ought to give some indication of how to find out more about the insects you have caught, and how to make known the new discoveries that you are certain to make as soon as you begin to observe insects more closely.

The early chapters, therefore, discuss where to look for insects, and how to catch them; how to bring them home, and how to make a permanent collection out of them. In all these matters each entomologist has his own pet ideas, and it is not possible to catalogue them all. The important things are the basic principles. Where one expert says he always mounts his specimens in ABC solution, another swears by XYZ; the secret of success in each case is usually not the special formula, but the skill and experience that each brings to the job. And when it comes to being recommended to use 'a mounted pin-feather of a snipe or woodcock', or 'an eyelash mounted in a matchstick', we are being given entertainment rather than instruction.

So far as collecting the insects is concerned, the real secret is not in having the right equipment, but in understanding the ways of the insects when they are alive, and that is why I have put observation first, and collecting second.

The chapters on studying insects will be found to deal mainly with identification, and the recognition and description of new species: not because this is the whole of entomology, but because it is the keystone upon which all the rest depends. It is the present fashion to look down upon systematics—and, indeed, upon natural history in general—as unscientific pursuits. 'It is probably true to say that, except in so far as they contribute to theories and generalisations, the scientific mind is not interested in facts [the attitude that] the scientific theory has less appeal than the facts themselves . . . is characteristic of the naturalist' (Wigglesworth, 1956).

Unfortunately, when theories conflict with facts, the facts always win. So if anything in this book should encourage you to become a systematic entomologist, be consoled by the fact that your work, unscientific though it may be, will probably outlive a good many theories.

It is a pleasure to express my thanks to the members of the Shell Film Unit for a most enjoyable visit to their studio, and to Professor R. M. Gordon and the authorities of the Liverpool School of Tropical Medicine for the use of the photograph from which Plate VII is taken. I am grateful to a number of friends who have given me the benefit of their experience in collecting and preserving insects. Most particularly, I am indebted to my wife and my son David, for their indispensable help at all stages of the work.

NOTE

The following arbitrary rule has been adopted concerning the use of hyphens in popular names ending in the syllable '*fly*'.

Names of insects that are true flies carry a hyphen; e.g. *house-fly*, *bot-fly*, *crane-fly*. Names of insects that are not true flies are written as single words; e.g., *butterfly*, *dragonfly*, *mayfly*. Exceptions arise when a proper name is involved or if the use of a single word seems grotesque. In such cases the word '*fly*' is printed separately, as in *Dobson fly*, *ichneumon fly*.

COLLECTING INSECTS

I

WHERE TO LOOK FOR INSECTS

Insects are everywhere. There is almost no place in the world where life is possible and where insects are not to be found. To begin to study them it is not necessary to go to distant countries, or to search in out-of-the-way places. You can make a start in your garden or, if you like, in the house itself.

At first, you will want to catch and look at nearly all the bigger specimens you see, but once you have a fair idea of the Orders of insects (see Chapter IX) you will do better to limit your interest, either to some group, such as beetles, moths, or dragonflies, or to some particular setting, say the insects of a sand-heath, or a pond, or those which live on one kind of plant. Whichever way you choose to approach your collecting, do not be in a great hurry to catch and kill the insects, but spend as much time as you can watching them going about their daily life.

To find the insects you want you will need to have some idea of how they live, and what they require at different stages of their life. Nearly all insects begin life as an egg which is laid in such a position that the newly hatched young insect will find food and shelter provided close at hand. In many groups, the young insect is very much like the adult, except for the absence of wings, and then you may expect to find the young and the adults together, or at least close by. Thus a colony of greenfly on a stem will include both adults and young; and dragonflies can be caught in the air over the water in which the nymphs are living.

In contrast to this, the more advanced groups hatch into a larva that is quite different in shape from the adult, so that if we did not know better we might well believe it was quite a different insect. Think of a honey-bee and its white, legless, almost helpless larva. Such larvæ may live in surroundings totally different from those of the adult insect, and for collecting purposes we must treat them as if they really were different insects. To enable these insects to rebuild themselves from a larva into an adult there is a resting stage, the pupa or chrysalis, and this again has its own habitat, often unlike that of either of the other two.

Remember, therefore, that catching the adult insects is only one part of collecting, and by itself gives a very one-sided view of their life-history. To know an insect well you have to find the young insects, keep them alive, rear them to maturity, and get them to mate and lay eggs. We shall return to this again in Chapter III.

The things that insects of all stages are concerned with are light, warmth, food, moisture and shelter, and it is by trying to see these things from their point of view that we can learn to anticipate the movements of insects, and to know where to look for them. Some skilled collectors show an uncanny, almost instinctive knowledge of the ways of insects, and always seem to take the rare or unusual insects, while other collectors at the same time and place are getting only the most commonplace species.

A good place in which to start collecting insects is a *flowering hedgerow* on a warm, sunny day. Certainly you can collect in winter, or on a dull, cold day, but then you have to be more patient, and more skilled, to be successful.

Before you do anything else, stand and watch for a while. See how the pollen-loving insects work over the flowers. Some, like the bees, go from flower to flower, wasting little time, and collecting almost continuously. Others, notably the butterflies, some moths, and many flies, love the warmth of the sun, and spend much of their time just basking, either quite still, or slowly opening and closing the wings. At the opposite extreme are the hoverers, which are able to remain poised in the air, apparently motionless, but with the wings moving at very high speeds. These look deceptively easy to catch, but try it, and see how quickly they can dart away in any direction. Some of them hover like this for mating purposes, making it easier for the two sexes to find each other: often it is the males that gather into a dancing swarm, like the midges on summer evenings, and in the tropics some hoverers have silvery or iridescent patches on the body, which glisten in the sunlight, and attract attention from a distance. If you know this, collecting them is made much simpler.

The leaves and stems of the plants shelter many insects. Underneath the leaves you may find clusters of eggs, or a hanging pupa, as well as many insects that are just keeping out of the way and trying not to attract attention. On the foliage you will see a number of adult insects, some of which are carnivores, and are looking out for a victim. Wasps look for caterpillars to carry off to feed their young, while the slender, small-waisted ichneumon flies look for a chance to lay their eggs on a caterpillar, so that their larvæ may feed upon it. Robber-flies and other carnivorous flies sit motionless until some other insect flies by, and then they take off and attack it in the air, seizing it and taking it to a leaf or stem, and quickly sucking it dry. Occasionally, after you have been looking at the same spot for several minutes, you will realise that there is a motionless insect, a light green long-horned grass-hopper, perhaps, or in warmer countries, a mantis or a cicada.

On the stems and under the leaves, you will not be surprised to find an encrusted mass of aphids (greenfly and blackfly) or coccids (scale-insects). Feeding upon these you may find the greenish, grub-like larvæ of hover-flies, and the active, six-legged larvæ of coccinellid beetles, whose adults, the ladybirds, fly and crawl over the foliage.

Ants, of course, hurry about everywhere, but to collect them, it is more profitable to find one of their runs along the ground, and follow it back to the nest.

We have said nothing yet about the beetles, other than the ladybirds. Some of the more brightly coloured ones, such as the tiger-beetles will be seen shining in the sun, and in the tropics you will see the Cassidinæ, or tortoise beetles, glistening like mother-of-pearl. Beetles in general, however, are not very active fliers, and will be collected mainly by beating, sweeping, pond-netting, or just by picking them up.

Insects that fly, and which are big enough to see easily, can be caught one at a time in a net, as described in the next chapter, but there are a great many smaller insects that keep still, or hide away, and are more difficult for the collector to deal with. You can find many of them by searching patiently, but even then it may be difficult to get them out of the middle of a prickly bush. Those above waist level are collected by beating the foliage with a stick, while holding underneath it a beating-tray, or an open umbrella to catch the insects. All the wingless ones will fall down in this way, and so will many of the sluggish fliers, which will often struggle on the tray long enough for you to put a tube or a pill-box over them. Beating is obviously easiest where you can get the tray in and out without trouble, and works best round about trees and shrubby plants—beating about the bush, in fact.

B

Insects that sit about below your waist level are best taken by
'sweeping'. When you have brushed the net through the foliage a
few times, it will have in it a very mixed lot of insects, and you
may be doubtful how to deal with them. First look out for any
angry bees or wasps: if you want them, take them out with a
pill-box, leaving the net lying closed on the ground; if you don't
want them, let them escape, as they will try very hard to do. Then
you can examine your catch by looking into the net as shown in
Plates III, IV.

The movements of many small insects are peculiar, and easily
recognised again: the looping motion of geometrid caterpillars;
the restless, jerky walk, and nervous waving of the antennæ of
many small wasps and ichneumon flies; the strutting and wing-
waving of some small flies. Insects like these become just as
familiar as people we know, and besides being interesting in themselves, such peculiarities are a quick way of spotting these groups
if you want to collect them.

Going back to the leaves, you are sure to find some that have
either mines or galls. Mines are tunnels produced when a larva
pushes its way between the upper and lower surfaces of a leaf.
They show up as a pattern, either in a paler green, yellow or
white, and are often very complicated. Galls are spongy or woody
outgrowths produced by the plant when its tissues are irritated
by the feeding of an insect: such, for example, as the marble galls
of oak or the pincushion galls of the rose. Both mines and galls
vary a great deal, and can be grouped and classified just like the
insects themselves, and many people study them without bothering
very much about the insects that cause them. This is rather a
pity, because it makes for confusion. It is generally true that one
kind of insect makes one kind of mine or gall on one kind of plant,
but this may not always be so, and there is need for much careful
study of the mines and galls and the insect together. Unfortunately
this means slow and patient work in collecting affected plants,
keeping them until the adult insects emerge, and then properly
classifying the insects, and this takes a long time (see Chapter
III).

Inside the stems of plants there are tunnelling insects, notably
beetles, moth larvæ, and those of the stem sawflies. Some attack
healthy plants, particularly young shoots, and then they may be a
serious pest of cereal crops, or young seedlings. Many more tunnel
into dead or rotting stems, and these hide a great many insects of
all stages, larvæ, nymphs, pupæ and adults. Many of these are

seeking shelter rather than food, and on a walk at any time, even in winter, and when you have no collecting gear, you can split open dead stems, or cut them off and take them home for examination.

A final place to look for insects along our hedgerow is in the soil about the roots of the plants. Move the foliage gently aside, and be ready with an aspirator to pick up the smaller insects before they can take cover; bigger ones need a tube or a pill-box (Chapter II). Stirring up the leaf-mould and other debris will flush a number of these insects, but for thorough collecting it is best to dig up a sample of the top inch or two of soil and take it home in a tin or a screw-topped jar.

So you see, a hedgerow has a tremendous population of insects, and if you have only a short time for collecting in some locality— say while you are changing trains, or in a few minutes after a picnic stop—the nearest hedgerow is the obvious place to go. But just because it is so obvious, you can be sure that other collectors have been there before you, and in a short time on a casual visit you will have to rely on beginner's luck to get anything unusual. If you just want a particular group that you know will be there, then you will be satisfied; but if you want to find the rare insects, and perhaps new ones, then you must look somewhere else.

Rivalling a hedgerow in having a variety of species in a small space is a *garden*. In fact it is often the place where young collectors first begin, but it has certain obvious drawbacks. You can seldom lash about with a net in the herbaceous border without becoming unpopular with the owner.

Garden collecting is rather sophisticated, and is the sort of thing the great entomologist does in a spare moment. Instead of labouring with a sweeping net in the hot sun, he strolls about in a superior way, and occasionally brings out a tube or a pill-box to pick up a single insect. If there are visitors present he tells them its name, and usually says it is a great rarity, so that they imagine him rushing off to his study as soon as they are gone to write a paper about it. What he usually does in fact is to forget it until his wife empties his pockets.

The one great advantage about a garden is that it is always there, that you know the plants intimately, and that it is easy to follow the comings and goings of the insect population all through the year. Some eminent entomologists have compiled lists of the species occurring in their gardens, and while it is easy to smile if they are pompous about it, such lists can show what a great variety of insects lives literally on our doorstep, and what a lot of passers-by there are during the course of a year.

For making a general collection, however, the most profitable area to tackle next to a hedgerow is a piece of *scrub land*, with low bushes of different species, long and short grass, and sandy or stony hollows, thus providing situations to suit a great variety of insects. Places of this kind include odd bits of land in the angles of cultivated fields; a hillside that is too poor for ploughing; a hollow that is simply left alone by the farmer; a railway embankment or a cutting, if you have access to them; and of course a quarry, a sand-pit or a chalk-pit. Besides most of the hedgerow insects that we have already talked about, you will get many predaceous and parasitic Hymenoptera and Diptera flying round the bushes, or sitting on the low twigs just above the level of the grass, waiting for something promising to turn up. Probably, too, one of the bigger dragonflies will come prospecting round. In the sandy or stony patches you will find the fossorial wasps and bees going in and out of their burrows, some flies which have a dusty or sandy appearance to suit their surroundings, and of course a great many beetles, especially if you turn over stones and loose pieces of bark. In subtropical and tropical countries you will find the pits made in the dust by antlions, and by flies of similar habits. If there are nests of sand-martins, or the nests of small mammals, these can be searched for fleas. With the trowel you should always take on collecting trips, you can dig for pupæ in bare or sandy areas.

An *open hillside*, of the kind shown in Plate I, comes next on the list. The insects are not so crowded together as in a scrubby patch, and you have to move about more, and work harder for your catch. On the other hand, there are many transient insects, moving most often up the hillside, or along its slope, and you have a good excuse for sitting down and enjoying the sunshine. If anything comes near, you can see it in good time to stand up and go after it.

Such a hillside often leads to a wood. *Woodland* collecting can be disappointing, unless you know what to expect, and where to look for it. In the depths of a wood, even a deciduous one, the light is poor, there are few flowers, and insects, too, are much fewer than they are outside. There is little on the wing, except an occasional butterfly, or a swarm of flies dancing in a patch of sunlight under a tree. Most collecting is done on the tree-trunks, or on the ground at the foot of the trees. Bigger insects can be stalked and trapped under the net; a net with a small frame, as shown in fig. 7, is useful because the ground under trees is often very uneven, and a bigger frame gives the insect more chance to find a way out.

The most interesting collecting in woods is to go round the tree-trunks with an aspirator as in Plate VI, keeping a pill-box or one or two tubes in your pocket ready for any bigger insects. Dig at the roots of trees with a knife or trowel. Pull off loose pieces of bark, and break open stumps and fallen logs with a jack-knife; but try not to overdo this, and do not go through the wood leaving a trail of wreckage behind. Do not neglect the debris at the foot of trees, or in rot-holes in the trunk; take samples (properly labelled, see Chapter V) away in a tin or jar, and also take back pieces of wood that seem to be infested with wood-boring insects.

The *edges of woods*, and open spaces inside them such as clearings, rides and glades—are much more attractive to insects than the unbroken plantation. These places have many of the hedgerow insects, and some of the woodland ones as well. A *stream in woodland* is even more attractive to the collector, since it provides all the water-loving insects in addition to the others mentioned.

The New Forest is a famous locality for collecting, and you can see there the tremendous local variation in the numbers of insects. The gloomy 'inclosures' of pines give you very little to collect except beetles and sawflies. More open, deciduous woodland is richer, and some of the patches that have been undisturbed for a long time (Mark Ash, for instance) are the places to go if you want the unusual insects. But the really productive localities in numbers are the more open, watered areas, the famous 'walks' (Rhinefield, for example), and streams such as the Highland Water.

A word of warning about these borderline, or 'fringe' localities. It is difficult to say, without previous knowledge, whether a particular insect that you have taken is a true forest insect, or belongs to more open country. More particularly abroad, in the tropics, for instance, you should take care how you label specimens from forest-fringe areas. People working away in museums and other places using your locality-names without your local knowledge, may come to quite wrong conclusions about the habits and distribution of the insects they are studying.

Grassland varies a good deal in character. *Lowland pasture* has a much less varied insect fauna than anything we have yet discussed, though the number of individual insects may be great. On the wing are mainly butterflies, with an occasional bee or beetle; most of the insects are hidden in the grass or around its roots. Sweeping is the obvious way to collect here, and will produce Homoptera, small Diptera and Hymenoptera, and beetles. Search the grass roots with an aspirator, and give special attention to clumps of flowers, and to pats of cow-dung; the last have a very varied insect fauna, according to age and dryness.

Open downland has a fauna of its own, such things, for example as the Chalk Hill Blue butterfly. Flowers are usually plentiful, and there are more insects than on many lush pastures. Many downland areas are celebrated collecting grounds, such as Box Hill, where you may actually see a man with a butterfly-net, in full cry after a specimen, just as they always show him in cartoons. *Heathland* has fewer flowers, but more scope for sand-living, fossorial insects, especially Hymenoptera and beetles.

The limestone *fells* have a thin, poor grass, and the windswept *moors* a peaty, acid soil, and both are impoverished from the entomologist's point of view; they offer connoisseurs' collecting, where the prospect of a few scarce insects makes up for the knowledge and patience required to collect them. The moors lead up to the mountains, and so on to the snowline. The study of the insects of high altitudes is a remote one in every sense, and appeals, perhaps, to those who have a responsive strain of Celtic melancholy in their blood. They find insects of peculiar structure, often with reduced wings, or flightless, sitting on or near the snow.

The 'mountains' of the British Isles are low ones, and getting to the snowline in Scotland is comparatively easy. In tropical countries there are often a number of successive vegetational zones between the valleys and the snowline, each with its quota of insects. The study of these zones, comparing the insects with those of other zones, and other countries, is one of the fascinating branches of ecology.

So far we have considered only terrestrial insects. Collecting in water—ponds, streams, rivers, lakes—is another side of entomology, and often seems to be followed by a different set of people; or rather, by two sets of people. There are those who are interested in catching the insects in the water, using the collecting methods described in Chapter II, and there are those who catch dragonflies, mayflies and stoneflies over the water. To try to do both means that you have to carry a double set of nets and the other gear such as sieves and dredges. The sea-shore has its insect population, some living and breeding among the wrack and stranded rubbish, others to be found as larvæ and pupæ in the sand. A few insects are to be found in deep water.

These are all the more general ways of collecting in daylight, but there are other places where you may look for a special and sometimes a peculiar fauna. All kinds of rubbish and debris have their insects, and can either be searched on the spot, or taken home in a tin or jar for detailed examination, or for putting through a Berlese funnel (see fig. 38). Do not be squeamish. Remember that rotting and decay are part of the natural cycle by which the essential elements, nitrogen, carbon, potassium, phosphorus, are sorted out and used again, and insects play a valuable part in this process.

Animal dung attracts many insects to lay eggs, and to use it as food for their larvæ. As the dung ages it goes through a regular sequence of drying and changing its temperature and chemical composition, and there is a corresponding sequence of insects visiting it. Some very beautiful work has been done on the succession of insects in a cow-pat. The same applies to the dead bodies of animals, and the carrion-feeding insects that destroy them. If you come upon a dead mouse or mole, cover it with a stone or a piece of wood, supported on stones as shown in fig. 31, and pay regular visits to collect the insects in and around it.

Many living animals have their *parasitic* insects. Some can be caught on the wing by waiting near a bait animal, such as a cow, a horse, a donkey, or a tethered goat, though you have to make friends with the animal first before it will let you wave a net around its ears. The larvæ of bots and warbles are found by inspecting carcases of freshly killed animals, looking principally under the skin, or in the throat, the intestine and the cavities of the head, including the nose. Unfortunately many of these larvæ cannot be reared to the adult stage unless they have quite finished their feeding when you take them out. You have a better chance with those which live in the intestine, and which generally drop out with the dung when they are ready to pupate. These are particularly worth looking for if you have the chance to examine fresh dung of large game animals; after all, this is the only way you are likely to get a specimen of the magnificent *Gyrostigma*, that breeds in the stomachs of rhinoceroses.

Ectoparasites are insects that live on the outside of other animals. Fleas and lice are the best known, but there are also some flies, and a few bugs. These generally stick closely to their host so long as it is alive, but leave quickly when it dies. Apart from picking them off the living animal, you have to be prepared to deal with the parasites immediately when you kill the host animal (for details, see Chapter IX). The fleas, and some of the flies, however, do not breed on the host, but their larvæ live in the nest or lair, either feeding there on debris, or resting there as a pupa until a new host arrives. Thus if you find a nest, even one that is no longer in use, search it for insects, larvæ and pupæ as well as adults.

But insects also live on other insects. The old doggerel about big fleas having little fleas on them is partly true. Thus dragonflies and Neuroptera may carry on their wings minute flies of the genus *Forcipomyia*, and a great many different groups of insects may be found to carry mites and pseudoscorpions, not as parasites, but as scavengers, living on dung or other matter with which their host's body is contaminated: a case of living on crumbs from the rich man's table. *Phoresy* is the name given to the trick of using some other animal to carry you about; an example is the fly *Dermatobia hominis*, which uses a mosquito as a transport animal. Some larvæ of aquatic insects live on crabs.

A number of ways in which insects may be *trapped* in the daytime are discussed in Chapter II. Traps have the advantage that they go on working when you are not there, but on the other hand the specimens they catch for you are often spoiled by being overcrowded, and crawling all over each other. Traps are not a way to get good material for your collection, but they do catch the shy and elusive insect, and they can also be used to give an idea of how common insects are, and at what times they appear. Used in winter as well as in summer, and in all weather conditions, they may upset some of our ideas of what insects are about in winter, or in the wet.

Some ingenious trapping methods have been invented. For example, you may hang bundles of twigs in trees and hope to lure wood-boring insects into them; cover dead animals as we have already described above; put a board on top of a freshly sawn stump so that unwary wood-borers will tunnel through into it without noticing the difference; or go up to the edge of a pond where the first dry soil lies, and pour water over it, to bring out the insects that do not like being submerged. There is a touch of poetic justice about one suggestion that at a picnic you should deliberately put out one sandwich on the ground and catch all the insects that are foolish enough to come to it.

Do not neglect the possibilities of a car. If you drive at about 20–25 m.p.h. some aerial insects will follow you, and when you stop they will fly round, and probably settle on the bonnet or the tyres, since these are both warm. But do not drive too quickly.

The legend that some flies travel at 800 m.p.h. is pure imagination, and the most recent authority puts the top speed of any insect at about 36 m.p.h. If you wish you may trail a net from a car, and you should certainly examine the radiator after a drive in the country; but the insects collect on the radiator proper, and not on the fancy chromium-plated grille. So many insects collect here that it was once seriously suggested they might be studied as evidence of the movements of suspected cars about the country. Unfortunately as collector's items these specimens are often distorted, and nearly always half cooked.

Indoor collecting can go on all the year round. Apart from pests, like fleas, bugs and flies, a number of interesting insects find their way indoors, and can be caught on the windows as they try to get out again. Others are brought in with fruit or flowers, or breed in odd, neglected corners (which exist in even the best-kept houses), or swarm indoors to shelter in the roof or the bedrooms in the winter.

Finally, you can collect *at night*. Organised collecting, with a proper light-trap, is discussed in Chapter II, and practical problems such as choosing a site, and the effects of different types of weather are discussed from long experience by de Worms (1939). Both he and Williams (1956) dispute the old belief that insects do not fly on moonlight nights; they say that in fact it is just that the trap does not seem so bright to the insect on such nights. De Worms warns against putting the trap in a convenient hollow which will fill with mist or even fog on a cool night. There is generally little insect activity when rain is on the way, but after a shower, and even during light rain, collecting may be good.

In addition to the elaborate trap, many other lights will attract insects. The bathroom is mentioned in Chapter II, and in the tropics the lamp by which you sit is surrounded by a ring of singed insects, while others settle on the wall nearby. The only bar to collecting is the competition of the geckoes, frogs and mantids. You will often see insects at street-lights, or on the outside of lighted shop-windows (where in the daytime you may collect insects on the *inside* of the same window). However, you are less likely to arouse the interest of a policeman if you use your own porch-light instead.

Enough has been said, I hope, to show that there is no lack of material for the collector of insects, and the only thing left to do is to get together the necessary gear, and begin.

II

CATCHING AND TRAPPING INSECTS

The next step after finding and observing insects is to obtain some of them for further study, either dead or alive. Equipment for 'catching' is that which needs to have the collector there to work it, and that for 'trapping' goes on working in his absence.

When you take up any hobby there are two extremes you need to avoid. One is that of buying every new gadget you hear about, because it looks so clever and interesting: if you do that you will find that you spend all your time admiring your equipment and never get round to using it. The other extreme is to take a pride in never buying anything ready-made, making all your own equipment from old tins, pieces of wire and so on. Try to keep a sense of proportion between these two extremes. The equipment should always exist to do the job, and not for its own sake. The aim should be to use as little as possible, and of course to spend no more on it than is necessary; but yet at the same time, not to carry round clumsy home-made gear if there is a cheap ready-made article.

A guiding principle should be to buy equipment that will serve as many different purposes as possible. This does not mean something like the schoolboy's penknife, with a gadget attached for every possible purpose, including taking stones out of horses' hoofs. It means, in the biological term, a generalised implement. The best collectors do not have a set of different nets for every kind of insect; they have found by trial a good general purpose net that suits their needs, and they stick to that. Nor do they carry about tubes and boxes suitable only for the rare insects they may never see; they have a few, well-tried sizes and shapes, and use them for everything.

This chapter deals with nets, for chasing and catching insects; tubes and other containers, to put the captures in; and traps to work while the collector is busy somewhere else.

26

An insect may be captured by net in one of several different
ways:

(a) By catching it in flight.

(b) By stalking the insect until it settles, and then dropping the
    mouth of the net over it.

(c) By 'sweeping': that is, by swinging the net, mouth first,
    through grass or soft herbage, so that the insects that are
    disturbed are trapped in the bag of the net.

(d) By 'beating': that is, by holding the net beneath bushes,
    or branches of trees, and beating the foliage with a stick so
    that the insects fall into the net.

(e) Insects in ponds and streams need special treatment, though
    the principles of pursuit and capture are the same as those
    in the air.

In theory, each of these types of collecting calls for a slightly
different kind of net-frame and bag, but in practice it is generally
possible to do everything except perhaps the water-collecting with
one general purpose net. We shall consider this first, and then
give details of the more specialised kinds.

General purpose net

The *frame* should be 12–18 in. across, and either circular or
pear-shaped (figs. 1–5). The pear-shaped frame makes it easier
to swing the net close to branches, tree-trunks, walls or the ground,
and so to scoop off the insects as they rise in alarm before it.
With this kind of frame, too, it is easier to put one's head into the
net to inspect the catch (Plates III, IV). A frame that can be
folded, or taken apart into several pieces, is convenient to carry in
the pocket or under the arm when not in use.

A well-tried kind of frame is made from three or more pieces of
cane, joined together either with brass hinges, or with brass tips
and sockets pushing into each other (fig. 1). Such a frame is light
and strong, and is elastic enough to withstand quite sharp knocks
against stones and trees. Unfortunately the brass fittings, and the
amount of workmanship, make these nets rather expensive today,
and unless both materials and workmanship are of the best quality
trouble comes from splitting, either of the cane or of the brass. A
cheaper type, with only the Y-piece of brass, and one, curved
piece of cane for the frame costs 10/6–12/6.

Metal frames are made more cheaply than the best brass and

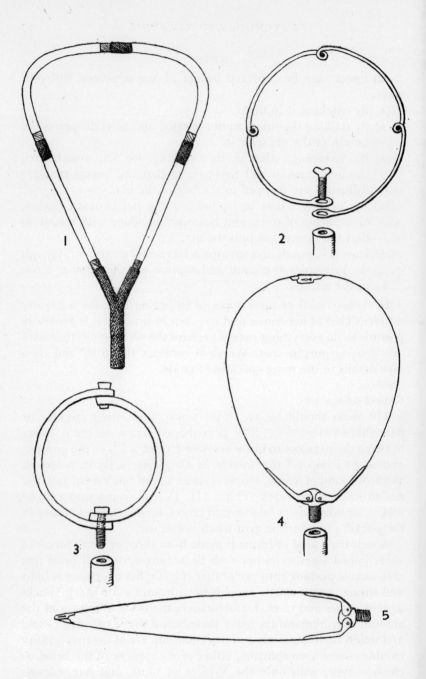

Figures 1–5. Net frames. 1, jointed cane; 2, 3, hinged metal; 4, 5, steel spring, shown open and closed.

53069

cane, and may be either a single ring of heavy metal rod, or two
or more sections joined together (figs. 2, 3). These are sturdy, but
are inclined to be heavy. The best all-round frame is made from
two pieces of steel strip, in one or two slightly different designs
(figs. 4, 5). When folded it makes a straight object, rather like a
ladies' umbrella. In use, the two strips engage by means of a
catch at one end and a screw fitting at the other, to form a pear-
shaped frame roughly 18 × 12 in.

The drawbacks of this type of frame are that the steel edge
wears out the hem of the bag fairly soon, and that when the net
is used for sweeping the frame is apt to chop off the tops of grasses
and other plants. This has the double objection of destroying the
flowers that may be attracting the insects you want to catch, and
of filling the net with a mass of foliage, so that it will not swing
properly, and so that any insects caught are difficult to find.

For this reason the light cane frame is still favoured by many
experienced collectors.

The *bag* should be at least twice as long as the diameter of the
frame, so that with a twist of the wrist it can be closed over the
frame, as shown in Plate II. The material from which the bag is
made should be light and soft so that as the net is swung the bag
opens fully (Plate I). A closely woven material is unsuitable
because, besides staying in stiff folds, it also holds a cushion of
air inside it, which may prevent small insects from going into the
opening. What is wanted is a net-like material (hence the name),
which will allow a rush of air through the frame, and yet which
is of a mesh small enough to trap the smallest insects in which
the collector is likely to be interested.

Mosquito netting, well washed to make it soft, or old lace
curtaining (but not too old!), will do; so will an interlock material,
like stockinette (bobbinet), provided that it has a cotton or nylon
yarn. Rayon materials are liable to tear when they are wet, and
all nets are likely to get wet often from moisture on the foliage.
The traditional material for the making of insect nets is millers'
bolting silk, but this is too expensive for general use.

If a ready-made net is bought the bag will be supplied, of
course, and will generally be cotton net of fairly open mesh,
costing four or five shillings: larger, 'Kite' net-bags, of finer
material, cost three times as much. It is a good idea to have
several spare bags to fit the same frame—and to make sure before
buying the net that the bag can easily be changed, and is not
stitched permanently on to the frame. The bag is certain to catch

on brambles sometimes, and tear. One or two small holes do not matter, but each one increases the risk of losing an insect that you have taken a lot of trouble to catch. Small rubber bands should be carried for tying up little holes; or, of course, a needle and cotton will make a more permanent mend. Even so you will need spare bags, if only because the first one will get wet and dirty. Bags can be made at home that will be quite good enough for spare or standby use, by using the bought net as a pattern.

Whatever bag is used, it needs to be attached to the frame. Some nets have metal rings, like curtain rings, that hook into a solid hem, or into a piece of the special tape used on curtains. These are rather fiddling to change, and also are liable to leave a gap between the frame and the bag, through which insects may escape. A better plan is to have a strong tubular hem of canvas or other heavy material, through which the pieces of the frame are threaded before they are joined together. Either kind of hem should be as strong as possible, because it gets a good deal of wear from hitting tree-trunks or scraping on the ground.

If the net is to be used for one kind of collecting only, the general-purpose net can be improved upon as follows:

(a) *For flying insects only*. Keep the aperture big, the net frame light in weight, and the bag of open mesh. If only big things like butterflies and dragon-flies are to be caught, the bag may be of very coarse netting, and may be black or dark green. Dark nets are also liked by some collectors of small moths, because these insects show up well against the net; on the other hand, small Diptera and Hymenoptera are seen best against a white net.

(b) *For stalking individual insects*. A smaller frame is an advantage, because the ground is generally uneven, and the bigger the frame, the more likely it is to leave a crevice somewhere round the edge where an insect can escape. A light, flexible frame is easier to press down to the ground. The bag should be long, so that the tip can be held up and the bag shaken, so that the captured insect will fly up into the folds of the net. A dark net is less likely to scare the insect away during the approach.

If you do a lot of collecting of individual insects from awkward places, in spiny vegetation, or among flower heads which you do not want to break off (e.g. bees), it is useful to have a net with a small, circular frame and a long, cylindrical bag, as shown in fig. 7.

Where even a small-aperture net cannot reach, there is a device called the *net-forceps* (fig. 10). This can be make from the wooden

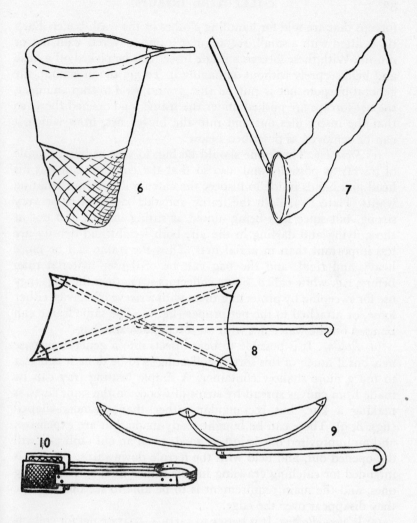

Figures 6–10. Nets. 6, sweeping net, strengthened with canvas; 7, small aperture net, with long bag; 8, 9, beating tray, top and side views; 10, net-forceps.

forceps that are sold for handling clothes in the wash-boiler. Each tip is fitted with a small, rectangular frame, covered with net or muslin. With these forceps a single insect can be picked off a bush and held securely without damaging it. To get the insect out, the general-purpose net is put on the ground, as if to trap an insect, the net-forceps are pushed under the frame, and opened there, so that the insect flies out and into the bigger net, from which it can be removed as described below.

(c) *Sweeping*. The frame should be big, to take as big a sample of insects as possible, and also so that the collector can put his head and hands inside to inspect the catch and take out what he wants (Plate IV). Both the frame and the bag need to be very strong, but since it is being aimed at sitting insects, and not at those flying and darting in the air, both weight and density are less important than in aerial nets. Thus the frame can be more heavy and rigid, and the bag can be of denser material than before, e.g. white calico. Some collectors strengthen the bags they use for sweeping by protecting them with a sleeve of canvas, either loose, or attached to the net proper (fig. 6). The same frame can be used on the water-net with an interchangeable bag.

(d) *Beating*. It is possible to beat insects into a general-purpose net, but if much of this sort of collecting is to be done it is better to use a more shallow container. A simple beating tray can be made from canvas spread by strips of wood, on the same lines as making a kite, but rectangular rather than diamond-shaped (figs. 8, 9). These can be bought ready-made, but are expensive, and an improvised one is just as good. Even an old umbrella will do, opened out, and held with the ferrule downwards. Beating is intended for catching crawling insects rather than actively flying ones, and the main requirement is to be able to see them before they disappear over the edge.

(e) *Water-collecting*. It is better to carry a separate net for collecting in water, because one that is used both in air and in water is not likely to be very efficient in either. The water net is used much more slowly, and meets with much more resistance than the air net, so that it can with advantage be heavier and stronger. Sometimes the same frame is used for water-collecting and for sweeping, with different bags. The frame need not be round, and it is often better to have a square, or a diamond-shaped frame, since this can more easily be pushed into loose gravel, or round the bases of water-plants. For regular collecting from the bed of the pond or stream, some form of trawl or dredge is needed (figs. 11–15).

I. Using a short-handled net.

II. Each stroke should finish like this, so that nothing can escape.

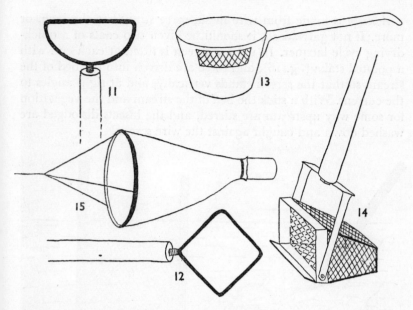

Figures 11–15. Equipment for water-collecting. 11, 12, net frames; 13, dipper; 14, dredge; 15, plankton net.

Those nets used on the bottom may have a container of wire gauze, copper, or galvanised iron, and the edge reinforced with some form of scraper. Nets that are to be moved through the water need a more flexible bag, similar to that of an aerial net. The material may be the same, but needs to be able to stand constant immersion, and frequent damp storage without rotting. The net is made less deep than an aerial net, because it gets full of debris and needs to be cleared out, and because aquatic insects, on the whole, are less active than those that live on land, or at any rate are less able to leap out of a shallow net. Small, light-weight nets are available, but of course this makes another different net to be carried.

A plankton net is made as in fig. 15, and is a cone of net-like material ending in a detachable glass tube, or an unbreakable plastic container. In streams this can be held or fixed in one position, when the flow of water will extend the net, and insects will collect in it. In still water the same effect may be produced by dragging the net through the water, or towing it behind a boat or a swimmer.

C

A screen is made from wire mesh, of 12 strands to the inch, or more. If not galvanised, it should be given two coats of a quick-drying cycle lacquer. In use the screen is fitted at each end with a pointed stake (fig. 16), and these are driven into the bed of the stream so that the screen stands vertically, and at right angles to the current. With a stick the bed of the stream and the vegetation for some way upstream are stirred, and the insects dislodged are washed down and caught against the wire screen.

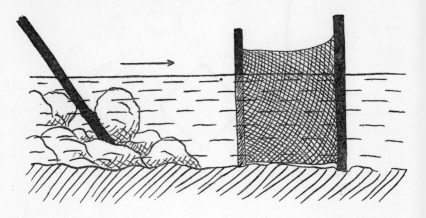

Figure 16. Water-collecting: disturbing stones and mud upstream of a wire screen.

Sieves are useful for collecting insects from mud at the bottom, or on the edges of a stream. A portable sieve, like a coal-riddle, is suitable for occasional use, but for a more thorough study of the mud-fauna of a particular stream a wooden stand with inter-changeable sieves is a great help (see fig. 17). The stand is like the frame of an occasionable table, but without the solid top. Into the recessed top fit sieves like seed-boxes, which instead of a wooden bottom have a wire mesh of different degrees of coarseness. In addition some form of jug or ladle is needed.

In use, the stand can be placed directly in the stream and a sieve placed in position. With the ladle a sample of the mud is taken up and poured on to the sieve, and the water and fine particles fall through back into the stream. If the sieve begins to get clogged with mud it is only necessary to take a ladle full of clear water and pour it through. The insects are picked off into tubes.

Handles for nets. A long handle is seldom needed for a collecting-net, except in water. Generally it will be found that a handle longer than about two feet is an encumbrance: the net is heavy at the end of such a long lever, and difficult to control, and the added strain on the collector's wrist prevents those quick changes of direction needed to catch a wary insect. Many collectors do not bother with a handle at all, other than the six-inch brass tube that is part of the frame of many nets. If a short handle is used it should be light and very strong.

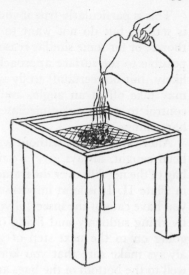

Figure 17. Water - collecting: washing mud through a sieve.

It is useful to carry a walking-stick with a ferrule narrow enough to be pushed into the brass tube of the net. Whatever stick is used it should fit very firmly on to the frame, because it is most annoying to reach out over a stream to catch dragonflies and see the net fall off into the water. For beating, the stick can be separated from the net and used to beat the branches, while the net is held beneath them in the other hand.

Water-nets need a long, strong handle, and generally something like a broomstick, firmly screwed to the ring, is needed to get enough reach and enough force for pushing aside plants, and against a gravelly bottom. Telescope handles of light alloy cost upwards of a pound, and are an extravagance.

Using the net in the air. Short strokes are more effective than long ones. A long stroke at arm's length is bound to be relatively slow, and becomes both slower and less accurate towards the end of the stroke. Get as near as you can to the insect before striking at it, and then make a short stroke, speeding up towards the end, not slowing down. It is during the latter part of the stroke, when the insect has seen the net coming, that it will try to dodge, and extra speed at this point is important. If your arm is not fully extended you have a better chance of making a quick twist of the wrist to beat the insect.

This is particularly true if you are trying to catch an insect that is settled, but do not want to drop the net over it, because of thorns, or for some similar reason. If you swing the net as close as possible to the surface approaching the insect from in front, it is likely (but not certain!) to fly up into the path of the net; but it may take off at an angle, and you need to have enough wrist control to make an immediate correction when you see this is happening.

After every stroke, without waiting to see whether anything has been caught, always give a quick flick to the frame so that the bag of the net falls over the frame, with the mouth closed, as shown in Plate II. It is most important not to peer into the net to see if you have caught the insect; if you do it will probably surprise you by rising suddenly and flying out before you can stop it. Before going on to the next step of getting the insect out of the net, always make sure that you know just where it is, and that it is well to the bottom of the bag, and is not entangled in any folds of netting. Insects are very clever at making use of such folds to avoid the tube or pill-box into which you are trying to entice them. If you are not entirely satisfied with the position of the insect, do not open the mouth of the net, but take a quick, decisive stroke through the air, quick enough to make the bag billow out, and the end with a closing flick over the frame, as before. Do this as often as is needed to get the insect safely into a position from which you can get it out without the risk of letting it escape. Be particularly careful with bees and wasps, and if you lose sight of them do not grasp the net with your fingers, nor let it rest on your bare knee. A sharp sting may make you drop the net, or, worse still, drop the killing bottle in your other hand, and lose much of your catch into long grass.

TRANSFERRING TO CONTAINERS

Getting the insect out of the net

Water insects are generally fairly helpless when the water is drained away, and then can be tipped into a jar or other container, or carefully picked up with forceps, or even with the fingers.

Insects not in water (aerial insects) are more active and generally more fragile, and it is seldom a good thing to pick them up if it can be avoided, especially while they are still alive. Use may be made of the following:

(a) *Tubes*, glass or transparent plastic, should always be carried by the collector (Plate VIII). In fact it is a good practice to keep a couple of small tubes in your pocket even when you are not on a collecting excursion, because, once you have become interested in insects it is surprising how often you will see an insect on a window, or a garden seat, or the bonnet of a car, and wish that you had something to put it in.

Useful sizes of tubes are $2 \times \frac{1}{2}$ in., or $3 \times \frac{3}{4}$ in. with corks to fit. Make sure in advance that the corks do fit. They should, when new, be slightly bigger than the opening of the tube, and rather hard. Put the cork down on a smooth floor (e.g. linoleum), and roll it gently under the sole of the shoe, with a slight pressure; this will make the cork much softer, and it can be fitted into the tube firmly, without any tendency to spring out again in your pocket. A cork with a plastic cap can be removed with the hand that is holding the tube. These tubes cost 1/6 to 2/- a dozen, and boxes to hold them neatly in compartments can be bought. This reduces the risk of breaking the tubes against each other in a bag or in the pocket.

When getting insects into and out of tubes make use of their inclination to walk upwards, and to move towards the light. If the insect is big enough to be seen clearly through the net, from outside, then the procedure is as follows. With one hand pinch off a part of the bag containing the insect, and with the other introduce the tube into the net from below (see Plate V). Bring the tube up under the insect until the net is tight across the open end of the tube and then give a sharp tap, so the insect falls into the tube.

If the insect cannot be clearly seen from outside then the best plan is to put one's head and one hand into the net, while the other hand holds the bag up and against the light (Plate III). The insects climbing up the inside of the net show up against the light, and it is easy to choose the one you want and place the tube over it from inside.

Resting insects, or those which are actively feeding, such as plant bugs or mosquitoes, can often be caught by putting a tube directly over them, without using a net (Plate VII). Sometimes they are so sluggish that you will need to move the tube sideways before they can be dislodged and will fly up into the tube. It is sometimes difficult to persuade the insect to fly far enough down the tube to get the cork in before it escapes, and a small piece of card is useful to have ready to slip over the open end while the tube is being moved. Cover the end with the thumb as soon as you can, and then find the cork and put it in. Indoors you will find that the attraction of the light is generally so great that, if you keep the closed end of the tube towards the window you have plenty of time for manipulating the cork, and insects will even stay in open tubes if they point this way. Out of doors the light is more scattered, and you will need to tap the tube sharply on the palm of the hand and then put the cork in quickly while the insect is struggling at the bottom.

If insects are taken home alive in tubes, make sure that the tube is not so big, nor the insect so small, that the latter can fly about, or be thrown about. In either case it will break its wing-tips, and possibly its legs. This danger can be reduced by pushing the insect into a small space at the end of the tube by means of a plug of twisted paper, or of cellulose wadding (see p. 90; not cotton wool because the fibres get entangled), but of course this reduces the amount of air, and may make the insect die sooner. A piece of blotting paper for the insect to stand on is useful, and this also helps to absorb any surplus moisture. If tubes are carried in the pocket on hot days, beads of condensed moisture will form on the inside of the glass, and the insect may be trapped in these and ruined as a specimen. If you can, it is better to transfer the insect quickly to a muslin cage as shown in Plate VII.

I have discussed tubes at some length because they are the cheapest and most generally useful pieces of entomological equipment.

(b) *Pill-boxes* (fig. 18; Plate VIII). These are cylindrical boxes like the doctor's pill-boxes, from which they take their name, but the entomological ones are stronger and have a glass bottom. It is important that they should have a glass *bottom* and not a glass top: this means that the glass is in the deeper half, not in the shallow lid. They are used, like tubes, for putting over insects in order to pick them up, and we want the insect as far as possible from the open end while the lid is put on.

Pill-boxes may be of metal, but these are liable to get dented, and they also encourage the formation of moisture inside, one of the collector's worst troubles. Strong cardboard boxes are very serviceable, and will last longer if they are painted on the outside with shellac or clear varnish, or with one of the clear lacquers sold for protecting brass or silverware.

Pill-boxes are sold in nests of graded sizes, fitting into each other, so that the whole nest when empty occupies only the space

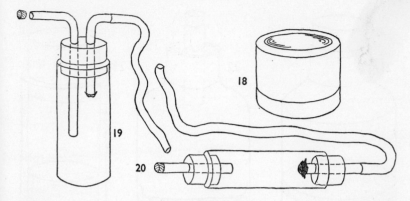

Figures 18–20. Equipment for picking up insects. 18, glass-bottomed pill-box (bottom upwards); 19, 20, aspirators.

of the biggest one. This is very convenient for storage, but that is about its only advantage. As soon as they are brought into use they at once occupy a great deal more space than previously, and this has to be remembered when packing the sachel or collecting bag. It is tedious to have to open all the others before you can get at the smallest one, and so there is a temptation to put insects into pill-boxes that are too big for them. The insects that are caught are seldom graded in size to match the pill-boxes, nor are they caught in the right order of size. A nest of seven pill-boxes nowadays costs about 15/–.

If you can, therefore, it is best to get single pill-boxes rather than nests, and to have a number of boxes of two convenient sizes: 1 in. and 1½ in. diameter, with perhaps a couple of big ones, 2½ in. or 3 in. for occasional use such as taking a larva or pupa with the soil in which it was found. Used singly, pill-boxes have the advantage over tubes that the glass is flat, and so can be seen through without distortion. This allows one to look at the insects with a pocket lens, or to put the box under a binocular microscope and watch the insects alive (see Chapter VI). A pill-box, especially a bigger one, can also be used in the field to confine an interesting insect—say an ant with its burden, or a predaceous insect with its prey—for a time while it is observed, and it can then be released again.

(c) *Collecting-bottles* (fig. 22; Plate XB). In its simplest form this is a variation of the tube, which in this case has both ends open and passes through the cork of an oval bottle small enough to be

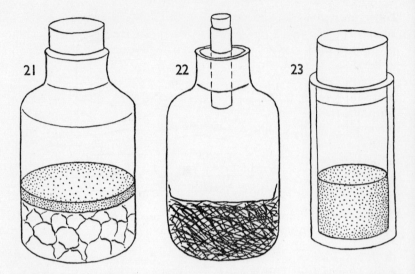

Figures 21–23. Killing-bottles. 21, cyanide lumps underneath a layer of plaster-of-paris; 22, collecting-bottle with laurel leaves; 23, bottle for liquid killing-agents, e.g. ethyl acetate.

held in the hand. The open end of the tube is placed over the specimen, and when the insect has flown or walked some way into the tube the end is corked. It is, in fact, a combination of a small aperture with a bigger receptacle, so as to get the benefits of both. Before taking out the cork to catch another insect, always look at the small tube and if there are any insects in it, shake them down into the bottle first. Such a bottle costs about 3/6.

The simple collecting-bottle can be converted into a killing bottle by putting into the bottom of it one of the killing agents, preferably one of the less poisonous ones, described below. Such a killing bottle is convenient to carry in the pocket for occasional use—say on an outing not specifically a collecting trip, or to keep in an office drawer during the week—but if you expect to make a big catch it is better to use a sucking tube and empty it periodically into a bigger killing bottle, as described below.

(d) *Aspirators* (sucking-tubes and suction-bottles; 'Pooters') (Plate II; figs. 19, 20). After the simple tube, these are the most generally useful of collecting equipment, and every collector should make one. They are used to collect small insects from a net or occasionally directly from foliage, from walls, or from the ground. A *suction-bottle* is made by taking a small bottle, like the collecting bottle already described, but fitting the cork with two small tubes instead of one. The two tubes are bent at right angles, or to any other angle that the collector finds convenient.

Bending a narrow glass tube like this is quite easy. It is heated, not in the hot flame of a Bunsen burner or a gas ring, but in the more diffuse yellow flame of a closed Bunsen or of an oil lamp, until a length of about ¾–1 in. of the glass glows yellow, and is obviously softened. Turn it gently and do not allow the soft glass to sag under its own weight. Both ends have to be held, and care is needed not to burn the fingers. When the glass is soft it is allowed to droop at one end till it assumes the smooth curve that is wanted, when it is taken out of the flame and allowed to cool. Do not put it down on a piece of metal or a cold tile, or it will crack.

The holes through the cork should from preference be made with a cork-borer, but they can be started with an ordinary twist drill, and then made bigger with a round file. Although the glass tubes must obviously be an air-tight fit, do not try to force them into excessively small holes, as they are likely to break at the bend and make a nasty cut in the palm of the hand.

As shown in fig. 19, one tube has a small cork at its outer end, and its inner end open; the other is closed at its inner end with a piece of muslin or a bit of an old net-bag, held on by rubber band or machine-cotton, while the outer end of this tube is fitted with a length of rubber tubing. Sometimes the rubber tubing ends in a glass mouthpiece, but this is liable to break if bitten in moments of excitement.

By sucking at the rubber tube, you can draw small insects into the bottle, and in the intervals of collecting the small cork is replaced to make sure that none of them escape again. The suction-bottle is used for taking small insects out of the net, the head and one hand of the collector being inside the net, so that the contents can be seen, and a selection made of the insects there. The bottle can also be used for direct collecting, and it is particularly useful for picking up insects from the trunks of trees and from walls.

As with other bottles and tubes, a most important consideration is to avoid moisture on the inside. A piece of blotting paper inside the bottle helps to keep it dry, and also provides a foothold for the insects so that they are not shaken about so much. The blotting paper should be big enough to line the sides of the bottle, or to be crumpled up into an immovable ball: it should not be free to move about and damage the specimens.

Many collectors prefer a straight tube about 1 in. or 1½ in. in diameter, in place of the bottle. This then has the two smaller tubes at opposite ends, as in Plate VIII. The tube may be made of glass or of celluloid or plastic material: glass is very liable to break at inconvenient times, and the other materials, though less liable to break, are attacked by some chemicals, such as ethyl acetate, that are used to kill the insects afterwards. A ready-made one costs five or six shillings.

The chief advantage of the suction-tube over the suction-bottle is that both ends can be opened for cleaning. The glass soon gets soiled with droppings from the insects, with condensed moisture, and with fumes of ethyl acetate, which may be unpleasant for the collector when next he uses the tube. A cloth can be pulled through the open tube for cleaning and drying, whereas a bottle is difficult to clean and dry properly, especially during the day, while actually out collecting.

The advantage of the suction-bottle, on the other hand, is that the collector can carry one cork with its two tubes and several bottles, each with a solid cork. When one bottle has been used, and a reasonable number of insects drawn into it, it can be tightly corked and another one used in its stead. Thus different batches of insects—say from different plants, or from different kinds of situation—can be kept separate, and can be taken home alive if this is preferred.

If you are doing a kind of collecting that calls for a number of small samples of insects it is useful to have what is in effect a suction-bottle, but to use as containers a series of tubes closed at one end, and about 3 × 1 in., a kind of tube commonly used in laboratories (see fig. 19).

Whether using suction-bottles or a suction-tube you will need to immobilise the small insects before they can safely be transferred to the killing-bottle proper. The easiest method is to pour a drop or two of ethyl acetate on to a small wad of cotton wool and hold this to the open end of the inlet tube, at the same time sucking *gently* at the rubber tube. Do not suck hard, or you will get a choking mouthful of acetate fumes. Stop when the acetate can just be tasted, and continue to hold the cotton wool in place, watching until all the insects have fallen over and are lying still. Before beginning make sure that no insects are in the small inlet tube itself, and if any are there, get them out by tapping the tube with the hand. Do not make the cotton wool so wet with acetate that drops of liquid are drawn into the tube, or they will make it

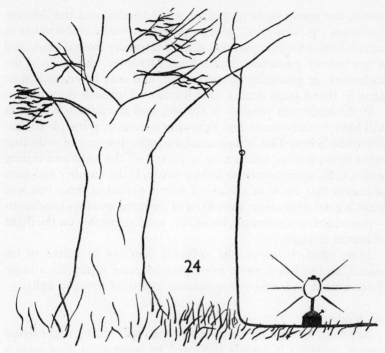

24

Figure 24. Sheeting.

difficult to get the specimens out. Wetting with acetate is less serious than wetting with water, because the acetate will dry without ill effect, but the specimen may be damaged during the time it is actually wet.

After emptying the contents of the tube or bottle into the killing-bottle, and having replaced the cork of the latter, clean out the suction-tube or suction-bottle thoroughly before using it again. This is where the advantage lies with the tube open at both ends, since it can be cleaned and polished with a rag on the spot, and immediately used again.

COLLECTING INSECTS AT LIGHT AT NIGHT

Everybody knows that insects are about at night, and will come to a light. The attraction of the candle for the moth is proverbial.

If you have a house that overlooks open country, or even one that stands high in a residential area, you will find that a lighted window in summer will attract many night-flying insects, not only moths, but many kinds of midges, some beetles, and the delicate lacewings ('golden-eyes') and stoneflies. A bathroom window is most effective for this purpose, since it is usually frosted glass, and is less heavily curtained than others. Moreover, the walls of the bathroom are generally light-coloured, and may be enamelled or tiled, so that a great deal of light is reflected towards the window.

If the bathroom window is opened, and the light left on, you will have a ready-made box light-trap similar in principle to that described below. This is a pleasant and effortless way of collecting night-flying insects, which may be picked off the walls and ceiling with a tube, suction-tube or killing-bottle. If the number and kind of insects that come in are noted over a period of time, you will learn a good deal about the effects of different weather conditions —moonlight, temperature, humidity, wind strength—on the flight of insects at night.

More often, however, the collector goes out in search of his insects, and so has to use a more portable, and if possible a more concentrated and effective apparatus to attract them to light.

(a) Sheeting

Although a single light out in the open will attract night-flying insects, its effect is greatly increased by using it to illuminate a white surface, such as a sheet. The sheet may merely be laid on the ground with the lamp in the middle of it. A hurricane lamp will give some results but an acetylene lamp (now seldom seen), a pressure paraffin lamp with a mantle, or an electric inspection lamp will be more effective. The 'Tilley' Storm Lantern, widely used in the tropics for ordinary house lighting, is excellent for this purpose and gives about 300 candle-power; it burns paraffin and is storm-proof.

A more usual practice is to hang the sheet from the branches of a tree (fig. 24), or to support it vertically with poles, and either to stand the lamp at its foot or to shine the light on to it from such a distance that the beam just covers the sheet from edge to edge. Motor-car headlights are useful for the last method, though to make sure of getting home again afterwards it is advisable to use a spare battery and an extra lamp for the illuminations rather than the ones installed in the car (see also discussion on theory of attraction to light, below).

Such a lighted sheet is effective chiefly in one direction, at right angles to the illuminated surface, and the sheet should be placed so that the insects coming to it will be flying upwind, since this is

found to give the best results. A
modification that allows the light to
be effective in all directions is to
place it in the centre of a square
enclosure of sheets, so that there are
four lighted sides, though here the
sheets must be fairly transparent.

In all cases where a vertical sheet is
used it should not stop short at ground
level, but should extend forwards at
its foot for about five feet along the
ground. This is because many moths,
having come to the light, settle as
soon as they pass out of the light into
the shadows round the base of the
sheet, and they are easily lost against
the bare ground or in grass.

Figure 25, a spirit lamp can
be used to diffuse ethyl
acetate in a light-trap.

Sheeting is very pleasant on a fine summer night, and results
in good quality material for the collection, because each specimen
can be noted as soon as it arrives, and captured with the greatest
care, before it has any chance to damage itself. On the other hand,
the sheet needs constant attention, or at least should be visited
at fairly frequent intervals: it is a common practice to operate
two or more sheets in different places, and to make a round of
visits in succession (compare *sugaring*, page 54).

To collect insects in any numbers, and especially to carry out
any comparative study of the abundance of insects in different
situations, or under different weather conditions, some form of
trap is necessary, so that it will go on operating in the absence of
the collector.

(b) Light traps

The simplest form is the *box-trap* (fig. 26) which anyone can
easily make. Five of the six faces of the box are solid. The sixth is
blocked by two overlapping sheets of glass, which slope inwards;
thus an insect seeking the light is guided through the narrow slit
between the sheets of glass, but it has a small chance of finding the
slit in the opposite direction. An open killing-bottle, or the lamp
shown in fig. 25, may be placed inside the box, so that the escaping
fumes will stupefy and eventually kill the insects; or the latter
may simply be left to crawl into corners of the box, or given
egg-packing material to rest on (see p. 70).

This type of trap has several drawbacks. It throws a light in one direction only, so that even if a good position is chosen collecting may be spoiled by pointing the trap in the wrong direction. A killing-bottle in such a box soon loses its effectiveness, and the bigger and more hardy insects may trample upon and damage the ones killed earlier. If the trap is not visited till next day, the appearance of daylight outside the trap attracts the surviving insects on the glass sheets and they may escape before the collector arrives.

The Hiestand Trap (fig. 27) is a simple device to attract insects from all directions and lead them into a killing-bottle. The light is not enclosed, but an open killing-bottle is slung below it, and is provided with a funnel leading into it. This trap makes use of the observation that insects appearing at a light frequently settle just below the light, if they can, or fly round it until they eventually fall down from exhaustion. The fumes rising from the killing-bottle help to bring this about.

The Williams Trap (fig. 28) is an elaboration of the same idea, and is, in effect, a combination of the box-trap and Hiestand's,

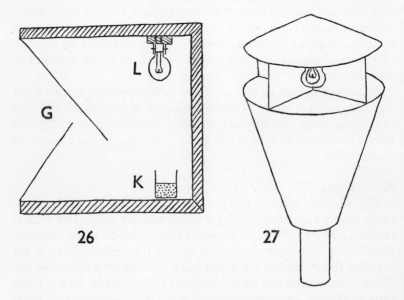

Figures 26, 27. Light-traps. 26, a simple box-trap: G, glass; L. lamp; K, open killing-bottle or spirit lamp diffuser, as shown in fig. 25; 27, Hiestand's funnel trap.

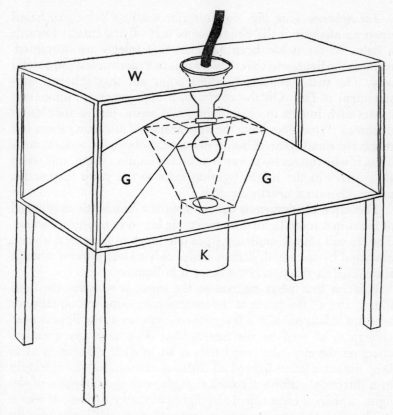

Figure 28. The Williams's type of light-trap: G, arrangement of sloping glass sheets surrounding the lamp; K, detachable container with killing-agent; W, wooden or metal cover.

as will be seen by comparing the diagrams of the three traps (figs. 26–28). One model was specifically designed for taking on collecting expeditions abroad. It therefore folds, not only into a reasonably small space, but into a shape convenient for packing and transport, the wooden legs completely enclosing the glass parts of the trap. The killing-bottle used was a Kilner or Foster fruit jar, the metal screw-cap being permanently fixed in the bottom of the trap just below the hole. As killing agent Williams used tetrachlorethane poured on to plaster of paris. He recommends rolling the plaster round the sides as it dries, so that the insects are still in contact with the vapour, even after a layer of dead specimens has covered the bottom.

The Robinson Trap (fig. 29) introduces a new principle, based upon an analysis of the behaviour of night-flying insects towards a light. So far it has been assumed that insects are 'attracted' towards the light, and that they fly to it in a more or less purposeful way. The two Robinson brothers point out that this is a misstatement of fact. On the contrary, a high general illumination causes such insects to cease flying, and settle, just as they do at daybreak. What does have the appearance of attracting them is a relatively small light at some distance, isolated in a dark area. That is why insects fly towards a distant lamp at night, but when they arrive in the bright lighting close to the lamp they settle, preferably into a nearby shadow.

The same phenomenon can be seen if a bluebottle is released at night in a room lighted by two table lamps in opposite corners. The fly will shuttle endlessly from one lamp to the other, always attracted by the small, distant lamp, only to lose interest when it is attained: a reaction not unknown in humans.

It seems that what matters to the insect is whether the light illuminates all the facets of the insect's compound eye equally, or whether it falls on only a few of these. As soon as the light is near enough to be seen by the insect—that is to have any chemical effect on the eye—the insect tries to fly in such a direction as to keep the same facets lighted all the time. This makes the insect fly in a direction making a constant angle with the direction of the light: a phenomenon called the 'light-compass reaction', of which a fuller account can be seen in entomological text-books, e.g. in Wigglesworth (1950, p. 202). If the light seen is at a great distance (e.g. the sun or the moon) the insect can fly in a straight line and still maintain a constant angle with the direction of the light. If, however, the light is not very far away, say only a few hundred feet, its direction soon changes as the insect flies in a straight line, and to keep the light shining on the same part of the eye the insect has to change direction towards the light.

Under certain conditions of direction of flight and distance the insect is merely deflected for a moment, and then flies on into the night. If, however, the insect passes somewhat nearer to the light the direction of flight is made to change more rapidly, and the insect then approaches the light in an ever-steepening spiral. There are, therefore, two distances that are important in the behaviour of the insect: that at which it first notices, and is affected by, the light; and that at which it begins the fatal, spiralling flight.

III. Putting the head and one hand inside the net is often the best way to corner a captive insect.

IV, To pick and choose out of a sweeping of small insects there is nothing like getting into the net with them.

V. Use a pill-box or a tube to take a middle-sized insect out of the net.

WARNING

It is dangerous to use Ethyl-acetate in light-trap because the vapour is inflammable. The devices in figures 26–29 should be used with tetra-chlorethane only.

Robinson and Robinson (1950) say that they: 'envisage a light source as the centre of two concentric spheres'. The inner, which they call the 'sphere of dazzle' is that in which the spiral flight begins. The space outside this, up to the limit at which the light is seen, they call the 'area of repulsion', and consider that in that space the insect is actually *repelled* by the light, but it seems to me that they have insufficient evidence that any actual repulsion takes place. This is not the place for a theoretical discussion of geometry and dynamics, but readers who are interested will find the Robinson's articles listed in the bibliography at the end of this book, and observations and comments by other people on later pages of the same journals.

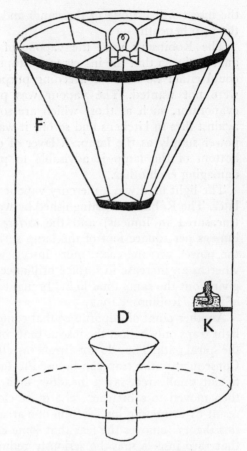

Figure 29. The Robinson type of light trap: F, funnel with vanes; D, drainage funnel for rain-water; K, spirit-lamp diffusing tetra-chlorethane, or ethyl acetate.

Be that as it may, the Robinson trap makes use of the fact that the approach to the light is not direct, but is a spiral path passing round the light, and close to it. The light is at the centre of a number of vertical metal vanes, arranged inside a drum-like container that is open at the top (fig. 29). The light is level with the top rim of the drum. If we visualise an insect flying towards the light, and then round it in a spiral path, unless the plane of the path happens by chance to be exactly horizontal, at one point the path of flight must dip inside the drum. As soon as this occurs the insect will hit one of the vanes and fall down the cone into the trap beneath.

The Robinsons used the vapour of tetrachlorethane as an anæsthetic, so that the insects were stupefied but not killed: they could either be used for breeding purposes, or released, if they were not wanted. The vapour was produced by an electric evaporator, such as those which are sold commercially for use against flies in kitchens and so on: it was worked from the same power supply as the lamp. A layer of cellulose wadding at the bottom of the lamp is advisable to prevent the insects from damaging each other.

The light used was a mercury vapour lamp, which is discussed later. The Robinsons distinguished between the *power* of the lamp (measured in lumens) and the *surface brilliance* (measured in lumens per square foot of the lamp surface). They state that as the power was increased more insects were caught in the trap, whereas an increase in surface brilliance (e.g. by a smaller lamp giving out the same total light) brought in more different species of insect (Robinson, 1952).

Another point of importance that comes out in this work is that light traps only collect the insects that come near enough to begin the spiral path. They do not attract insects from a greater distance. Consequently the trap can be used to take a sample from a particular small area, say a meadow, or a patch of woodland, and then moved to somewhere else quite close, without spoiling the result by attracting insects from one area into another. Moreover this theory removes the fear that some collectors have expressed, that rare insects may be seriously reduced in number, or even exterminated by the use of light traps. The fact that only the insects that would be passing through that limited area anyway can be caught means that only a very small percentage of the insects of the neighbourhood can possibly be trapped.

A portable version of the *Robinson Trap*, for taking on collecting expeditions, has been patented, and is made commercially. It can be obtained from Messrs. Watkins & Doncaster and costs about £7 10s. without electrical fittings, or £15 10s. with all fittings for mercury vapour light, except the long-distance flex.

An Under-Water Light Trap. Three American authors (Hungerford and others, 1955) have described experiments in the use of a light trap under water, for capturing water-beetles, water-bugs, and the aquatic nymphs and larvæ of flies, mayflies and dragonflies. The principle is exactly the same as that of the box-trap used in the open air, but there are practical problems to do with keeping the light working under water, and preventing silt and debris from clogging the trap, or obscuring the light.

In the final version, a 21-in. length of galvanised iron flue-pipe formed the body of the trap, and was used horizontally. Into one end was placed a cone of copper gauze, of 40 meshes per inch, and about 9 in. deep with a 1-in. hole at the apex. The other end of the pipe was closed by a wooden plug, through which were

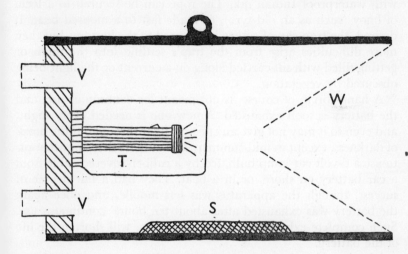

Figure 30. Hungerford's underwater light-trap: W, wire funnel; T, torch, protected in a Kilner jar; V, well traps; S, lead sinker.

inserted four short lengths of 1-in. pipe, each closed by copper gauze like that of the funnel (fig. 30). These were called 'well-traps', and allowed the water to drain out as the trap was lifted, so serving to concentrate at least the smaller items of the catch into convenient receptacles.

On to the middle of the wooden plug was screwed the top of a Kilner jar, or a water-tight preserving jar of a similar kind, together with a fitting to take the end of a pocket electric torch. The authors removed the screw cap from the end of the torch and fixed this permanently in the middle of the jar-top: but if it is preferred, one of the clips used in wireless sets to hold a big condenser could be used to hold the torch.

A lead sinker is attached to the side of the tube in one place, and immediately opposite is bolted a strong eye for the attachment of a length of window-cord or clothes-line. The balance of the various parts is adjusted so that the trap lies horizontally, or with the open (cone) end very slightly raised.

To set the trap, the torch is fitted with new batteries, fixed in position, switched on, and the glass jar screwed into place. The plug is pushed into the iron tube and fixed with screws or hook-bolts. The trap is then gently submerged and lowered by the rope to any desired depth, the rope being marked off in suitable lengths with waterproof Indian ink. The rope can be secured to a form of buoy (such as an old tyre), or made fast to a moored boat. If desired, the trap can of course be lowered to the bottom, but then more difficulties arise from the trap's settling into the mud, or getting filled with silt carried along on a current or the light being obscured by vegetation.

A hand-torch, of course, is not meant for continuous use, and the battery is soon exhausted. A new one is needed every night, and even so it may not give an effective light throughout the hours of darkness, except in mid-summer. The authors describe attempts to use a 6-volt car lamp bulb, fed by a rubber-covered cable from a car battery on shore, or in a boat. They had a fair degree of success, though the apparatus was less mobile, and once again the battery was exhausted after about ten hours' continuous use. Such complete exhaustion, if repeated often, will shorten the life of the battery.

Warning: if such a trap is constructed, no attempt should be made to use mains electricity to light it. Besides infringing the Regulations, it would be extremely dangerous, because of the risk of leakage to the water. Even with a car battery it should be remembered that, although the voltage is deceptively low, the battery is capable of giving a very high current, of the order of 50 amps, if it should be accidentally shorted.

The Mercury-Vapour Lamp. An electric discharge lamp containing mercury vapour is widely used in light traps, because it gives a light with a high content of ultra-violet. Since the bulb is just like an ordinary electric light bulb of the big, 200-watt size, it can be used in any of the usual traps, but is particularly successful in the Robinson Trap. The electrical properties of the lamp need explanation.

Inside the outer bulb is a small quartz tube containing mercury vapour, and it is the passage of electricity through this that gives off the light. The electric current is carried by charged particles, or *ions*, and when the lamp is cold these are few in number.

Consequently the mains voltage produces at first only a small current, and when the lamp is first switched on it gives only a weak glow. The passage of the current automatically generates more ions, and so the discharge steadily increases, and the lamp glows more and more brightly.

If the lamp is connected directly to the mains supply, this process will go on until so much current is passing that the lamp will overheat and burn out. To prevent this the lamp must be put in series with a *choke*, which will allow a small alternating current to pass, but which progressively impedes, or 'chokes' the flow as the current increases. The current is thus automatically kept down within the safety limit of the lamp.

Because the MV lamp looks so much like an ordinary light bulb, there is a danger that it might be mistaken for one. To make sure that it cannot be used in an ordinary mains socket the brass cap of the MV lamp is fitted with three small side-pins instead of the usual two, and it will fit only into a special socket which has three notches to correspond.

The full equipment, therefore, includes the MV lamp, 80 w. or 135 w.; the lamp-holder to be screwed into the light trap, and the correct choke. Lamps cost about £2 5s.; chokes, £5 4s.; and the complete outfit about £8, plus the cost of the extra long lead.

The other end of the lead is plugged into the ordinary domestic lighting circuit (5 amps), and if a fuse is not fitted into the equipment it would be as well to use a fused plug. The supply must be alternating current, only, of 50 cycles per second. Differences in the supply voltage, within the usual range of about 110–250 volts, can be adjusted at the choke, but for countries where the frequency is not 50 a different choke will be needed.

The 80-watt lamp consumes one unit of electricity costing a little over one penny, in 12½ hours; the bigger, 135-watt lamp in just under 8 hours. A generator suitable for the MV lamp is made by Coventry Climax, and costs about £40. It weighs about 80 lb., but will go into the boot of a small car.

OTHER TYPES OF TRAP
Baits and Bait-traps

An obvious principle in setting baits for insects is to use either a natural substance that is known to attract them, or a synthetic substitute giving off the same odours in even greater concentration. Nevertheless, there are a few substances that appear to be highly attractive to insects even though, as far as is known, these compounds are not naturally present in anything the insect normally encounters.

The first group, natural baits, may be roughly divided into the products of fermentation and vegetable decomposition on the one hand, and the nitrogenous products of animal decay on the other.

Fermentation is always attractive to insects because of the alcohols, esters and similar organic compounds that are released. The perfumes of flowers are obviously of a similar nature, and they can be imitated by synthetic chemical compounds, as is done in the perfumery industry. Brewing, wine-making, or even the serving of fermented liquids inadvertently attract insects, and naturally this has suggested the use of sweet and fermenting baits. The oldest of such processes is sugaring.

Sugaring is used principally by collectors of night-flying moths, but there is no reason why it should not be tried as an experiment, in daylight as well as at night, by any general collector.

The bait is a fermenting mixture of sugar, treacle or molasses, and beer, rum or some other form of alcohol. The British Museum *Handbook for Collectors* gives the general proportions as about 1 lb. treacle, 2 lb. brown sugar, $\frac{1}{2}$ pint of beer, and a little rum, but it is emphasised that every collector has his own formula. This is one of those matters already mentioned, in which the acquiring of a personal knack is more important than looking for a magic formula.

The mixture needs to be boiled in an old pan, and stirred into a uniform brew. The longer it is boiled the stickier it gets, and the collector will find by experience what consistency suits him. The best way of sharing the spirits between the sugaring mixture and the collector himself is also one for a personal decision, taking into account the hour of the night, and the state of the weather. A sugaring mixture can be bought ready-made from entomological suppliers.

The sugaring mixture may be simply painted on to trees, fences and walls, or on to specially prepared surfaces, such as sheets of cork or hardboard. Pieces of cork or old sponge may be fixed on to short canes, and the mixture poured over the head, or the head dipped in it. There is no golden rule about where to put the patches of sugar except that generally they should be in positions where the odour can be carried down-wind. The general practice is to go for a walk round the area, leaving patches at a number of likely spots, and coming back to the starting-point. You then have a 'round', and can go round and round it, carrying a hand-lamp, and stopping at each patch in turn to see what insects have come to it, and to take off those you want with a tube, pill-box or killing-bottle. Insects that have been feeding on the sugar will not preserve well if killed while full of it, and may void a sticky mess when they are killed. They are best kept alive until the following day.

As with light-trapping the effect of the weather is complex, and no clear rules can be given, but in general warm, humid nights, when scents are strong, may be expected to give better results from sugaring than cold or windy nights.

Wounded and 'Sappy' trees. Trees that have been wounded by pollarding, by the breaking off of a branch, or by the attacks of the larvæ of the Goat-moth, *Cossus*, may have a patch where sap oozes on to the surface and runs down the trunk. This is a natural sugaring patch, and attracts a great many insects, notably butter-flies and moths, bees and wasps, and flies. When such a tree is discovered its position should be noted, and frequent visits made, both by day and by night.

Rot-holes in trees. In a wound like those mentioned above, in any tree-hollow, in the angle between two branches, or in the exposed end of a cut-off branch or stump, decay may set in and result in a *rot-hole* filled either with a pulpy mass of vegetable matter, or with water that is dark with organic matter. Such holes are always worth investigating. The water may contain mosquito larvæ (some vicious biters among the mosquitoes breed in these holes) or larvæ and adults of any other group that can tolerate life in water containing very little oxygen.

Besides the species that find this a suitable breeding-ground there are other, carnivorous, forms that feed on the first group, or on insects that accidentally fall into the water. The fauna of these rot-holes has never been completely explored, especially in the tropics, where they are abundant, and some very rare and beautiful insects are known only by breeding from larvæ found in such situations. No opportunity of collecting them should be missed.

The water can be explored by means of a small strainer or dipper (fig. 13), or can be baled out or siphoned into a screw-topped preserving jar. It should then be taken home and allowed to stand overnight, when the clear liquid with its insect contents can be decanted off the sediment. The pulpy mass surrounding the hole, including any growth of moss or mould, or any rotting wood, should be cut out with a knife and also carried home in a jar or tin for more detailed examination there.

Figure 31. A pitfall for catching ground-living insects.

Baited traps. Some baited traps are made in the form of wire cages. The general principle of all of them is the same, that the insects are attracted to the bait in a shallow container, and then when they rise up after feeding they enter a wire enclosure from which escape is difficult.

Such traps are effective only for flying insects of course, and the bait is varied according to the insects that the collector wishes to attract. Decaying meat, fish, bones, and animal excreta are commonly used to attract the scavenging and filth-feeding flies, and also, be it noted, butterflies.

Sweet and fermenting baits—decaying and over-ripe fruit, honey, syrup—may also be used in such traps, and will attract any of the insects that normally go to flowers. A little stale beer is an old-established bait in a household fly-trap.

Care should be exercised in using a trap with a sweet bait in a district where honey-bees are about. Apart from the risk of unpopularity with bee-keeping neighbours, the attempt to rescue and release a number of angry bees is not a pleasant experience.

Pitfalls (fig. 31). Crawling and running insects may be caught in baited traps sunk into the ground so as to form pitfalls, from which the insects cannot climb out again because the sides are too steep and smooth. Glass jars make the most convenient containers: tins may be used, but they quickly rust.

A piece of wood or a slab of stone is supported over the mouth so that frogs and toads do not get in and steal the insects, nor a heavy shower make the trap water-logged. For the same reason, the mouth of the trap should be level with the top of a gentle rise of soil, not set at the bottom of a hollow.

The baits used are the same as those in the baited traps for flying insects, described above, but with more emphasis on the animal baits to attract, in particular, the dung-feeding and carrion-feeding beetles. Like all traps, pitfalls should be examined frequently, not only because any insects that die will quickly spoil if they are not removed, but also because carrion as a bait attracts a succession of different insects as the process of decay goes on.

Animal baits without traps. The animal baits mentioned above, for traps and pitfalls, may also be set out on the ground, and inspected at intervals, much as in sugaring. This is more laborious than setting a trap and going away and leaving it; but it is also more rewarding in the quality of the specimens taken, since each can be taken up individually in a tube or pill-box, and killed and preserved at leisure.

There is a certain natural distaste about visiting and examining these baits of carrion and animal excreta, but this can be quickly forgotten in the interest of watching the succession of insects that come to such a bait, and the community of insects that grows up in and around it. Besides the adults that come to carrion or dung there are many kinds of insect larvæ that develop in it, moving out into the surrounding soil when they are ready to pupate.

The Malaise Trap

Anyone who has ever been camping will know how insects continually find their way into the tent, and, in the daytime at least, how they waste their efforts in endlessly climbing up to the roof in a vain attempt to find a way out towards the light of the sky. Every now and then one drops to the ground, but it nearly always starts again to fly up on to the wall of the tent, and then to climb towards the roof. Seldom does an insect, of its own accord, go to the open door of the tent and escape that way, unless the door is the brightest part: i.e. if the tent is pitched in a cave, or under dense foliage.

Almost all insects, winged or wingless, show the same general instincts: to move towards the light; when they meet an obstacle such as a wall, to climb upwards; and after a period without success, to let go their hold, fall to the ground, and begin again.

Dr. Rene Malaise, of Stockholm, had the idea of making a tent of netting, and modifying it in such a way that it became an insect trap. His original material was black fishing net, but any net may be used that would be suitable for making a hand-net for the same insects. One might expect it to be more successful if it were dark and difficult to see, but Malaise traps have been worked successfully in pale materials, and the tents from which the idea arose are also generally pale. The first Malaise trap was a cube, six feet each way, but his later ones had an opening twelve feet wide and six feet high. The roof sloped up to one corner as in the sketch (fig. 33). This was chiefly a matter of convenience, so as to bring the collecting cylinder to the side so that it was easier to empty. A ridged trap, like a tent, may be used, but the ridge should slope up to one point as shown in figs. 32, 33. At this point a flapped opening leads into a smaller net chamber, and this in turn rises to one high point at which a brass tube is sewn into place.

Constructional points recommended by Malaise are that all edges and seams should be reinforced with cotton bands ¾ in. wide, and that the foot of the side-walls should consist of a strip of cheap, strong canvas about a yard wide, half of which makes the lowest 18 in. of the wall, and the rest is laid on the ground and weighted with stones. This part quickly rots if the tent is used much, and so it should be attached in such a way that it can be easily removed.

At as many points as possible of the seams are attached loops of tape for the supporting lines, which are attached to trees, or pegged out with tent pegs, according to the nature of the site chosen. It is important that the exit from the peak of the trap to the collecting-tube should not be obstructed by allowing the netting to sag over it; if necessary, a light wire frame may be built round this opening, or an old lamp-shade frame may be used.

The *killing-bottles* used by Malaise are fitted on to the brass tube at the top of the trap, the tube being slit longitudinally so that it can be pushed tightly into place. Fig. 34 shows the bottle designed by Malaise, which consists of three chambers, screwed together, and joined by two funnel-shaped openings. Hanging from the lower funnel is a spirit lamp filled with ethyl acetate (fig. 25), which vaporises slowly and acts as the killing agent.

The insect, having worked its way up to the top of the netting trap, sees the light of the sky through the gauze in the top chamber of the bottle, and flies into this. After trying vainly to get out, it drops down on to the first funnel, perhaps already partly overcome by the vapour of the ethyl acetate. Falling through the funnel into the middle chamber, the insect is completely overcome by the vapour, and then falls down into the lowest chamber. Here the catch of insects is preserved, in a relaxed state, protected from the weather and carnivorous animals, and free from mould, for an indefinite period. According to Malaise, the insects will remain in good condition for up to a week in humid climates, but need to be removed twice a day in very dry climates, otherwise the insects get dry and brittle.

The position of the trap is very important. It is possible that it might have attractive properties for some insects, since rather similar traps are used for catching tsetse and other biting flies.

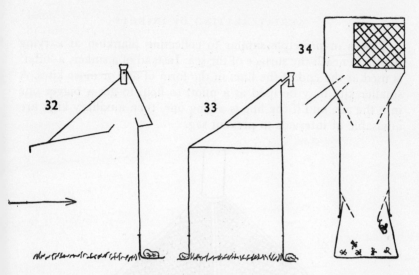

Figures 32–34. The Malaise trap. 32, 33, the trap in side view and front view; 34, Malaise's special type of insect container and killing-bottle.

For practical purposes, however, it is best to assume that the Malaise trap merely takes a sample of the insects that would in any case be passing through the space occupied by the opening of the trap. It must, therefore, be placed where insects congregate. On the edges of woods, across paths and rides, or lanes between hedges—these are likely places. Since most insects tend to fly against the wind the opening should point *downwind* and not the reverse, as might be thought on first consideration. If the wind is fairly strong Malaise recommends putting some branches or low shrubs into the mouth of the trap, because insects use the shelter of such objects to make their way against the wind by stages, and so they might be enticed into the mouth of the trap.

Ideally, such a trap should be carefully set according to the wind at the moment, but one of the advantages of the killing-bottle used is that the trap may be left without attention for several days, and in the meantime the wind may have changed round. To allow for this the trap may be made double, or bilateral—i.e. like two traps back to back, with a Y-shaped tube at the top leading into one killing-bottle. If the trap is to be left unattended it needs to be protected against interference by animals (and humans), and brushwood may be used to fence it round.

AERIAL NETTING OF INSECTS

This is in principle similar to collecting plankton at varying depths beneath the surface of the sea. Instead of a sinker, a 'lifter' is used at the end of the line, in the form of one or more kites. A smaller kite may be used as a pilot, to help to get a bigger one into the air, and if the line is a long one, then auxiliary kites are advisable at intervals to prevent sag.

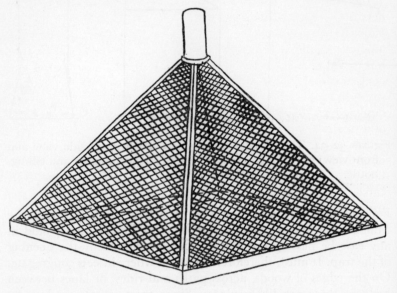

Figure 35. An emergence cage (see text).

The net is bigger than an ordinary collecting-net, and about 3 ft. in diameter is a useful size. That used by Professor Hardy was made of fine silk gauze, and tapered to a point, ending in a collecting-tube; it was, in fact, much the same as a marine plankton-net.

This is not a method for building up a collection of insects quickly, though the average of about seven insects per hour compares not unfavourably with the specialised collecting of any restricted group; if you plan to become an expert on some small family you will not catch them much more quickly than this. Aerial collecting is essentially a comparative method, to find out what insects are about at different heights and in different areas. Consequently there must be some way of opening and closing the net by remote control, so that a sample may be taken between any two desired heights.

The method used by Professor Hardy and his colleagues was to allow nitric acid of different strengths to eat through copper wire in two different tubes. The breaking of the first wire allowed the net to stream open, and the breaking of the second allowed the net to fall, so that a cord strangled it and closed the mouth. The net could then be hauled down at leisure.

In addition to kites, Professor Hardy and his colleagues operated nets from radio masts, ship and trains. To do this on a similar scale to theirs requires a great deal of organisation, and a certain amount of influence with the official bodies likely to be involved; but experiments of a less ambitious kind may be undertaken with comparatively simple apparatus. Suitable kites are available in stores that deal in government surplus equipment, having been designed for use either in meteorology, or for carrying the aerial of a dinghy radio.

Suction traps are a variant of aerial netting, in which a current of air is drawn through the net by some kind of fan, rather on the lines of a vacuum cleaner. Apart from increasing the size of the catch, they allow a known volume of air to be filtered in a given time, and so make possible quantitative studies of the prevalence of different kinds of insects.

COLLECTING INSECTS FROM DEBRIS

A very large number of small insects live in debris of various kinds: leaf-mould, decaying vegetation, garden rubbish, rotten wood, birds' nests, litter from the nests of small mammals, debris washed up by the tide, or left behind after a flood. Some insects can be removed by patiently turning over the material and using an aspirator, but to get a fair sample of the insect inhabitants the mass must be treated in one of two ways.

(a) *Emergence cage*

A wire cage, like a meat-cover, can be put down over a mass of rubbish, so that any insects flying up from it will be trapped. Fig. 35 shows such a cage with a small glass bottle or tube attached, into which the insects gradually pass. This type of cage is suitable for taking out into the field and using on the spot. If you can bring the rubbish back to the laboratory, or your home, in a tin, box or screw-topped jar, it can best be dealt with there in a *separator*, which employs the same principle of attraction towards the lightest place (fig. 36).

The separator is a wooden box which, when closed, is quite dark inside, except at one point where a tube or bottle opens out of the side. Again, the insects coming out collect in the bottle, which is attached by a rubber ring or a screw fitting, so that it can easily be replaced.

If the rubbish is first brought home in a tin or box, obviously this must be quite free of any holes, otherwise the insects will make their way to these in just the same way as they do towards the tube of the separator.

(b) Berlese funnel

Only a small proportion of the insects in the debris will come out of it on their own accord, and these are mainly the winged ones that have developed from nymphs, or emerged from pupæ. The other insects are presumably in the debris because they like moist, dark conditions, and to get them to come out we have to make things too warm and dry for them.

This is done by putting the debris on to a fine wire mesh fitted across the top of a funnel, and immediately underneath an electric lamp (fig. 38). As the debris dries from the top downwards, the insects gradually move downwards to remain in the conditions

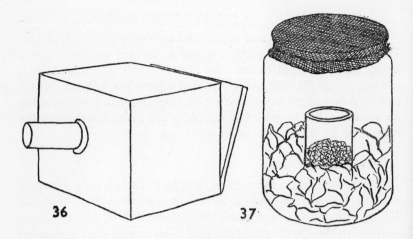

Figure 36. A separator, or emergence box.
Figure 37. Rearing from larvæ: larvæ and food-material in open tube, with crumpled paper or packing material for pupation.

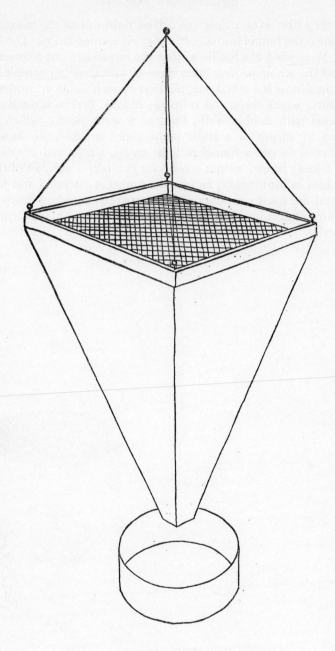

Figure 38. A Berlese funnel (see text)

that they like. When they are driven right out of the mass they fall down the funnel into a bottle of spirit waiting below. The heat must be applied gradually, so that the insects are not harmed by it, and the whole process takes three or four days per sample.

If the funnel is a metal one, the lower part is liable to condensed moisture, which traps and ruins the insects. Berlese himself used a funnel with double walls, forming a water-jacket, which was heated by means of a spirit lamp under a side-limb. Modern practice is to use a funnel of light metal, hardboard or plastic, on a folding frame, so that a collector can take a number of them with him in his luggage. In use, the funnel is extended and hung up, and the spirit container is quite separate, standing below the aperture (fig. 38). Heat is not essential except in very humid countries.

III

KEEPING, REARING AND BREEDING
INSECTS

The first two of these activities are much easier than the last. It is not difficult to keep most insects alive for some time after capture, and to induce the larvæ or pupæ to complete their development in captivity. *Breeding*, however, means maintaining them through a complete life-cycle, mating, oviposition, hatching, successive nymphal or larval moults, pupation, and emergence of a new generation of adults. If all these can be successfully accomplished, then a breeding stock of the insect can be kept going.

The two points at which breeding attempts commonly fail are mating and the feeding of the first-stage larvæ. It is probable that these are critical stages in nature, too. Insects that are active and disperse widely, especially if they fly, may have a slender chance of meeting the other sex unless they have some rendezvous and method of recognition. Mating swarms serve this purpose. A dancing swarm of male midges on a summer's day is a conspicuous sight, and a female has only to approach to be pursued immediately. This kind of mating is obviously difficult to arrange in captivity. In other groups where such congregations of males do not occur, the two sexes may still meet normally in flight, and may be unable to follow through the necessary behaviour-pattern unless they are confined in a very big cage in which something like normal flight is possible.

Once a female is impregnated, the development of the eggs goes on whether she is free or captive, so long as she can get the necessary food, or has already fed sufficiently. Hence oviposition takes place readily in captivity, and the eggs generally hatch fairly easily. Keeping the young larvæ alive is another matter. They are often tiny and delicate, and a great wastage may normally occur in nature at this stage. The first larval stage of many insects is

E

unknown, and it may be passed in some curious or restricted situation: in mud of a particular consistency and organic content; in a particular part of a particular plant; or in some unsuspected crack or crevice. In a great many of the holometabolous insects (see p. 239) we know almost nothing about the requirements of the very young larvæ, and consequently we cannot reproduce them in the laboratory.

The insects that can be successfully bred continuously in the laboratory are, generally speaking, those whose immature stages are all passed in a uniform and stable medium, and of which the adults are relatively sedentary. This includes insects living in dry stored products (beetles, moths); some of those living in decaying or fermenting material (notably the fruit-fly, *Drosophila melanogaster*), though this statement has to be qualified if the medium changes as it ages; and of course the social insects (bees, ants, termites) which make their own artificial surroundings.

KEEPING ADULT INSECTS ALIVE

The simplest container is a glass jar, covered on top with muslin or netting: the same material that is used to catch the insect may be used to keep it in the jar. The insect needs somewhere to rest; enough moisture, but not too much, and protection from extremes of temperature.

It is usually best to put some sand or soil at the bottom, with a stone, or perhaps one or two plants, so as to provide something like natural conditions. For ground-living insects such as many beetles, the artificial ground should be like the natural one: do not put insects from a dry sandy bank into damp loam, or mud-loving insects into dry sand.

Moisture

This can be provided by damping the soil daily but this is an uncertain process, and the moisture may collect in one corner, and quickly result in the formation of mould. It is better to put the water on to a definite spot, such as a piece of sponge, or to put into the cage a small glass tube, filled with water, and its mouth plugged with cotton wool (fig. 41). The tube should lie on its side, so that the cotton wool is kept wet. In a bigger cage, a small spirit lamp may be filled with water, and the wick will keep on passing out moisture to the atmosphere (fig. 25); or an inverted tube as in fig. 40.

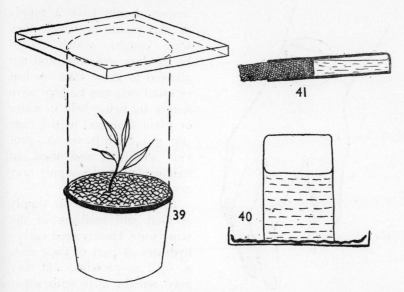

Figures 39–41. 39, rearing cage for insects living on a plant; 40, a device for supplying water to caged insects; 41, a wick-tube, using a wick of rolled gauze or cotton wool.

At all times when handling living insects it is essential to avoid the condensation of drops of moisture on the inside of the container, because these may trap the insects, and damage or kill them.

Temperature regulation

This will seldom be necessary during a short period after capture, unless the insects have been sent from a tropical country. Thanks to air transport, it is now possible to receive living insects from the tropics or the Arctic within a few days of their capture, though immigration restrictions make it less easy for a private individual to do this than an institution. The point to remember is that the tropics are not always intensely hot, nor the Arctic always freezing cold. It is only necessary to protect the insects against extreme temperatures that lie outside their normal range. More will be said on this point later, when we discuss rearing insects.

Food

Food must be provided. Caterpillars, bugs and other plant-

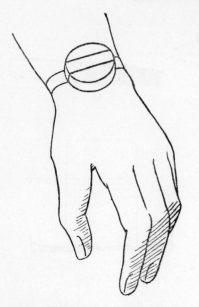

Figure 42. A gauze-topped pill-box strapped to the wrist for feeding bloodsucking insects.

feeders should have a supply of the plant on which they were caught, which should be regularly renewed, and not allowed to grow stale. A leaf or small twig can be kept alive longer by being held in water or planted in soil in the cage (fig. 39). Such leaves also provide moisture, and then an independent water-supply may not be needed.

Raisins are a useful supply of food and moisture at the same time. Insects need carbohydrates as part of their diet, as well as proteins, and they may remain alive with sugar and water, though they may not be able to produce eggs in the absence of protein food. The raisins should be chopped, or pulled apart, dropped into the cage, and renewed if they show signs of mould.

Carnivorous insects can be given prey as nearly as possible that which they normally take, and blood-sucking insects can be allowed to take blood, either from a laboratory animal (rabbit, or guinea-pig) or from a human volunteer, if one is available. Fig. 42 shows how a gauze-topped pill-box can be strapped to the skin with sticking-plaster, to allow the insects inside it to take a meal of blood. The use of humans for feeding such insects is best restricted to insects that have been bred in the laboratory, and are having their first feed, so that there is no risk of transmitting any infection.

Insects that normally live in stored products (flour, grain and so on) are adapted to great dryness, and can be kept alive indefinitely in their own food material, without a special supply of either food or water. The main problem here is cleanliness. Flour moths (*Ephestia* or *Sitotroga*) will breed happily in a jar of flour or breakfast cereal, but they soil it with their droppings, and mat the food together with the webs that they spin before pupating. If nothing is done, the culture will begin to moulder and smell, and the insects will die. Every ten days or so, therefore, the jar should be emptied on to a sheet of paper, and the insects be sifted out, or picked out with forceps. The jar should be cleaned, carefully dried, and given a fresh supply of food, into which the insects of all stages are replaced. Remember not to clean out the jar with strong detergents or other chemicals that may be harmful to the insects afterwards.

REARING INSECTS FROM LARVAE

Insects may be brought home in an immature stage—nymph, larva or pupa—and kept alive until they develop into adults. This is quite easy to carry out with the insects infesting stored products, as described above, or with those living in dung, decaying vegetable matter, compost or rotting fruit, provided that these materials are kept fresh, and renewed as necessary.

Often it is not essential to use the natural food-material, particularly if that is objectionable, decomposing or offensively smelling. Generally speaking, some degree of fermentation is necessary in order to produce the yeasts that the larvæ need, and dry, sterile media may be unsuccessful, even though in theory they contain enough protein and carbohydrate for the insect's needs. West (1951, pp. 306–365) describes in detail a number of artificial foods for rearing larvæ of house-flies, which may be used for other insects too. They are mostly made up from bran, oats or powdered milk, which is moistened, but not saturated with water. Sometimes yeast and malt are added to give a start to the necessary fermentation.

Messrs. McGregor & Co., Quayside Mills, Leith, Edinburgh, make a composite mouse food for the feeding of laboratory animals, and this can be used for some insects, including omnivorous ones, such as cockroaches and crickets.

Carnivorous larvæ, such as those of the blow-flies, can be reared on ground lean beef, provided it does not contain too much fat, which produces acids that are less favourable to larval growth. Dog-biscuits, and patent dog- or cat-foods may be used for this purpose, and larvæ have been reared on an entirely artificial medium consisting of Agar, baker's yeast and salt.

To all media likely to decompose rapidly, the addition of a little formalin (40% formaldehyde) will delay bacterial action. The amount must be regulated by trial and error to avoid killing the larvæ.

Providing sites for pupation

Once again the insects infesting stored products will look after themselves in this respect, and so will many aquatic insects, but those whose larvæ live in a semi-liquid or decomposing medium usually need a drier place in which to pupate. Those, like caterpillars, which feed on leaves in the open, need at least support for the pupa, and usually some degree of shelter as well.

Fruit-flies (*Drosophila*), reared in milk bottles or similar containers, will climb up and pupate on the glass above the culture medium, and will cement themselves very firmly to the glass. They can be assisted by pushing a piece of cardboard down the side of the bottle, so that it is partly below the level of the medium, and partly above, thus increasing the area to which pupæ may be attached.

Many insects pupate in the soil, and for these it is sufficient to put the vessel containing the larvæ and their food material inside a larger vessel, and standing on a layer of soil, in a jar like that shown in fig. 37, but with soil in place of the crumpled paper. Sand may be used instead of soil, but in either case the problem is to give just the right amount of moisture. Too little is liable to cause the pupa to dry up and die; too much leads to the growth of moulds and fungi.

Insects that are fairly resistant to drought in the pupal stage (e.g. blow-flies) will pupate successfully in any crumpled paper, and a most useful material for this purpose is the rough corrugated or cellular material that is used for packing eggs. This can be broken up into small pieces, or used as a folded sheet. It is particularly successful for Lepidoptera, many of which spin a silken cocoon, or suspend the pupa with threads of silk, and the rough packing material gives a good anchorage. It also satisfies the instinct that many larvæ have to press themselves into a crevice, with as much as possible of their body touching a surface (thigmotactic reaction).

The regulation of moisture during pupation is a matter on which no general rule can be given, except to be guided by what is known about the pupation-sites in nature. In excessively dry conditions pupæ may lose moisture through their skin, and through spiracles. If they are kept in a warm place entirely without moisture the pupal skin becomes so brittle that mechanical injury may lead to death, even if desiccation does not.

On the other hand, too little moisture is less risky than too much, which will quickly bring mould and fungus. The atmosphere may be kept moist enough by using a small wick-tube (fig. 41), and just a trace of 40% formalin in the water will help to keep away mould.

Temperature requirements of pupæ

Many insects that now occur in temperate countries are of tropical origin, or are closely related to tropical groups, especially the domesticated species like the house-fly, the blow-flies, fruit-flies, and many household beetles. Others, like the social Hymenoptera, or the wood-boring beetles, pass their early stages in places where they are protected from extremes of temperature. In some at least of these groups, breeding may go on continuously if the larvæ and pupæ are kept warm, and the life-cycle may, indeed, be shortened by raising the temperature to tropical heat.

On the other hand, insects that are fully adapted to living out-of-doors in temperate countries have to be able to withstand low temperatures, often far below freezing, in the winter. They may do this by going into a state of immobility and arrested development known as *diapause*, which is akin to the hibernation of, say, tortoises, and which may affect any stage of the insect, from egg to adult. The physiological state of the insect during diapause is only partly understood, but it may be an essential part of the life-cycle, so that the insect cannot complete its development until it has been chilled, or even frozen.

Consequently, if you collect pupæ of Lepidoptera or beetles in exposed places, in shallow soil, under a light covering of leaves, in the angle of a tree, or by splitting hollow stems, do not try to 'hatch them out' by bringing them indoors and keeping them in a warm place. Put them in soil or sand in a wire cage out of doors, or in an unheated garage or shed. Do not try to protect them from frost any more than you found them protected in nature, but see that they have good ventilation, and do not get sodden with condensed moisture. Most pupæ need moisture when they are getting ready to emerge, when obviously rapid chemical changes are going on. If you have identified your pupæ you will know roughly when they are likely to emerge, and about a fortnight before that they should be transferred to damp sand, which is kept moist by occasionally spraying with water from a fine spray, but is not made sodden.

Rearing of Microlepidoptera

A paper by Ford (1940) describes techniques particularly suitable for Microlepidoptera, but with principles that can be applied to other insects. For example, he covers the breeding-jars with a sheet of plate-glass, and grinds the rim of the jar with silver sand and water until it makes complete contact with the glass. For keeping insects on growing plants that are rather dry, or liable to wither quickly he uses a glass jar, but if the plant is a succulent one he prefers a flower-pot, to avoid drops of condensed moisture. He points out that larvæ which feed in the spring and pupate in summer usually need to pupate in earth, or at least among dry rubbish or hollow stems. Those which pupate in winter are the more hardy ones and may be kept exposed in tins in a cellar or cold outhouse until they are put into sand for the last two weeks of the pupal period.

Rearing of leaf-mining insects

The technique described by Spencer (1956) for AGROMYZIDÆ applies to leaf-miners of other groups too. He puts the leaf straight into an air-tight tin, or a screw-topped jar, to avoid loss of moisture from the mine. As soon as the insect is seen to have pupated it is removed from the leaf, otherwise it soon gets mouldy. The pupæ are kept in small, labelled tubes until they emerge, when they are killed and mounted with the empty pupal skin on the same mount. For these pupæ, too, periodic damping is required, and frosting if they are exposed to this in nature. Spencer warns that a high rate of mortality is normal, and must be expected.

Sleeving of larvæ

Where it is not convenient to remove part of the food-plant of a larva and grow this in a small cage, one can do the opposite, and place the cage round the insects where they are found. Thus caterpillars that are found feeding on a shrub may be confined by enclosing the twig on which they are feeding in a sleeve of fine muslin (fig. 43). This not only keeps the larvæ from wandering away, but protects them from attack by birds or parasitic insects. It is necessary to watch them, and if they have eaten up the food available, to move them to a fresh branch of the same shrub.

Larvæ that do not pupate in the soil will make their cocoons inside the sleeve, and the twig can then be cut off and moved to a gauze cage, ready for the emergence of the adult insect. For those

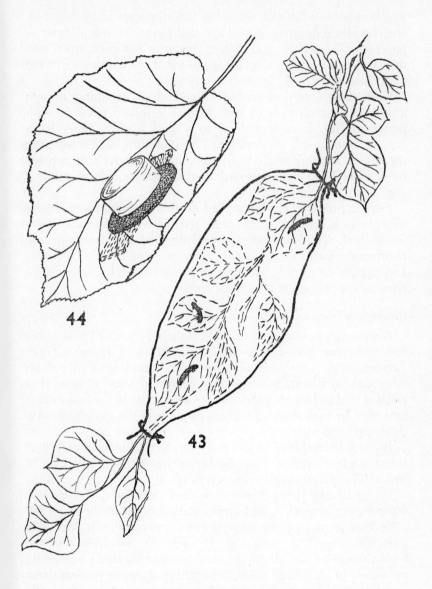

Figures 43, 44. Keeping leaf-feeding insects under observation. 43, by sleeving a branch; 44, by Kaloostian's magnetic cage.

which pupate in the soil, when the larva appears to be fully fed, one end of the sleeve is opened and tied round the rim of a pot or jar containing soil or peat. When the larva has gone down into this the jar is transferred to a cage to await the emergence of the adult insect.

Kaloostian (1955) describes a method of confining minute insects on a small area of leaf. A small celluloid pill-box, with perforated lid, is cemented on to a steel washer, using balsa cement, or a similar preparation. This miniature cage is put over the aphids, or other small, leaf-feeding insects, and is held in place by a small bar-magnet pressed to the opposite side of the leaf (fig. 44).

A similar method can be applied to aquatic insects by enclosing nymphs in a wire or gauze cage, part of which projects above water-level. You will have to provide food for them: for the carnivorous forms mosquito larvæ, fly maggots, *Drosophila* larvæ, Daphnia, meal worms, 'ant eggs'; for those which browse on algæ on stones, a few suitably covered stones.

Rearing and breeding locusts

A recent pamphlet, written by P. Hunter-Jones, and obtainable free from the Anti-Locust Research Centre, 1 Prince's Gate, London, S.W.7, gives detailed instructions and advice for those who wish to maintain a breeding colony of these insects. It is stressed that locusts are particularly easy to raise in the laboratory, and may be used with advantage in place of the cockroach as a demonstration insect.

If you want to breed locusts this pamphlet is indispensable, and it has much to say that is applicable to the rearing of any kind of insect. There is no single correct type of cage, but 'anything from a jam jar to a large tea chest can be used'. Similarly, 'Controlled-temperature rooms . . . and thermostatic control in the cages are unnecessary, except for experimental purposes'. In fact this pamphlet illustrates admirably the general principles that we have already set out: simple methods; uncomplicated equipment; avoidance of condensed moisture; untiring attention to cleanliness with frequent and regular removal of droppings and uneaten food; periodical disinfection of the cages and their fittings; avoidance of extreme temperatures outside the normal range tolerated by the insect; and patience.

IV

HOW INSECTS SHOULD BE KILLED,
AND PRESERVED TEMPORARILY

How an insect is killed may have an important effect on its permanent preservation, and this should be borne in mind when deciding which method to use. Do not be unnecessarily hasty in killing all the insects caught, because as long as they remain alive they are not only interesting in their behaviour, but are also surprisingly tough. Living insects are able to survive without damage a shaking that would knock scales and bristles, and even limbs, off a dead one.

On the other hand the bigger insects are very liable to damage themselves by fluttering about in captivity. Flies and dragon-flies may break the tips of the wings, while butterflies may beat off most of the scales, and completely change their appearance. If bigger insects are to be kept alive in tubes or pill-boxes, they should be given something to provide a foothold: a leaf, or a piece of paper, or, perhaps best of all, a piece of the rough material used for packing eggs. The container should be kept in the dark as much as possible, so that the insects will rest quietly, and not spend their time trying to beat their way out.

Take great care to avoid the condensation of drops of water inside the glass, which easily occurs if tubes of pill-boxes are left lying in the sun, or carried in a warm hand, or in the trouser-pocket. The danger is greater if fresh green leaves are put in with the insect, and that is why paper or other absorbent material is to be preferred. Even a small drop of moisture may trap the insect by a wing or a leg, and it will then break itself to pieces trying to get free.

A drawback to bringing the specimens home alive is the space needed to give each one a separate container, and numbers of small insects must usually be killed in the field. If they can be kept together without risk, the muslin cage shown in Plate VII is excellent.

If you intend to collect one particular group of insects you should find out what methods of killing are recommended by specialists in that group, making allowance for the fact that a specialist in any subject is inclined to take his own fads too seriously. Chapter IX gives some indication of methods suitable for each Order of insects. For making a mixed general collection, any of the killing-bottles described below will do, but the bottle containing plaster-of-paris moistened with ethyl acetate is generally to be preferred.

KILLING-BOTTLES

All chemicals that will kill an insect quickly are bound to be poisonous to the collector to some extent. With ordinary care the risk is small, but killing-bottles of all kinds should be treated with great respect. Always keep the killing-bottle tightly corked, except when insects are being put in or taken out. The bottles should be packed carefully, away from sandwiches and other food, and should not be carried in warm pockets, because this causes the killing agent to vaporise too much, as well as encouraging drops of moisture to condense inside the bottle.

Glass bottles should not be allowed to rest against each other, or against other glass-ware, because in this way they break very easily. A killing-bottle that is broken or damaged should be destroyed, as described below.

(a) Cyanide bottles

These are made in a strong bottle or tube with a specially well-fitting cork. In the bottom is placed a layer of broken potassium cyanide about $\frac{1}{4}$ in. deep, and powdered plaster-of-paris is used to fill the spaces between the lumps of cyanide, and shaken down to a level top. Some more plaster-of-paris is mixed with enough water to make a thick cream, and this is poured over the previous mixture, like a layer of icing (fig. 21).

The setting of plaster-of-paris is an exothermic reaction, in which much heat is generated, and much water vapour given off. It is necessary, therefore, to set the bottle or tube aside, *open*, for a day or so, until the plaster is hard and dry. During this process, bubbles may form in the plaster, and must be broken and filled in while the plaster is still soft. When drying is finished, the cyanide will be held safely under a hard, but porous layer of plaster, and the gradual decomposition of the potassium cyanide will release hydrogen cyanide, which will percolate through the plaster, and fill the interior of the bottle.

Naturally, during the drying process the bottle must be kept in a dry, *well ventilated place*, well out of reach of any people who might not know what it was, or of children or domestic animals. Make sure, too, that the heat of reaction has not cracked the glass.

The cyanide bottle is liable to sweat a little in use, and a circular piece of blotting-paper may be placed on top of the plaster, and renewed when damp. The used blotting-paper must be burned.

Cyanide is an effective all-round killing agent, though it is said to make some kinds of insects brittle, and it sometimes acts slowly. This is particularly true of beetles, and big beetles that have apparently been dead for some time in a cyanide bottle may afterwards come to life again.

These bottles are much used by professional entomologists, who can get them made up in a laboratory under proper supervision, and who can store them safely when not in use. *Although the construction of these bottles is described here, collectors are strongly advised not to attempt to make their own, but to get a chemist to do it.*

The size and shape of the bottle used is a matter of personal preference. If only one is used during a day's collecting it has to be opened again each time a new capture is made, and it is very easy to tip out some of the specimens previously caught, or even to drop the whole bottleful. This risk is reduced if one bottle is kept for taking specimens out of the net, and killing them; as soon as the insect is inert it is transferred to one of several storage bottles, which can be arranged according to the groups of insects, or according to their locality. For this method, tubes about 3 in. long and $1\frac{1}{2}$ in. across are very convenient (as in fig. 23).

Warning: Potassium cyanide is an extremely dangerous substance to handle, and if you intend only to collect occasionally, you should consider whether it is worth while to use this type of killing-bottle. Besides the risk of breakage, there is the responsibility of having the bottle about the house, keeping it away from other people, and eventually of safely destroying it. (For advice on destruction, see below.)

(b) Laurel leaves

This is an old-fashioned, and rather slow, killing agent, but has the advantages that it can be safely prepared at home, and that it keeps specimens relaxed (i.e. soft and flexible) indefinitely, and prevents the growth of mould.

The leaves are picked and crushed or chopped; an old kitchen mincer is said to be effective, but it should be one that is not to be used for food again. A layer of the chopped leaves is put into a tube or bottle of the shape and size described above, and is covered with a piece of blotting-paper. A container of this kind is needed for catching the insect, or taking it out of the net, and a wide-mouthed bottle or tube like the cyanide bottle can be used for medium-sized and big insects. For the very small ones a collecting-bottle of the type shown in fig. 22, with a small tube through the cork, can be converted into a killing-bottle by putting a layer of laurel leaves into it; this type of bottle can of course be used with cyanide, but there is a danger of the escape of poisonous fumes.

In addition to bottles and tubes, tins and boxes small enough to be carried in the pocket may be equipped with a layer of laurel leaves covered with blotting-paper, and may then be used for carrying the dead insects and keeping them in a relaxed condition.

Like most other materials, 'laurel mixture' can be bought from the dealers if you prefer to do so: 2–3 shillings per tin.

Liquid killing agents

These cannot just be placed in the container, like the laurel leaves, but need something absorbent to hold the liquid. Tubes or bottles, including the collecting-bottle shown in fig. 22 may have a layer of plain plaster-of-paris (*without* cyanide this time!) poured into them, and allowed to set, forming a porous block. Unlike the cyanide bottle, this kind of bottle is permanent, and can be used over and over again, with any of the liquid killing agents.

If this type of bottle is used in light traps, the specimens pile up on top of the plaster, and the lethal effect is dispersed. The specimens caught later in the night are liable to move about and damage the others, before they are overcome. Williams recommends that the bottle should be rolled while the plaster is still wet, so as to get a layer all round the sides of the jar, and this remains effective much longer.

Just before setting out on a collecting trip, a little of the liquid is poured on to the plaster, taking care that no more liquid is used than the block can soak up. If any remains free on the surface it will wet the specimens and spoil them. The cork is replaced tightly, and the bottle is ready for immediate use. If necessary, the killing-bottle can be replenished during the day from a small bottle of the liquid, carried for the purpose. This bottle should have a screw top, and should be carefully tested for leaks, because some of these liquids, particularly ethyl acetate, are very fluid, and leak easily.

Another method of holding the liquid in a wide-mouthed bottle is to hollow out the cork and fill the cavity with cotton wool, held in place by a strip of gauze stuck over it. *Killing-tubes* for smaller insects may be made by pushing a tight plug of cotton wool to the bottom of a glass tube, and moistening the plug with the killing-agent. Pieces of celluloid (the real thing, not some of the plastic substitutes) will absorb ethyl acetate, and rubber (in the form of rubber bands, or a rubber bung) will absorb chloroform.

Whatever form of container is used, it is most important to see that there is no liquid that is not absorbed, and that the tube or bottle is not left in the sun, kept in a warm pocket, or clutched too long in a hot hand.

Killing-liquids in common use include *ethyl acetate* ($CH_3COOC_2H_5$); *ammonia* (NH_4OH); *benzene* (C_6H_6); *chloroform* ($CHCl_3$); *carbon tetrachloride* (CCl_4); *trichloro-ethylene* (C_2HCl_3). Such highly volatile substances as ether, petrol, and lighter fluid are not recommended for general use, since they are not only dangerously inflammable, but they evaporate so quickly that they last only a short time in the field. Lighter fluid is sometimes used for killing moths after bringing them home alive (see p. 85).

Undoubtedly the most generally satisfactory liquid killing agent is ethyl acetate; all the others have some drawback, such as being more poisonous, or inflammable, or leaving the specimens dry and brittle, but they can be used on occasions.

Ethyl acetate is a clear, mobile liquid: i.e. it flows very easily, and escapes easily from corks and stoppers. It has a distinctive smell, rather fruity, but not quite the pear-drop smell of its relative, amyl acetate. Though the vapour should not be inhaled more than can be avoided, it is not dangerously poisonous to humans. It acts quickly on most insects making them unconscious almost at once, though it takes rather longer to kill them. Even those who use a cyanide bottle for killing their specimens find it necessary to have a stock of ethyl acetate as well. When small insects are caught in an aspirator (figs. 19, 20) they need to be made quiet with ethyl acetate before they can be transferred to the killing-bottle. It is also most useful to have available at home to deal with those specimens that people will bring to you, alive, in a match-box or a jam jar. The awkward problem of how to get the insect out without letting it escape is solved by putting a few drops of ethyl acetate on to a small piece of cotton wool, opening the box or jar as little as possible, and pushing the cotton wool in. In a few minutes the insects will be immobilised, but not killed, and they can afterwards be revived, or killed in a killing-bottle as desired.

Insects killed in ethyl acetate often die in an extended condition that makes them easier to study, and they also remain limp and relaxed for a reasonable time, though not indefinitely.

Ammonia is favoured by some collectors, especially collectors of butterflies and moths, because it leaves these insects in a good condition for setting. Another advantage used to be that it was available in every household as the domestic ammonia solution, now largely replaced by synthetic detergents, and peroxide or chloride bleaches. In any case domestic ammonia is a diluted solution of uncertain strength.

To use ammonia effectively, one should have the full-strength '·880 Ammonia' of the chemist, but in this form it is unpleasant to handle. It burns the skin, and the fumes attack the eyes, nostrils and mouth: either fumes or liquid may give dangerous blistering if inhaled or swallowed.

Entomologically, ammonia has the disadvantage of sometimes altering the colour of specimens.

Chloroform is not recommended as a general killing agent for insects, but a small bottle of it is useful at times, if it can be safely stored out of harm's way. It will burn if lighted, but is not inflammable in the ordinary sense, and although, of course, it is used as an anæsthetic, the rather pleasant-smelling vapour is not harmful in small quantities. Chloroform decomposes and becomes more poisonous with age, with the formation of carbonyl chloride (Phosgene): it should be kept in a dark bottle, and thrown away if it has not been used for some time.

Chloroform is useful for anæsthetising, or killing, small mammals and birds, in order to collect their parasites. A few drops may be put on to pinned insects in the collection, if these show signs of being attacked by pests.

Benzene, like chloroform, is not a good general killing agent, but is a useful fluid to possess for other purposes (e.g. for cleaning, see figs. 47, 48). It can be used occasionally in the killing-bottle if nothing else is at hand. Benzene is *highly inflammable.*

Destruction of killing-bottles

This applies principally to cyanide bottles, since the other kind

VI. An aspirator is used to collect from tree-trunks, posts and walls.

VII. Biting flies (and other insects), taken in a tube (*left*) or a simple aspirator (*right*) can be carried home alive in this muslin cage, which is airy, and gives good protection against the shocks of the journey.

of bottles with an absorbent layer for using liquid killing agents may be used over and over again.

It is seldom wise to try to remove old cyanide so that the bottle can be used again, because it is very difficult to chip out the plaster-of-paris without breaking the glass.

Never throw old cyanide bottles into dustbins, or on to dumps of any kind, because someone might pick them up who did not know what they were. For the same reason, do not let them be forgotten on a shelf or in a cupboard. Do not keep glass cyanide bottles or tubes in a drawer, because the opening and shutting of the drawer is liable to cause them to break: there is less risk of this with plastic bottles.

Take out the cork of the cyanide bottle, and bury the open bottle in damp soil, taking care that this is not where a dog is likely to see you, and dig it up again. Do not get rid of it by throwing it into a stream. It may be burned in an incinerator, a garden bonfire, or a furnace, but see that it gets really hot, and it is not left lying about in the ashes.

OTHER METHODS OF KILLING INSECTS

Pinching

The bigger insects, notably butterflies and moths, can be killed by pinching the thorax between thumb and finger in one neat, quick, decisive movement. This is a knack, and is learned only with practice. Its advantage is that it kills the insect instantaneously, without giving it a chance to struggle and break its wings, or knock off the scales. Naturally, it is only a worthwhile method if the pinching is expert enough to kill the insect with less damage than using a killing-bottle.

Injecting

The bigger insects, again, can be killed by injecting one of the killing fluids with a hypodermic needle, which costs 7/6 from entomological suppliers.

Drowning

Killing by direct drowning is obviously not suitable normally for insects that are fragile, covered with hair or scales, or have a powdery covering to the body: exceptions are the very volatile liquids, benzene, petrol, lighter-fluid, which are used by some lepidopterists. Tough insects such as beetles and some bugs may

F

be killed by drowning, but the method is used chiefly for killing larvæ.

Many larvæ are adapted to living under very unfavourable conditions, with little oxygen, and so they are able to close their spiracles and resist poisonous gases more successfully than can adult insects. If these larvæ are put into an ordinary killing-bottle with adult insects, the larvæ may crawl about and damage the others, as well as soiling them with excreta. When larvæ die they quickly shrivel and rot if they are not put into a fluid.

Hot water (not boiling) can be used at home, in a laboratory, or in camp. The larvæ are dropped alive into a small quantity of hot water, which is then allowed to cool before the larvæ are transferred to 80% spirit (see p. 132). Larvæ that are killed in hot water must be transferred to the spirit as soon as possible, because if they are left lying in the water rot will set in. Once a specimen has begun to decompose, putting it into spirit cannot repair the damage already done.

Since *spirit* is to be used for storing the larvæ, the latter may be dropped into it alive. In its struggles against asphyxiation, the larva will swallow spirit, and so ensure a complete penetration, but the killing process is slower than in hot water, and may be distasteful to the collector. Some larvæ are difficult to kill in plain alcohol.

To overcome this drawback, and in particular to coagulate the proteins of the cells more quickly, so as to preserve the internal structure as much as possible, *fixatives* are used. The moment a living tissue dies, chemical changes begin inside the cells, and to forestall this a fixative must have great penetrating power, and something of the powerful action of a tanning agent. Such substances as potassium bichromate and picric acid have this property, and a picro-chloro-acetic formula is given in the section on formulæ. The insect is left in the fixative for 12 hours, and is then rinsed in several changes of 80% alcohol, and finally stored in 80% alcohol.

Material so fixed is good for cutting into thin sections for observation of cell-structure, but is too hard and brittle for ordinary identification purposes, and simple dissection of the bigger organs. For these purposes a less drastic fixative is needed. Such a one is Pampel's Fluid, or the variant of it recommended by van Emden, or the Embalming Fluid (see section on Formulæ, p. 303). The insect (adult or larva) if it is large must first be killed in chloroform in a killing-bottle, and then transferred to the fixative, after first making a slit in the body to let the fluid enter. Smaller adults and larvæ may be put into the fluid alive, and in that case a few drops of ethyl acetate should be added, to anæsthetise the insect, and cause it to struggle less.

In this type of fixative the insect is left for a period varying from 24 hours to a week, according to size. It may, if desired, be permanently stored in the fluid, or it may be transferred to 80% alcohol, the latter being changed after the first week.

SPECIAL METHODS OF KILLING CERTAIN GROUPS

Dragonflies—in order to preserve the colours

Dragonflies are often a great disappointment to the collector, because the colours of both the wings and body of some of the most beautiful species are liable to fade quickly after death. There is no simple, generally accepted, and infallible way of preventing this, but suggestions appear from time to time in the entomological journals. Two fairly recent ones are given here, a simple technique, and a more complicated one.

(a) *Method of Fraser* (1949). Lt.-Col. F. C. Fraser, a well-known collector of dragonflies for many years writes: 'The specimens are gutted immediately after killing, and then set upside down on a piece of cork (setting, p. 105), in a dish of methylated spirit, or 75% alcohol for not less than four hours. After this the specimens may be removed to the cabinet.' Specimens treated in this way retained their colours after ten years.

(b) *Method of Moore* (1951). Moore considers at length the special problem of the colours of dragonflies. The following is a précis of his account, which should be consulted for more precise details.

The need for special care applies only to those colours that are produced by pigments lying beneath the insect cuticle. Those produced by pigments within the cuticle, or on its surface, need no special treatment, beyond ordinary careful handling.

The destruction of these *subcutaneous pigments* after death is apparently brought about by decomposition of the body contents, and the same result can be achieved in the living insect by the application of ammonia vapour.

Five methods of dealing with dragonflies are listed:

1. Degutting, followed by oven drying at 110° F. (see p. 107).
2. Degutting, soaking in spirit and drying in air. (This is Fraser's method, given above.)

3. Vacuum drying (see below).
4. Drying under a solvent (see below).
5. Retaining permanently in spirit.

The method of killing is part of the preservation process, if colours are to be preserved. Moore recommends that the dragon-flies should be brought home alive, each pushed head-first into a glass tube so that it cannot beat about and damage itself. A separate killing-tube is prepared, with powdered potassium metabisulphite and citric acid (both obtainable from photo-graphic chemists), covered with a wad of blotting-paper, and moistened with water, when it gives off sulphur dioxide. Each dragonfly in turn is carefully tapped out of its tube into the hand, and then inserted into the killing-tube. The latter can be used several times, until it ceases to work.

The dragonfly should not be allowed to remain in the original tube so long that it dies there, since, once the processes of decay have set in, the rest of the treatment is largely wasted.

This method is recommended particularly for red species but also for yellow, black and yellow-brown species. Those in which other colours predominate can be killed with ethyl acetate (see above, p. 79), using the same kind of killing-tube.

As soon as the dragonfly is killed it should be set (see p. 100): this is the reason for bringing it home alive instead of killing it in the field and bringing it home in papers, or between layers of wadding. The set specimen can be either air-dried or vacuum-dried. For *vacuum-drying* it is put into a chemical desiccator with phosphorus pentaoxide as a drying agent, and exhausted by a water-pump: obviously a method likely to appeal only to someone who collects a great many dragonflies, or who has access to a well-equipped chemical laboratory. The abdominal sternites (i.e. the plates underneath the abdomen) should be punctured to avoid distortion as pressure is reduced, and the abdomen supported by pins until it is dry. Anisoptera (i.e. generally the bigger dragon-flies, see p. 227) need full vacuum, Zygoptera (the smaller Damsel-flies) need only a partial vacuum. The drying takes 24 hours. This method is described in more detail in Chapter V, p. 109.

If the abdomen is marred by grease it should be taken off, cleaned in ethyl acetate, and replaced.

For *solvent-drying*, the dragonfly is killed, set on a small setting-board and immersed, board and all, in ethyl acetate in a suitably-sized preserving jar overnight. When it is taken out the ethyl acetate will quickly evaporate, and leave the specimen ready for the cabinet. The jar may be used three or four times for each filling of ethyl acetate.

Burnet Moths

For these, and for all other moths that either are difficult to kill in cyanide, or go greasy very easily and so lose their natural appearance, Wallis-Norton (1950)* recommends the use of lighter fluid as a killing agent. The moth is brought home alive, and is picked up in forceps and held in a jar of the lighter fluid for three or four minutes. Then place it right side up on blotting-paper in a current of air, when it will dry quickly, and return to full colour. Set immediately. Do not use for butterflies, nor for moths with delicate wings.

BRINGING THE SPECIMENS HOME

Bringing the specimens home alive has already been discussed earlier in this book (p. 38) when various types of tubes and pill-boxes were described. Those insects that are killed at the time of collecting, or soon afterwards, may either be pinned in the field, or brought back for more leisurely pinning at home. In the latter event, they will begin to dry and harden, and must be protected against damage on the way home.

On no account should dead insects be carried about loose in a tube, or in any other container. I know one eminent entomologist who carries dead insects about in his coat pocket, but his eminence does not rest on the beauty of his collections.

Pinning in the field

Generally speaking, an insect can only be pinned once, so if you are going to pin it on the spot you must do so properly. Do not think that it can be spiked in any old way for the time being, and put right afterwards at home. Any attempt to re-pin it later on will only leave an ugly hole in the thorax, if it does not break the specimen completely.

A practised collector can pin very small insects on 'minuten' pins (see p. 111), with the naked eye only, while he is supporting everything on his knee in a tent, but most people will find it better to do this under a magnifying-glass, or the lowest power of a binocular microscope, at home. It is better at first to pin in the

* See *References*, p. 318.

field only insects bigger than, say, half an inch, and bring the rest home in papers or layers, as described below.

The methods of permanently mounting insects by direct pinning, and by staging, are described later in Chapter V. In the field you will have to choose between the two methods, according to the insect concerned, and to choose a suitable pin: a longer, headed pin for directly pinned specimens and a smaller, stainless steel point for those that are afterwards to be staged. The latter are not staged in the field, but are brought home on their small points only.

If you are going to collect insects that are normally set (see p. 100), it may be convenient to carry one or two miniature setting-boards, so that some specimens at least can be set during the day, say while sitting after lunch. Most insects are not set in the field, and many groups—Diptera, Hymenoptera, Hemiptera, Coleoptera, for instance—are seldom set at all. In these groups a little spreading of the legs and wings, while the insect is still soft, is a great help afterwards not only in improving the appearance of the collection, but also in helping identification by making all parts of the insect visible.

Single specimens can be pinned into the inner surface of the cork of a suitably-sized tube. This is a safe method of transit, provided the tube is not broken, but of course it takes up a lot of space. It is more convenient to pack the pinned insects into small pocket-boxes.

Making pocket-boxes. These can be very simple, and many collectors save cigarette-tins or any other tins about an inch deep, and of a size and shape to go easily into the pocket. Rectangular ones, or those with gently rounded corners, are less wasteful of pocket space than circular ones. Plate IX, left, shows a kind of tin that is admirable, after its original contents have been enjoyed.

In the bottom should be stuck a sheet of cork, balsa wood, or one of the synthetic substances ('peat', or 'moll') that are supplied for lining insect store-boxes (see Chapter V, p. 124). The top of this layer should be neatly finished by sticking a sheet of white paper over it, overlapping about a quarter-inch on to the sides of the tin. Apart from improving the appearance, this paper gives a white background to the specimens, against which they can be seen better, and upon which you can mark off groups of specimens with a pencil line, and put down the locality in which they were collected. Balsa cement, as used in making model aeroplanes, or

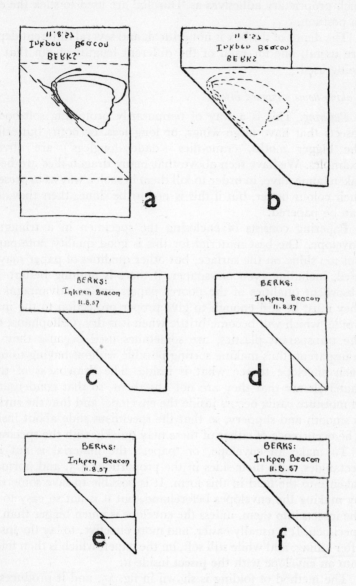

Figure 45. Successive stages of papering an insect. Note how the paper is labelled before being folded.

such proprietary adhesives as 'Durofix' are used to stick the cork in position.

The depth of the box is not critical, and several different depths are useful, one for each of the different lengths of pin that are being used.

Taking home unpinned insects

Papering. This is a way of temporarily protecting soft-bodied insects that have large wings, or long legs, or both: butterflies, the bigger moths, crane-flies ('daddy-longlegs') are obvious examples. We have seen above that many dragon-flies are better taken home alive, in order to kill them in such a way as to preserve their colour better, but if this is not to be done, then they, too, can be papered.

Papering consists of enclosing the specimen in a triangular envelope. The best material for this is good quality note-paper, not too shiny on the surface, but other qualities of paper may be used, including even newspaper, if there is nothing better. The absorbent qualities of the poorer papers are an advantage, but they must be stiff enough to give proper protection to the insect inside, which will become brittle when it is dry. Cellophane, and the transparent plastics, are sometimes used because they are transparent, thus making sorting possible without having to open each envelope to see what is inside. The drawbacks of these materials are that they are not absorbent, so that condensation of moisture easily occurs inside the envelope, and that the surface is smooth and slippery, so that the specimens slide about inside. The occurrence of either of these may quickly ruin the specimen.

To make an envelope, or 'paper', the material is cut into rectangles, with their sides in the proportions 3:5, and normally taken into the field in this form. It is possible to save some time by making the envelopes beforehand, but it is not so easy to get the insects into them, unless the envelope is much bigger than the specimen. It is usually easier, and more effective, to lay the insect, after killing, and while still soft, on the paper, which is then folded into an envelope with the insect inside it.

The method of folding is shown in fig. 45, and it produces an envelope in the shape of an isosceles triangle. Clearly, the length of each of the equal sides will be the breadth of the original rectangle of paper, and so if you know what kinds of insects you are likely to collect, you can cut bundles of papers of one or two convenient sizes before setting out for the day. The smallest that is likely to be worth using is about $1\frac{1}{2} \times 2\frac{1}{2}$ in., while 3×5 in. will take most butterflies. If dragon-flies are to be papered, still bigger envelopes will be wanted.

The bigger the envelope, the more rigid the paper should be, because when the insect has dried it becomes very brittle, and each time the envelope is handled there is a risk of bending it, and breaking the specimen inside. *Only one specimen* should be put in each paper: if two or more are put in the risk of their damaging each other is considerable, and then you will not know which of the legs, wings or heads belong to which specimen.

The soft and flexible insect is laid on the paper rectangle, the wings are raised above the back, and the legs drawn up. The other folds shown in the diagram are then made, taking care each time that no part of the specimen is lying across a fold.

The question of *labelling* of specimens is given special mention later (p. 118), but in papering, the labelling is an integral part of the process. The data—details of date, time, and place of collection, collector's name, and so on—are written on the part of the envelope that will form a flap, before this is folded over. Do not write on the paper with the specimen inside it. In order to avoid having to open the envelope unnecessarily, to see what is inside it, it is a good idea to write on the outside some indication of the nature of the contents. If you can give the genus and species, so much the better: if not, the name of the genus, or the family, or just 'butterfly', or 'lacewing' is better than nothing.

The paper envelopes are carried and stored in a box, which must obviously be broader than the biggest envelope that will be used. On no account be tempted to crowd papers into a box that is slightly too narrow, so that they do not lie flat. A tin is convenient, and permissible for carrying the envelopes home, but it should not be left in the hot sun, nor stored in either a very warm, or a very cold place, because of the risk of condensation of moisture inside it. A wooden or a cardboard box is better, because it will absorb quite a bit of moisture (Plate IX).

The envelopes should be packed just tight enough not to move, but should not be so tight that the insects are crushed. Before carrying the box, if it is not quite full, pack it gently with newspaper, so that the envelopes do not move about.

It may sometimes be necessary to store insects for a long period in paper envelopes. This is a useful way of keeping duplicates, ready for exchange with other collectors, and avoids the expenditure of time and space on pinning and setting them. In this event, care must be taken to see that the envelopes are quite dry before putting them finally away. The papers may be laid out singly in a warm room for a few days, or for a short time in an airing cupboard, but not overheated. Then they should be stored in a tightly closed box, preferably a wooden one, with a few crystals of silica gel to absorb any remaining moisture, and a little paradichlorobenzene to keep out pests. They should be inspected at least twice a year.

Papered specimens are in a compressed, unnatural attitude, and are seldom in a state fit for study without further treatment. Sometimes, especially in clear-winged groups, the insect may be mounted as it lies, on a point (see p. 116), with great care in handling because of its brittle condition. Generally, however, papered specimens will need to be relaxed and permanently mounted, as described in Chapter V.

Layering. When a large number of small insects have been caught it is often not possible to take them home alive, and not convenient to pin them, or mount them on points, as soon as they are dead. A most useful way of storing the dead insects temporarily—and 'temporarily' in this connection may mean anything from a few hours to a number of years—is to pack them in layers between sheets of cellulose wadding.

An outer container is needed, and this may be any kind of box that is available, with the reservation that metal or plastic boxes are best avoided if possible, because they do not absorb moisture, and so increase the risk of mould. Wooden or cardboard boxes are best. Collecting expeditions often take with them nests of cardboard boxes, each box fitting into the next bigger, like a Chinese puzzle. These have the same good and bad points as the nests of pill-boxes: before use they are very compact, and occupy only the space of the biggest box, but once they are brought into use, they take up a surprising amount of space for the return journey.

The material used is *cellulose wadding*, obtainable in rolls from chemists' shops. It consists of innumerable layers of a tissue-like material, rather dusty in use, but quite free from fibres. Do not use cotton wool, because the strands get entangled in the specimens and cause breakage.

On expeditions, or collecting holidays, it saves space on the way out to carry the boxes in nests, and the wadding in the roll, but for a day's or a week-end's collecting the box should be filled beforehand. Cut rectangles of wadding to such a size that they will just fall into the box: the *lower half*—it is irritating to have cut them all and then to find that they fit neatly into the lid. If they are cut too small, then the specimens will shake out of their respective layers, and fall to ruin down the sides of the box. If the sheets of wadding are too big, and turn up at the sides, the specimens will tend to jumble in the middle of each layer, but this is better than the other.

In use, a layer of wadding is spread with freshly-killed insects, and put in the box, followed by another layer of wadding, and another of insects, and so on sandwich-like, till the box is full. At all times the box should be kept so full of wadding that the specimens will remain in position, and do not shake to the sides; yet not so tightly jammed that the specimens are crushed out of shape.

Each layer of insects must have its *locality label*, preferably a paper one, and not too small, so that it, too, stays in its proper place.

The great problem of layering is to avoid mould, which will certainly grow if fresh specimens are shut up and left even for a few days. They may be layered and brought home for drying the same evening, but in camp, or on a collecting trip, it is better not to shut them up until they have been at least partly dried. The best way of drying is to leave them in the sun for a few hours, but then they must be watched to see that a breeze does not scatter them, nor ants take them.

Ants are a great hazard to collectors. Once they have discovered a layer of freshly-killed insects, ants will form a procession to the spot, cut up the juiciest specimens (which by coincidence are invariably the rarest and most interesting), and remove them piecemeal. When a layer of insects is left overnight to dry, it should be placed on a small stand, such as a laboratory tripod, the legs of which stand in small pots filled with paraffin. Better still, dry the specimens in the daytime, and shut them up at night.

When most of the moisture has been removed, the rest will be taken up by the wadding and the box, provided that you are not working in a very humid climate, when these materials will be almost saturated with moisture already. In such conditions it is a good plan to bake the box and the wadding before a fire, just prior to bringing them into use. Into each layer should be put one or two granules of silica gel, which absorbs water without itself becoming wet and sticky.

Very fleshy specimens, or those with a bulky abdomen, should not be layered with other insects, unless they have first been

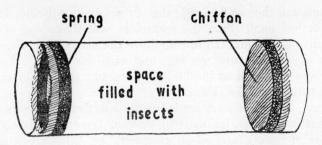

Figure 46. Tube as used by Dr. Malaise for bringing home small insects (see text).

squeezed out with a pencil, as described on p. 106. In any event, the layers of specimens should be examined every few weeks, if they remain in layers for a long period.

Dr. Malaise describes a convenient way of bringing home great quantities of small insects. They may be packed into air-tight glass bottles, like the killing-bottles shown in fig. 23, but with a layer of damp sand to which a few drops of ethyl acetate have been added to prevent the formation of mould.

His alternative method is to use glass tubes, closed off at each end with a sheet of chiffon or fine wire mesh: the latter is more ant-proof. The end material is held in place by a spring clip which slides into the glass tube, as in fig. 46, and which can thus be moved in or out. In use, the tube is filled with mixed insects, which are shaken loosely together, and the clips moved inwards until the mass is just held immobile.

The porous end-pieces allow the contents of the tube to be dried. For the first day they are put in the shade, because too vigorous heating causes moisture to condense inside the glass. When this danger is past the tubes are thoroughly dried in the sun, and then packed into cardboard boxes. For collecting in climates where hot sunshine is not available, a lamp or an oven can be used, but the same principle of gentle drying at first should be followed.

PRESERVING AND
EXAMINING INSECTS

V

PREPARING AND MOUNTING FOR
PERMANENT PRESERVATION

So far we have dealt with the temporary preservation of insects, how they should be killed, and protected against the immediate onset of decay. To make them permanently available for study or display they will need further attention.

Methods of permanent preservation fall into four categories: preserving the specimen dry; keeping it in a liquid; immersing it in a resinous material; and mounting on a microscope slide. Resin or plastic mounts are outside the scope of this book.

In spite of advanced techniques, the pinned and dried specimen is still the commonest and most generally useful for ordinary purposes. Insects, with their external chitinised skeleton, have the great advantage over mammals or birds that most of them can be left to dry naturally, and will do so without offensive decay, preserving to a great extent their natural appearance.

Exceptions are those which are very bulky, and whose body encloses an unusual amount of soft tissue; those whose external skeleton is weakly chitinised, so that they shrink and shrivel; and those whose colour changes on drying, either through structural deformation or chemical decomposition. Special treatment appropriate to these has been indicated in the preceding chapter; in the present one we shall consider the average adult insect.

Dried insects are extremely brittle, and will not survive even a touch without the risk of damage. Ideally, therefore, all manipulation of them should be completed while they are still fresh, and the dried specimen should never be touched again, being handled entirely by its mount. That is why pinning in the field has been advised wherever possible, but it is inevitable that some specimens will have to be brought home for the final handling: the very big ones, especially Lepidoptera and Odonata, and the very small ones that are too numerous for handling on the spot.

Drying and hardening can be postponed by using ethyl acetate or laurel leaves as a killing agent, and leaving the specimens in the vapour. Some collectors find that ethyl acetate overdoes the relaxation, and keeps the specimens rather mushy. Simply keeping the specimens in a tin with green leaves or moistened blotting-paper will delay drying, but there is a risk of the growth of mould or fungus unless a few drops of ethyl acetate or phenol are added. Any plump or fleshy specimens should be slit open and the body-contents removed, before decay can set in and turn the specimen black; rolling gently with a pencil will squeeze out the soft tissues without damage to the rest, so long as the insect is still quite soft.

In practical collecting, however, it is generally necessary to bring home at least a part of the catch in papers or between layers of wadding, and these specimens will be quite hard and brittle in a day or two. Both for this material, and for the further study of pinned and dried specimens, if it is necessary to move a wing or a leg to see details behind it, a technique of *relaxing*, or re-softening of the external skeleton is essential.

Relaxing

This can be done simply by keeping the specimen in a humid atmosphere until the integument absorbs enough moisture again to become soft.

For this purpose *relaxing tins* are sold, made of zinc or other rustless metal, and with a tightly fitting lid (Plate X, D). In the bottom is a fairly thick layer of cork, balsa wood, pith, or other synthetic cellular material of an absorbent texture, but firm enough to support a pin. It is better to have an upper layer of cork and a separate absorbent layer beneath it so that the moisture is not in contact with the insects directly. A closely fitting layer of blotting-paper inside the lid will stop the moisture that condenses on the lid from running into drops, which might fall on to the specimens.

When putting specimens into a relaxing tin, handle them as little as possible. Layered specimens should be picked up carefully with fine forceps, if the specimens are big enough, and very small ones should be gently tapped into the tin. Papered specimens should not be removed from their envelopes, since this would almost certainly break them. The entire envelope should be put in.

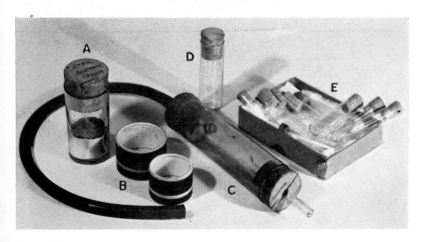

VIII. Take these when you go collecting. A, a killing-bottle for use with ethyl acetate; B, pill-boxes; C, an aspirator; D, a few larger tubes; E, a box of small tubes.

IX. Two ways of bringing back insects, after killing them in the field. *Left*, pinned on steel points, in a pocket-tin (see text); *right*, in papers.

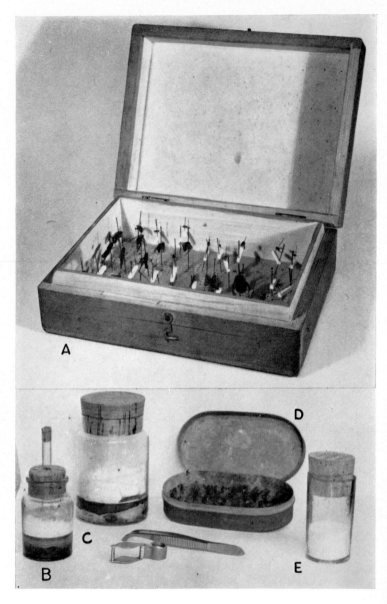

X. Some necessary equipment. A, a standard small store-box;
B, a collecting-bottle, with small tube through the cork, and in this
case containing cyanide; C, a large cyanide bottle; D, a relaxing
tin; E, a small killing-bottle for ethyl acetate. *Centre*, pinning
forceps and a pocket lens.

The absorbent layer is moistened with plain water. The specimens are meant to relax in a moist atmosphere, but not actually to be wetted, so do not allow water to appear on the surface of the absorbent layer. Take care, too, that moisture does not condense in drops on the inside of the lid in spite of the blotting-paper there. Do not move the closed box suddenly from a very warm room to a very cold one, or vice versa.

An exposure of twelve to twenty-four hours will relax most specimens, according to size, but exceptionally big insects, old ones, or greasy ones, may take longer. To prevent mould in the relaxing tin it is desirable to put in either a little solid naphthalene or paradichlorobenzene, or a liquid such as phenol or ethyl acetate. Some people prefer to use glacial acetic acid instead of water in a relaxing tin to minimize mould-formation.

To relax single specimens, and in particular to produce local softening quickly, so that wings or legs may be rearranged, a *relaxing fluid* can be applied with a paint brush to the area concerned. Watkins and Doncaster and other firms of naturalists sell a ready-mixed relaxing fluid. When using this, be careful to allow a reasonable time for the fluid to act before you try to move the insect, and test the limb carefully with a fine pin before using any force on it, so as not to break it off before it has softened.

Note that this fluid, unlike plain water, can be put directly on to the specimen. It seems to ruin the appearance, but quickly evaporates, and may even have a slight cleaning effect.

Cleaning specimens

On the general principle that insects should be handled as little as possible, it is well to avoid cleaning if possible. As with pictures, a little discoloration may be preferable to permanent damage. Much can be done by collecting carefully; by not overcrowding specimens; by not allowing them to be jumbled together, either alive or dead; and above all by keeping Lepidoptera strictly apart from other Orders, using different containers for them, so that their scales do not stick to everything else; or better still, by not collecting Lepidoptera if you have progressed beyond this stage.

Nevertheless, cleaning is sometimes unavoidable, and it is best done on relaxed material. Solid matter, scales, pollen dust can be picked off with a small camel-hair brush, but great care is needed not to break off bristles, nor scratch the surface. Beetles can be handled more roughly than most other insects, and may

G

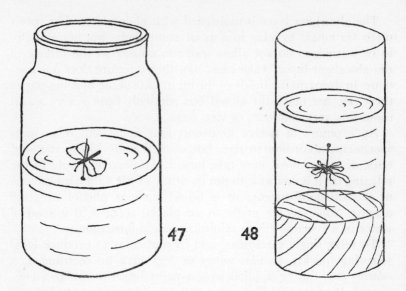

Figures 47, 48. Cleaning specimens. 47, dropping the pinned specimen into the fluid; 48, specimen pinned into the cork of a tube,
which is then inverted as shown.

be gently scrubbed with water or weak alcohol to help to loosen
the particles. These operations may take place under the binocular
microscope for greater safety.

More fragile insects, and those which are dry and rigid to start
with need to be immersed in a fluid. If the specimen is relaxed, or
has dried between layers of wadding, or while papered, it should
be picked up very carefully in fine forceps and dropped into a
small dish of the cleaning fluid. Pinned specimens, if they are
small, should be pinned into the inner surface of the cork of a
small tube, chosen so that the insect will go in without touching
the glass. The tube is then filled with fluid, with the specimen
hanging in it upside down, as shown in fig. 48. Bigger pinned
specimens, or those which are set, are dropped into a jar of the
fluid and left to float on the surface (fig. 47).

Just plain dirt, dust and grime are best removed in water, to
which one of the synthetic detergents (such as 'Tide', 'Surf', 'Daz'
or many others) has been added. These have the advantage of
acting as wetting agents, since very dry insect cuticle is often
difficult to wet with plain water.

To dislodge the dirt after wetting, a soft brush (size 0 or 1) may be used, with great care, under the low power of the binocular microscope, in the same way as on the dry specimen. A fine jet of water from a glass pipette, drawn out to a fine nozzle, is kinder to the specimen than a brush.

Special attention should be given to cleaning the wings of insects, so that the pattern can be seen as distinctly as possible. This is particularly important in wings to be mounted on slides and photographed, since quite insignificant specks of dust will show up as black spots by transmitted light.

Greasy specimens, where fatty material from the body contents has oozed out and destroyed the surface pattern—a common occurrence in most groups of insects except the smallest—need an organic solvent such as ethyl acetate, benzene or ether. Ether is recommended for specimens that are contaminated with verdigris. When the specimen is covered with mould or strands of fungus, these can be removed with a paint brush dipped in phenol (carbolic acid). When using these solvents, remember that some of them are highly inflammable, especially ether and benzene, and the heavy vapour may creep some distance along the table or floor. So do not get more than a few ounces of these liquids at a time, and do not leave the bottle standing open, even at some distance from any light. Phenol is corrosive if dropped on the skin.

If the specimen to be cleaned is mounted on a point (figs. 64, 65), it is generally best to remove it, and afterwards mount it again; the solvent will probably loosen the specimen anyway, and possibly may soften and distort the mount. The solvent to be used for dismounting the specimen must be suited to the adhesive that was originally used. Try water first, in case it is just a gum; then try 30% alcohol, 90% alcohol, ethyl acetate, amyl acetate, acetone and xylol. Apply locally with a brush, rather than immersing the specimen and its mount.

After cleaning, those specimens that have been treated in water or weak alcohol can be returned to the relaxing tin. Those which are to be mounted immediately should be placed for a short time in 95% alcohol, then in absolute alcohol, then dried on a piece of blotting-paper in a gentle current of air. They should be pinned before drying off, or pointed afterwards.

Specimens that have been immersed in the volatile fluids mentioned above can be merely dried in air. Though they may seem to have lost all colour and pattern while wet, they will have a restored brilliance when dry.

Setting

This operation is called 'spreading' in American works, and that term is more descriptive of the craft of arranging the soft, relaxed insect with its wings extended horizontally, and allowing it to harden in that attitude.

The advantages of doing this are that a drawer of set insects looks much neater and more orderly than a collection in irregular attitudes; that setting makes it much easier to study the wings, either with naked eye or with a binocular microscope or a lens; and that the insect so stretched in one horizontal plane can be moved from box to box, and the labels examined, with less risk of accidentally touching part of the specimen and breaking it off.

The drawbacks to setting are the time it takes; the extra space required to house the specimens; and a certain difficulty in seeing underneath the spread wings to examine the sides of the thorax.

Most Lepidoptera are set as a matter of course, because in this group the pattern of the wings is of primary importance, and specimens are more convenient to study, as well as making a better display. Other insects with large and conspicuous wings—Odonata, Ephemeroptera, Megaloptera, Neuroptera, many Orthoptera, and cicadas among the Homoptera—often look better if they are set. Diptera and Hymenoptera may be set by the collector who handles

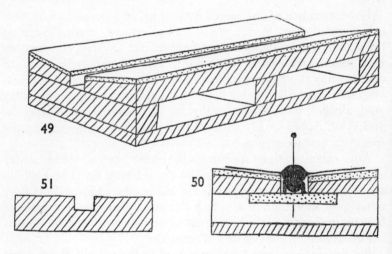

Figures 49–51. Setting-boards. 49, general pattern; 50, cross-section of board; 51, cross-section of a simple board, cut from a single piece of cork.

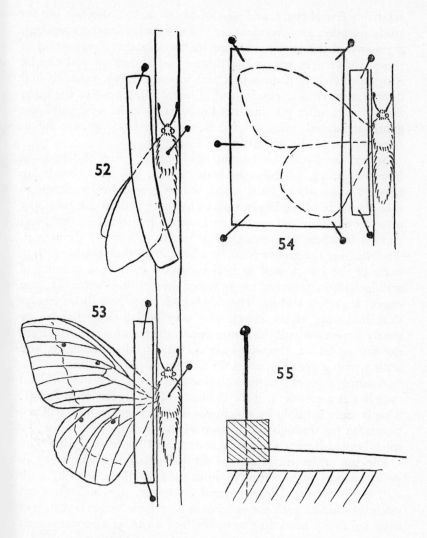

Figures 52–55. Setting. 52, narrow strip of setting-paper, pinned at front end only; 53, wings spread, and held by headless pins behind veins: paper strip pinned down at both ends; 54, a broader piece of setting-paper pushed down over tops of headless pins, and secured by a number of round-headed pins, which do not pass through the wing; 55, a setting-bristle, mounted in a cube of cork.

relatively few of them, and who wishes to make a display, but for study purposes set specimens are not always the most convenient. So many of the structures that are used in the classification of these two Orders are on the thorax and abdomen, and can be seen more clearly if the wings and legs are drawn upwards and downwards respectively, instead of being spread out to the sides. Such insects, after pinning, need only to have the wings and legs gently separated, using a long, thin pin, and taking care not to break off any hairs or bristles.

Setting boards can be bought ready-made, or easily made at home. Figs. 49, 50 show the construction. The side boards are covered with cork or balsa wood, with a groove in the middle to take the body of the insect, and its legs too, if these are not to be spread out. This groove has underneath it a sheet of cork, soft enough to allow an entomological pin to pass freely through it. The width of the groove must be a little more than the breadth of body of the insect, and so it is necessary to have a number of setting boards, covering the range of sizes of the insects that you expect to collect and set. The side boards must be a little broader than one wing of the insect, and may be either horizontal, or gently sloped towards the centre: when the insect is removed from the setting board, the wings always tend to droop slightly, and setting with a gentle upward tilt will compensate for this.

A simple form of construction is to take a thick sheet of cork and merely cut a groove in it for the body of the insect, as in fig. 51. This is more suitable for specimens on short pins, which will not penetrate far through the bottom of the cork. For long pins, or thick-bodied insects a properly constructed board is needed.

For use when travelling, or for collecting few specimens in perfect condition by setting them in the field, there are sold small setting boards fitted into a metal container, in which they can safely be carried with the specimens attached. Single boards cost from 1/6 to 6/– according to width, and a case of assorted boards may cost about £3.

The specimen is thoroughly relaxed, and pinned through the body on a long pin of appropriate thickness (p. 112). It is adjusted to the desired height on the pin with the 'steps' shown in fig. 56, and is then carefully pinned into the groove of the setting board, pushing the pin right through so that the body of the insect is correctly settled into the groove. In butterflies and in other groups where the wings are of paramount importance, the legs are tucked into the side of the body, in the groove, and the specimen made to rest with the wings on the board so that they can be set flat. It is important that the bases of the wings should be just level with the side boards: if they are higher the hind-wings will tend to spring up afterwards; if the body is too low, the setting-paper may leave a mark across the wings.

In other groups, such as flies or Hymenoptera, in which the legs, too, need to be displayed, the specimen is not pushed down so low, so that the legs can be drawn out symmetrically over the surface of the board: this results in a slight droop of the wings

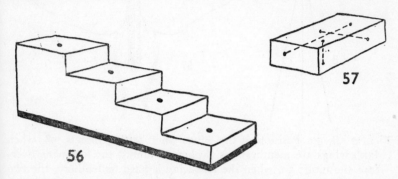

Figures 56, 57. Regulating the height of the insect and the labels on their pin. 56, 'steps', with a brass strip below: the pin is pushed into a step of suitable height, as far as it will go; 57, a block which can be turned over to give three different lengths of hole, when placed on a hard surface.

when set. The antennæ are always displayed, if they are long enough to do so.

The general practice about the position of the wings in setting is that where both wings are membranous they are set with the hind margin of the fore-wing at right angles to the body, and *overlapping* the hind-wing, so that the pattern of the fore-wing can be seen in its entirety (fig. 58). Where only the hind-wings are membranous, as in Orthoptera, the fore margin of the hind-wing is arranged at right angles to the body, and the fore-wings are drawn forwards, clear of it (fig. 59).

A strip of setting-paper is pinned at the front end (fig. 52), and the fore-wing is drawn forward to the correct position by inserting a *fine* pin (oo or ooo) behind one of the strong veins, or through the vein itself. This must be done very carefully, so as not to tear the wing-membrane. When the wing is correctly placed it can

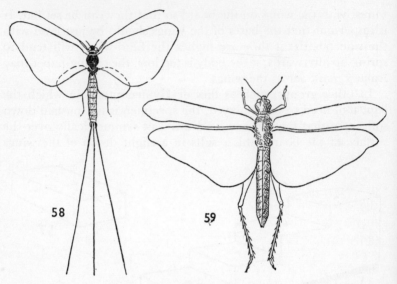

Figures 58, 59. Position of the wings when setting insects. 58, when both wings are membranous (Ephemeroptera), the fore-wing overlaps the hind; 59, when the fore-wing is hard or leathery, the two are not overlapped (Orthoptera).

be held there by pushing the fine pin into the board. If you use a headless stainless steel 'point' instead of a headed pin, you need not remove it until you have pressed the setting-paper into position, and it is holding the wing. Using pins to hold the wing is liable to leave visible holes: it is better to press down on the paper with one hand, and so hold down the fore-wing until the hind one is positioned; then clamp both down by pinning the other end of the paper. A *setting-bristle* may be used to hold down the wings while the paper is being adjusted. It is made by inserting a hog bristle or horse hair into a small piece of cork or linoleum and an ordinary entomological pin at right angles, as in fig. 55.

It may be found easier first to get the wings into position by using a narrow strip of paper across the bases, and then to pin a broader strip across the rest of the wing, making sure that this is flat and uncreased (figs. 52–54). Use fairly thick pins (No. 2 or No. 3), and as many of them as seem necessary to flatten the wings, since these pins pass only through the paper, and not through the wings.

The antennæ may be held under the narrow strips of paper, or may be positioned independently, and held by pins. Similarly the legs, if they are to be displayed, are teased into position with a pin, and held there by crossed pins. If the abdomen is inclined to droop into the groove it should be supported by crossed pins placed beneath it.

Upside-down setting is sometimes advisable, especially for insects such as grasshoppers, which have a large body, and would need a very large groove to accommodate them in the normal way. The relaxed insect is pinned upside down on to a plain sheet of cork and fixed with paper as before. Remember that the overlapping of the wings, when seen thus from below, is the reverse of that described above. The legs are stretched out, and also laid out in the same plane as the wings. When the setting is complete, the main pin is removed, since it passed through the thorax in the opposite direction to the usual one. Such specimens are usually set for exhibition in glass-topped boxes, when they are supported against the underside of the glass with cotton wool.

Do not forget about the collecting data for each specimen. It is easy to lose sight of the labels in the interest of setting, and so to end up with beautifully displayed specimens of no scientific value. The best plan is to write out at once a formal label for each specimen, and pin it to the board alongside.

The length of time taken for a specimen to harden cannot be estimated, since it depends on the amount of moisture present, and on temperature and humidity during drying. Generally speaking, freshly killed specimens will take longer to dry than those which have previously hardened, and have been relaxed. A period varying from four or five days up to three weeks may be needed. It is better not to use artificial heat to hasten drying, and of course to make quite sure that the specimen is hard before it is taken off the setting board. This may be tested by *gently* pushing against a leg or the abdomen with a pin: when dry it should spring back when the pin is removed.

Take off the specimens most carefully, removing the pins, and finally drawing out the specimen on its mounting pin. Put the label on to the mounting pin at once, and if possible put the specimen into a store-box or cabinet drawer forthwith. Do not leave it standing in a moist atmosphere.

Blowing and Stuffing

Any insect that has a large, soft abdomen will shrink badly on drying, as well as being discoloured by the decay of the internal tissues before drying is completed. Whenever there is any doubt on this score, the abdomen should be emptied as soon as the insect is dead.

To empty the abdomen, the insect is placed on a hard surface, such as a sheet of wood or hardboard, and a round pencil is placed across the base of the abdomen. Rolling the pencil gently towards the tip of the abdomen, with moderate pressure, but not enough to burst the skin, will cause the intestine to bulge out of the anus. The protruding part is snipped off with scissors or chopped off with a razor-blade. The rolling is now continued until all the contents of the abdomen have been pushed out.

Sometimes, to avoid damaging the rest of the specimen by crushing it down on to the board, it may be better to cut off the abdomen at the base, and then roll from the tip, so that the contents are expelled from the large hole at the base. Done in this way, it is easier to inflate the abdomen before sticking it on again, by blowing into the base with a fine pipette. If the abdomen is larger it may be packed with cotton wool moistened with phenol or ethyl acetate. In either case the abdomen is left to dry then carefully stuck back on again with mending cement (p. 117).

Insect larvæ, particularly caterpillars, can be preserved dry by a similar process of rolling and blowing, but in this case almost the whole body is emptied, and more care is needed when re-inflating, if the true shape is to be restored. It is advisable to keep the larva alive, without food, for a day or two, so that much waste matter from the intestine may be voided. The larva is then killed in an ethyl acetate killing-bottle, and immediately rolled as described above, starting the pencil just behind the head. When the skin is empty, it is inflated, and kept inflated during the period of drying in a warm atmosphere.

Fig. 60 shows the usual form of apparatus. A piece of glass tube is drawn out (p. 41 as for bending, but pulling it when hot) until it is fine enough to be inserted into the anus of the larva. It is clamped in position by a wire clip, made from watch spring or other spring steel (fig. 61). The skin can be inflated by mouth, but since it has to be maintained under pressure while it is drying, a period of up to an hour, it is better to arrange some form of pressure reservoir. Rubber tubes with double bulbs are available at medical stores, or an ordinary scent-spray bulb can be coupled to a simple reservoir made from a toy balloon, as shown in fig. 60. In either case, the outer bulb is used to inflate the skin, and the reservoir keeps up the pressure until the skin is dry.

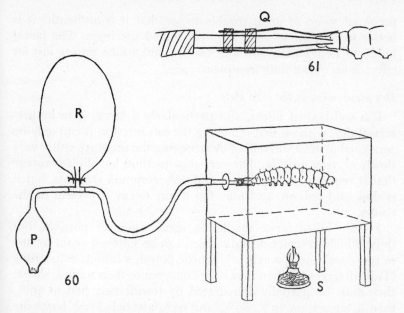

Figures 60–61. Inflating a larval skin. 60, general arrangement of
apparatus: the bulb P creates a pressure, which is stored in the
reservoir R, while the spirit lamp S provides gentle heat until the
skin is dry; 61, details of clip (Q) made from two pieces of spring
steel, holding the anus of the larva on to a fine glass tube.

Do not blow it up too hard, so as to distort the larva beyond its
natural appearance, or even to burst the skin.

The drying oven can be a laboratory incubator, but it can
equally well be a biscuit tin with a spirit lamp beneath it. Warmth
is required, but no great heat, otherwise the specimen may become
distorted, or even charred. A spirit lamp is the form of heat
usually recommended, but an electric light bulb or a tubular
heater may be used instead. An outfit for this purpose including
oven, lamp, tubes and mouthpiece can be bought for 17/6 with a
further 8/6 for the double bulb (1956).

Most colours are preserved well by this method, except green,
which is almost impossible to make permanent.

The dry skin is carefully removed from the tube and mounted.
It may be stuck on to a card or polyporus stage, which is then
pinned, or it may be stuck on to a preserved leaf or artificial
foliage. Unless you wish to make a demonstration case, and are

prepared to go to great trouble to see that it is authentic, it is better to be content with a simple staged specimen. The larval habits of Lepidoptera are well known, and a false setting just for effect is an out-of-date treatment.

Dry preservation in the solid state

If a soft-bodied insect, and particularly a larva, is to be preserved dry, without first removing the soft interior, it can only be protected against shrivelling by removing the moisture either very slowly or very quickly. The very slow method has the advantage that it requires no apparatus, and only common reagents, but it is slow and tedious, and may fail if any decay is present in the tissues.

Freshly killed larvæ should be used, wherever possible, but those which have accidentally dried can be softened again by one or two days' immersion in 2% caustic potash solution, or in strong 'Tide' detergent. When they have come out to their natural shape, they must be partially dehydrated by transferring first to 40%, then in succession 70%, 80%, and 95% alcohol. Fresh larvæ are put straight into the 95% alcohol.

Small larvæ are kept in 95% alcohol for one week, and bigger ones for correspondingly longer periods. Then come three changes of absolute alcohol, for at least a day each. At this stage the tissues should be completely dehydrated, but of course if the larva were now exposed to the air the absolute alcohol would quickly re-absorb water. It must therefore be replaced by a fluid without affinity for water, and xylol is used for this purpose.

The larvæ are transferred first to a mixture of one part of xylol to two parts of absolute alcohol; then two parts of xylol to one part of absolute alcohol and finally to pure xylol. If time allows, a day in each mixture would make a good job. The finished specimen is blotted dry, and may then be pinned or staged, like the blown skin (above).

The above method is described by van Emden (1942).

The quick method of dehydration is by freeze-drying, which has already been briefly mentioned in the previous chapter, as one method of preserving the colours of Dragonflies.

Freeze-Drying

The use of an excessively high vacuum to hasten the drying of insects and other zoological specimens, is limited by the distortion of the specimen that is liable to occur, and which may even lead to complete disintegration. Freezing may be used to support the tissues of the insect against this occurrence, and a method has recently been described in detail by Mr. D. A. L. Davies (1954).

This method requires equipment such as is likely to be available only to institutions, or to individual entomologists who have access to a laboratory. The chief need is for an oil-pump that will give a pressure down to 0.02–0.01 mm. mercury, and for a 'deep-freeze' cabinet that will give — 12° C. and will accommodate an ordinary laboratory desiccator.

Animals that have little or no resistance to desiccation lose water easily under vacuum, and the resultant loss of the latent heat of vaporisation ensures that they remain frozen. Most adult insects are fairly resistant to desiccation, and so there is danger of local thawing, and consequent distortion, unless a much lower temperature is used.

The method described was to put the specimen into a glass tube, immersed in a dish of acetone, and to drop into the acetone lumps of solid carbon dioxide, till they ceased to melt. This gives a temperature of — 65° C. The specimen is then quickly put, in its tube, into the desiccator, using phosphorus pentaoxide as a drying agent. The pump is started before putting the desiccator into the freezing cabinet, so as to make sure that the grease round the rim is not frozen, and gives a good seal.

The desiccator remains in the cabinet at — 12° C., with the pump going, for a period which varies from overnight to three or four days. Drying is complete when the weight is constant at above 30–40% of the original.

The resulting specimen has a curious, rubbery texture, and is not fragile like a normal dried insect. The original colours are preserved during the drying process, but green pigments may afterwards be altered by chemical change.

METHODS OF PINNING, AND CHOICE OF PINS

The only insects that can be pinned through the body are those of which the skin (more usually called the *cuticle*, or *integument*) is tough enough to grip the sides of the pin, and strong enough to support the weight of the specimen while doing so. Very small, fragile, or soft-bodied insects are damaged, or even ruined, if they are pinned, and so, if it is desirable to have them preserved dry they must be stuck on to a card or celluloid point as described below. Insects of a number of groups, notably the small and soft-bodied Apterygota, Thysanoptera, Aphids and their relatives, and the lice, fleas and other parasitic groups, are unsuitable for study if they are preserved dry. They need to be made transparent and mounted on a microscope slide (see p. 136).

Insects that are preserved dry become very brittle after a short exposure to the air, and the pin can only be passed through them while they are still soft. Any attempt to push a pin through a dry specimen if it does not cause immediate breakage, will give trouble eventually, because the cuticle will not grip the pin, and the specimen will turn round on the pin, to the danger of other specimens.

Pinning should be done while the specimen is still fresh if possible, but if a hardened specimen is to be pinned it must be relaxed as has been described above. Generally speaking, the best specimens for the collection are obtained by pinning as soon as the insect is dead, and so reducing the amount of handling to a minimum, but of course it is not possible to do this with every specimen in practice, and a compromise must be reached between quality and quantity. By using several killing-bottles, and such agents as ethyl acetate and laurel to keep the specimens relaxed, pinning can be deferred until the evening, when there is more time to decide which are to be pinned at once, and which are to be allowed to dry between layers of wadding, for attention in the future.

Whenever pinning takes place, the collector has to have some idea of how the specimen is to be preserved permanently, so that he can use a suitable pin from the start.

Choice of pins

This is very much a matter for personal experiment and only general indications can be given. As I have observed in the Introduction, some people feel very strongly about their favourite methods, but the fact is that there is no magic number, length or thickness that is correct.

Pins fall into three general series, 'English', 'Continental' and 'points' (or 'minuten').

English pins offer a range, not only of thickness, but also of length, particularly in the range 18–30 mm. They were developed in conjunction with the English preference for Lepidoptera set low down, near the bottom of the drawer, and allowing the drawers and boxes to be kept shallow. English pins are preferable if you want to stage your specimens (see below), since they are stout, stand up well to handling with forceps, and are easily

replaced if they do become bent. The shortness of the pin is compensated for by the fact that it carries only the stage and the labels,
not the specimen, and it gives less trouble than Continental pins
in touching the glass, or the pins of specimens in the other half of
the box.

'Continental' pins are intended for direct pinning, and so they
concentrate on length, thinness and sharpness of point. They are
generally in varying thicknesses, but in one of three lengths:
35 mm. (Nos. 000, 00, 0 and 1–7); 38 mm. (Nos. 8–10) and
50 mm. (Nos. 11, 12); Nos. 2 and 3 are useful sizes for general use.
They are very convenient if your specimens, and your boxes, are
suited to direct pinning, and the time and the handling of staging
are avoided. The thinner pins bend easily if the cork of the box
is not very soft, and once a direct pin bends it is never the same
again. Attempting to straighten it usually breaks the specimen,
and many a fine specimen that starts out bravely on a long
Continental pin ends up ignominiously with the pin cut short,
staged on polyporus, and mounted on an English No. 11.

An abomination is the Continental pin with a separate head,
that is not a moulded part of the shaft. These either pull off with
a jerk, leaving the pin now thin and headless, or push right down
the shaft. Any pin with a big head is also a nuisance, because it
slips in the grooves of the pinning forceps and suddenly flips the
specimen sideways.

True 'minuten' are very fine, black pins, used for pinning the
smallest and softest insects, and are extremely fragile in use. They
are used exclusively for staging (see above). For this purpose are
also used stainless steel 'points', which are headless, but stouter
than the minuten (though they are nowadays often called by this
name), and which are also used for direct pinning of Microlepidoptera. Their lengths are 10, 15 and 20 mm., in about six
thicknesses. The biggest ones overlap in size and thickness with
the English headed pins of sizes 9, 10 and 20, which may also be
used for staged specimens. Good quality points are obtainable
from Emil Arlt (see p. 320).

The series of numbers used for the different classes of pins, and
their relation with length and size, do not follow a very logical
pattern, and it is best to get a dealer's catalogue, and select what
seem best from what he has available. If the dealer will let you
have a mixed sample for trial, so much the better. A start might
be made with Continentals of sizes 2, 3 or 5, and 8; English
Nos. 11 or 13; and either Nos. 9, 10, or (preferably) stainless steel

points for staging. English pins, made of plated brass are called 'white' if they are untreated, and are slightly more expensive if they are covered with black lacquer, which improves the appearance, and reduces corrosion. A similar effect can be got by treating white pins with ammonium sulphide. English pins are generally sold by weight, quarter-ounce, half-ounce or one ounce. Continentals and steel points are sold by the hundred.

Pins fall into two classes, according to the purpose for which they are used.

(a) Direct pinning (fig. 62)

Here one pin passes through the specimen, and through all the various labels, and still has enough length to hold firmly into the bottom of the box or drawer. The pin must be sharp as well as long, to go through everything cleanly, without tearing a hole. A defect of some 'white' pins is the bluntness of the point. Steel pins are generally sharper than brass ones, but are more springy, and so there is more danger of a sudden flick damaging the specimen. What is wanted in long pins is a combination of sharpness and stiffness sufficient to make it penetrate a label, even if it has to be pushed from the top. If there is room to do so, of course, the pinning forceps should be inserted between the labels, and as low down the pin as possible.

The pin should not be absurdly thick compared with the insect. A big insect perched on a twisted pin like a hair, and a small one apparently impaled on a lamp-post are equally to be avoided.

The *length* of the pin needs to be related to the depth of the drawer or store-box in which you expect to keep it, including the depth of the cork or peat lining. Use the longest pin that can be accommodated, and pin the insect about three-quarters of the way up it. The pinning steps shown in fig. 56 are helpful in getting all the specimens to the same height, and in spacing the labels evenly down the pin. These details greatly improve the appearance of the collection.

The drawbacks of direct pinning are that where the specimen is small it is difficult to choose a pin thin enough to suit the specimen, and yet stout enough to hold all the labels firmly and stick into the box without bending; and that once the pin has been bent it is nearly impossible either to get it truly straight again or to remove and replace it. A third drawback is that the act of taking off labels to read them, and replacing them, easily breaks off legs or wings of the brittle insect.

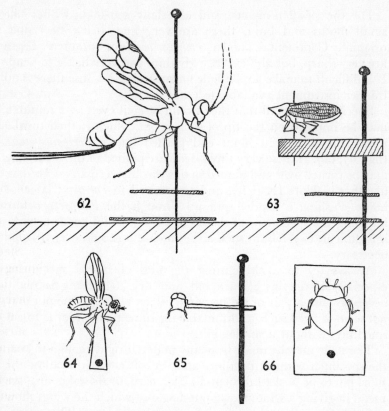

Figures 62–66. Various types of pinning. 62, direct pinning on a
long 'Continental' pin: two labels shown spaced out below specimen;
63, staging on *Polyporus:* labels on the staging pin; 64, gumming on
a card or celluloid point; 65, tip of a point turned up, and gummed
to side of specimen; 66, a beetle carded.

These risks are reduced by the following three methods of
double-mounting (staging, carding and pointing), though they
are replaced by other shortcomings.

(*b*) *Staging* (fig. 63)

This term is usually restricted to the type of double mount
shown in the figure, where the insect is pinned on to the support,
or stage. For medium-sized insects a stainless steel, headless pin is
more reliable than one with a head, since the latter is liable to
twist suddenly in the pinning forceps and damage the specimen.

H

For the smaller insects, and especially soft-bodied ones like small moths and bugs, there are very fine, black steel pins, originally Continental, known as *minuten nadeln* or 'minuten'. These are very sharp, but also exceedingly thin, and very liable to bend. It is difficult to make a pilot hole for such pins, because there is no thinner instrument available to make it.

Specimens so small that they would be split even by a minuten may be impaled on the tip of such a pin, which is then turned upside down, and its blunt end pushed into a *Polyporus* stage (figs. 67, 68). If these very tiny insects are pinned in the field, they may be turned over and pinned in this way into a small pocket-box like that in Plate IX (left), and transferred to *Polyporus* later, at home. Pushing a headed pin up through the *Polyporus* before impaling the specimen, as shown in fig. 69, is not good, because it is difficult to remount such a specimen if it should ever become necessary.

Always try to avoid cutting the pins of staged specimens, especially if the insects are old and dry. If cutting is really necessary, use a pair of strong wire-cutters: although the pin may not seem to need such a formidable instrument, the aim is to cut smoothly, without a sudden jolt.

The stage may be made from any material rigid enough to bear the specimen without bending, and yet soft enough to allow the short pin to be pushed through it. Thin card, or Bristol board, are useful in giving a white background against which the wings show up well, and light is reflected into the shadows. This is not 'carding', which means having the specimen stuck down as in fig. 66.

A card stage may make it difficult to see the underside of the specimen, unless it is carefully cut as small as possible. Celluloid was much used at one time in the belief that its transparency would allow the specimen to be inspected from below. This is only partly true, because the celluloid is usually uneven and scratched, and distorts vision so much, especially under the microscope, that no reliable examination can be made.

The best stage is a narrow, rigid one, and the best material is *Polyporus*, the white material of the great bracket fungus found attached to old trees. In theory anyone can find one and cut it up, but in practice it is easier to buy it ready-cut from a dealer (Plate XI). A quarter-ounce, costing about three shillings, is an ample supply. It is supplied in strips about three inches long, and square in section, each of which is cut with a scalpel or razor-blade into three or four stages. Pins go through it easily, and the stage neither deteriorates, nor corrodes the pins.

In default of *Polyporus*, cork, pith, or balsa wood may be used.

All these narrow stages have the merit of not covering up the underside of the specimen, but on the other hand they do not protect the specimen so much if it is accidentally dropped.

Many entomologists, especially in North America, dislike staged insects, and prefer direct pinning. It is true that stages are liable to work loose on the bigger pin, and may then move round, and perhaps damage specimens next to them in the box. This risk increases with the size of the specimen, and stages are seldom advisable for insects bigger than half an inch in length. A stage, even a narrow one of *Polyporus*, does have a noticeable protective value against many of the shocks of ordinary handling. Staging is particularly valuable when the longer pin gets bent through pushing it into a hard box, since this pin can be renewed without difficulty.

Re-staging specimens. Sometimes it is necessary to rescue a directly pinned insect whose pin has become bent, by cutting down the pin and fitting it on to a stage. The pin should be cut with the best cutters obtainable, in order to jolt it as little as possible. If possible, the point of the pin should be pushed through the stage before cutting it off. Not only does this give support to the pin at the moment of cutting, but it also gives an entry hole smaller than the diameter of the pin, and so ensures a good grip. The blunt end of a cut pin (or the blunt end of a short 'point', if desired) can be pushed into *Polyporus* with fair success, but will seldom hold in celluloid or card.

(c) Carding (fig. 66)

A rectangle of white card or Bristol board (see p. 170) may be used as a stage, but with the specimen stuck on to it instead of being pinned. Suitable adhesives are discussed below, under 'pointing'.

This method is popular with Coleopterists, who are dealing with insects that are comparatively robust, even when they are dead and dried. For more fragile insects the method is suitable for display rather than for study, since it prevents detailed examination of the underside of the specimen. Such specimens are usually set, with legs, and often wings spread out, and the tip of each gummed to the card.

Although in theory the specimen can be taken off the card by

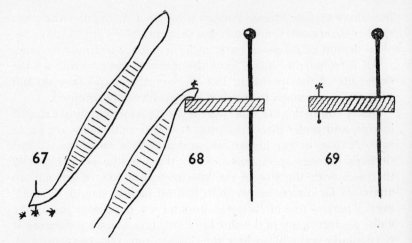

Figures 67–69. Pinning on the tip of a minuten, or steel point. 67, pushing the tip of the point into, but not through the specimen; 68,
inverting the pin, and pushing its blunt end into a *Polyporus* stage;
69, a small, headed pin pushed through the polyporus from below,
and the specimen impaled on its tip—not a good method, see text.

softening the adhesive in a suitable solvent, this process is likely
to result in permanent damage to the specimen; beetles, again,
being exceptional in their tolerance of such treatment.

(*d*) *Pointing* (figs. 64, 65)

This is the best way of mounting the smallest dry specimens. A
small triangle, sometimes with a blunt tip, is cut from thin white
card, Bristol board, or celluloid. As we have seen already, the
transparency of the celluloid is no great advantage, and there is
a tendency to curl and droop, especially if preservatives are used
in the box which have a solvent effect on celluloid. Thin card, or
Bristol board make the best points.

There is a special punch, like a ticket collectors' which can be
used to cut points at great speed, and of uniform size and shape,
but this is not worthwhile unless a large number is required.
Points can be cut by hand if a little care is taken to get them
uniform. First cut a strip of the card, its breadth equal to the
required length of the points. This is then cut across, with cuts
slanting alternately to left and right, taking care that the tips of
the points are as broad or as narrow as you want them. Normally
the tip of the point should be a little broader than the thorax of the

insect to be mounted on it, but sometimes, if the insect has long
and fragile legs, it is desirable that the point should not overlap the
sides of the thorax.

The long pin is carefully pushed through the point, on the
middle line, and near the base, not leaving too much card sticking
out behind the pin. Take care not to use too thick a pin, because
if you start a split in the card the mount will eventually fall apart.

As an adhesive, almost anything may be used that is available,
provided that it is tacky enough to hold the insect firmly even
when the adhesive is wet, and that it does not become too brittle
when dry. A useful adhesive for this purpose, and also for mending
broken insects, can be made by dissolving small pieces of celluloid
(*not* a 'Polythene' or 'Perspex' substitute) in amyl acetate (which
smells of pear-drops, and is not the same as the ethyl acetate used
as a killing agent). Put the pieces of celluloid into a small bottle
and moisten them with the acetate. As the celluloid softens, so
add more acetate in small quantities, until the mixture can just be
stirred into a thick fluid of uniform consistency. It should be just
viscous enough not to drip off the rod; if you make it too thin it
will run over the point and fail to hold the specimen, as well as
dripping down on to the bottom of the box. The consistency can
be varied by adding more acetate or more celluloid as required.

Commercial adhesives of a similar nature, such as the cement
sold for making model aeroplanes, usually dry too quickly to allow
the method of mounting the specimen which is described below;
even for the repairing of broken specimens these adhesives dry so
quickly that, say, a head cannot be placed in position with the
care and deliberation that is necessary. Colourless nail varnish
does not dry quite so quickly, and allows enough time for
manipulation.

Water-soluble gums are handy, because they are easy to obtain,
and because they can easily be softened again by moistening,
leaving the specimen relaxed. The risk of damage is therefore less
if the specimen needs to be re-staged. There is some risk of mould
developing, especially if the gum is stale when used. Some proprietary gums incorporate a mould-resisting chemical. Spirit gums
can be used, but they are generally less readily available than
water-gums, except in theatrical households. A recent Canadian
collectors' guide recommends the use of shellac gel, or of pure
white shellac.

More important than the nature of the adhesive is the way in
which it is used. It is useless to immerse the specimen in a large

bead of gum or celluloid, and the result will not look like a fly in amber. The best method is to put a spot of adhesive on each of a series of points, already mounted on their long pins. Taking the first one by its pin, it is turned upside down and used to pick up one of the tiny insects. For best results this should be done under the binocular microscope (low power), and the specimen quickly manipulated with a needle (or a pair of fine entomological pins) so as to display it to the best advantage. Take care not to push the specimen deeply into the adhesive, not to smear the adhesive on to legs, wings or any other part of the insect that should remain clean and dry for study.

It is sometimes an advantage to turn up the point of the card as in fig. 65, and then stick this to the side of the insect. The specimen then stands upright in the collection, not on its side, and if rather a lot of adhesive has been used, the insect does not sink down into it. This method is favoured in America, especially for beetles.

LABELLING

Specimens without labels are practically useless. It is difficult to think of any purpose for which unlabelled insects can be used, except to make those dreadful mosaics that once were fashionable, or to feed other animals. Collectors sometimes display a drawer of unlabelled insects, and then stand by to explain personally where each one was caught, but this is a short-sighted, not to say a lazy, practice.

Every pinned or papered specimen, and every batch of layered (or spirit material) should have its label (fig. 70).

What information should be given?

The *locality* is essential. The name of the country should come first, and should be written in full whenever possible. Sometimes a long name must be abbreviated, but this should be done in an obvious way: e.g. 'Port. E. Africa', rather than 'P.E.A.'. Initials lead to confusion, especially when more than one language has to be considered. Thus, 'B.O.A.' is British East Africa to a German, but 'A.O.F.' is French *West* Africa; similarly IFAN, in spite of its Arabic appearance, is not a place at all, but an organisation, *l'Institut français de l'Afrique noire*.

Difficulties arise through alteration of international boundaries, but if the date of collecting is also recorded, as it should be, it is usually possible for later workers to find where the boundary ran at the relevant date. A minor point when collecting in other people's countries, for the sake of amity, is to try not to offend them by using a name that they dislike, at any rate if the locality is to be published.

If your collecting will be confined to the British Isles it may seem needless to say so on every specimen, but if you later exchange specimens with friends overseas a full locality is a great help: those who feel it necessary to speak, and write, of 'Paris, France' will appreciate a little help with Sutton-under-the-Whitestone-Cliff. In any event all British material should be clearly labelled with the County.

Next comes the detailed locality, and this should be both clear and precise. Precision is important, of course. Far too many collectors label their material with the name of the town that is their headquarters, when in fact the collecting sites may be ten or twenty miles away, in varied surroundings. But even more important than precision is to name a place that can be identified by other people.

That is why I am discussing labelling in this chapter, and not in the previous one. In the field, temporary preservation is accompanied by temporary labelling, and as long as the collector ensures that the various batches of material are correctly identified, it is permissible to rely upon his memory for the full details when he gets home. An exception is that when material is sent home in advance it should either be clearly marked not to be handled until the collector returns, or else a covering letter should be sent, giving full and explicit details of all collecting stations.

Thus, in the first instance, a collector may label his various lots of material with the names of villages and local features—river valleys, hills and so on—for his personal convenience. When the material is being permanently labelled he should make sure that all the names used appear in gazetteers and atlases, and if they do not, he should translate them into a form in which they can be understood by strangers. Thus, a specimen labelled 'WESTERN AUSTRALIA: Ballinyoo' gives one about a third of a continent to choose from; 'about 100 miles N.E. of Geraldton' narrows the search considerably; and the approximate latitude and longitude would be an even better guide.

Add to this the date of collecting, and the collectors' name, and we have as much as can conveniently be put on one label. Any additional information is best put on a second label, which is then placed higher up the pin. Such details as 'at light', 'dancing in a

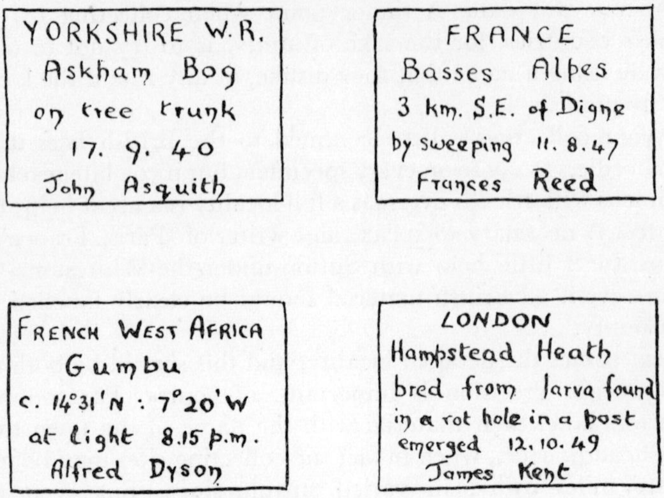

YORKSHIRE W.R. Askham Bog on tree trunk 17. 9. 40 John Asquith	FRANCE Basses Alpes 3 km. S.E. of Digne by sweeping 11. 8. 47 Frances Reed
FRENCH WEST AFRICA Gumbu c. 14°31'N : 7°20'W at light 8.15 p.m. Alfred Dyson	LONDON Hampstead Heath bred from larva found in a rot hole in a post emerged 12. 10. 49 James Kent

Figure 70. Four examples of labels.

swarm', or 'on tree-trunk' are well worth recording for the guidance of anyone who wants to look for more specimens of the same kind.

Making labels

The best material is thin white card. The thinnest Bristol board is excellent, but expensive. Plain index cards will do, if they are smooth of surface, and of a good white colour. Cartridge drawing-paper is not suitable for the tiny lettering that is needed.

The neatest labels are printed ones, using the small type sizes, from Diamond ($4\frac{1}{2}$ pt.) up to Minion (7 pt.). The lettering for one label, arranged as in fig. 70, can be set up on a small hand-press, such as the Adana, and large numbers of impressions made in neat rows on each piece of card. Try to space them as regularly as possible, leaving just enough room between them for a neat cut. The labels are then cut up with scissors, making each an even rectangle, cut as close to the type as one can. This is a tedious operation, and when a large number of specimens have to be labelled, it is more congenial to cut a lot of labels first, and have them ready, rather than to cut one at a time.

If the work is done by a small jobbing printer it may be possible to have the impressions regularly spaced over the card, so that they can be cut quickly with a guillotine, or a photographic print-trimmer.

Writing labels is a necessary part of the collector's art. Even if printed labels are used for long series of specimens there will still be many labels of which so few copies are wanted that it is not worth while to have them printed.

'Written' labels should more properly be called 'hand-printed', since ordinary cursive script is rarely successful, unless you can write copperplate on a very small scale. Hand-written labels tend to become too big, and the only way to keep them small is to learn to print letters of about the same size as the kinds of type already mentioned. Use a simple mapping pen, and ordinary Indian ink, or one of the manuscript black inks that are sold by dealers in artists' materials. Ordinary writing ink is less contrasty when new, and does not give so clean a line, while it may change unpredictably with age.

If a long series of labels is needed, and type-printing is not possible, the labels can be duplicated photographically. There are two methods of doing this, with and without a camera.

For the first method you will need a sheet of 'Kodatrace', a thin, transparent plastic sheet, one surface of which is matt, for writing upon. You also need a packet of cut film, size $3\frac{1}{2} \times 2\frac{1}{2}$ in., grade 'Fine Grain Ordinary'. Cut a piece of the Kodatrace the same size as the film, and upon the dull side of it write a series of labels in Indian ink, just as in fig. 70. When this is quite dry take it into a photographic dark-room, in a bright red safe-light, open the packet of cut film, and put a sheet of the film with the emulsion side against the dull side of the Kodatrace. It is easiest to do this in a small printing frame, but it is sufficient merely to place the two sheets on the table, with the Kodatrace on top, and cover them with a piece of plate-glass.

The exposure is made by momentarily switching on the white light. The length of exposure must be found by experiment and the easiest way to get consistent results is to have a reading lamp shining down on to the frame (or glass), and to switch on and off for a measured number of seconds. For economy a sheet of film may be cut into about eight pieces, and these used for trial exposures at the first attempt. The film is then developed and fixed in the usual way, and gives a negative of white letters on a dark ground. When this is dry, any number of contact prints can be made from it, each of which will cut up into eighteen or twenty labels.

The alternative way is to take a sheet of white card about 7×5 in. (i.e. twice the linear size of the negative required) and to write the eighteen labels correspondingly big, having first divided up the space into eighteen one-inch squares. This is then copied with an ordinary camera, provided that this will extend to the necessary one-and-a-half times the focal length of the lens, and a negative is produced, as before. This method is rather more troublesome than the first, because of the necessary adjustments of the camera and subject, and in particular because of the problem of getting really even lighting of the background; variations of lighting that are scarcely perceptible to the eye will show as grey tones on the finished labels. On the other hand, there is the advantage that the image is reduced and so the printing appears cleaner and neater; moreover, it can be reduced to a size smaller than one could conveniently write direct.

If you expect to do a lot of collecting in one locality it would be useful to make a negative of 'skeleton' labels to which the final details can be added in ink later. Another most useful negative is one of determination labels, for which there will be a permanent use. This last kind of label should be left in sheets until required, because the names of insects vary greatly in length, and it is convenient to write in the name in ink and then cut the label neatly round it.

While we are discussing labels we might mention the labelling of spirit collections (*see* below). Printed labels are excellent, of course, and so are those written in Indian ink, provided that the latter are quite dry before they are put into the liquid. The practical difficulty is that one often needs to write a label and use it almost immediately, and Indian ink is not waterproof for quite some time after writing. Many people write their labels for spirit collections in fine pencil, which does not run, but after long immersion in spirit it becomes paler and may be almost illegible.

The only effective safeguard with spirit collections is to inspect them at regular intervals, not too long apart, and to check the label at the same time. If the label is badly faded, do not throw it away, but add a new one written clearly.

It is a sound practice in both dry and spirit collections, never to remove and destroy any label, however unnecessary or incomplete it may seem. If you wish to add a better-looking, or more detailed label, do so by all means, but keep the original one underneath; if it is a large, ungainly paper label, fold it, like the one shown in Plate XIII, C. Queries that arise long after the specimen has been collected can often only be settled by referring to the original label, and it is surprising how much can be deduced by a little detective work.

Make all labels self-sufficient, as far as possible, and avoid the practice of using letters or numbers that refer to a separate field-book or card-index. There are exceptions to this rule, when the data are sent in a letter ahead of the specimens, or when the field-notes are much too long to go on the label, but you may be sure that sooner or later the letter and the field-notes will vanish, and the specimens will be left bearing cryptic symbols that can no longer be interpreted.

Spacing of labels on pinned specimens

Nothing spoils the look of a collection more than labels that are roughly cut, or untidily placed on the pin. The ideal is to have the lowest label resting on the paper which lines the box or drawer, and the others evenly spaced above it, all parallel, and each capable of being read without having to move any of them. Moving of labels round on the pin is to be avoided as much as possible, because this enlarges the hole until the label droops and twists uncontrollably. The aim, therefore, is to get each label straight into its correct position, and to leave it there. The 'steps' shown in fig. 56 are a gadget for this purpose. Each step has a vertical hole slightly thicker than the thickest pin to be used. After having staged the specimen, and pushed the staging pin through the mount, the label that is to be uppermost is impaled on the tip of the staging pin. This pin is then placed over the hole in the top step, and pushed down as far as it will go, keeping the label parallel to the specimen. The process is repeated with the second label, on the second step, and so on.

An alternative to the steps, and somewhat easier to make, is a block of wood or soft metal in which a row of holes is drilled, to gradually increasing depths or a block like that in fig. 57. *Never* use one large label and pin several specimens into it; in fact never have more than one pin going through a label that is attached to an insect. When you want to take out one of the pinned insects you will find it difficult not to damage the others.

STORAGE IN BOXES OR CABINETS

Permanent collections of pinned insects are kept either in store-boxes or in cabinets of drawers.

Store-boxes (fig. 71; Plate X), may be either of wood or of cardboard, but they must be strong, and carefully made, because they are expensive, and ought to last a long time. Although smaller boxes for temporary storage or posting may exist in a variety of sizes and shapes, boxes for permanent storage are invariably rectangular and flat, so that they can easily be stacked in a pile, or arranged neatly like books on a shelf. They used to be made with a rounded edge, to imitate a row of books, but in these more austere days they are normally flat on all sides and edges, as in Plate X.

The sizes in common use range from 10 × 8 in., up to 18 × 12 in. When you start your collection it is well to look ahead, and to choose one suitable size and stick to it. A collection looks neater, and is easier to handle, if all the boxes are alike and interchangeable. The size to choose depends on what you mean to collect. Butterflies, or dragonflies, or stag-beetles need the bigger sizes for even a modest number of specimens. For most other insects one of the smaller sizes is to be preferred. A box 18 × 12 in. will hold about 300 miscellaneous flies or beetles in one side, or double if the lid can be used as well. Every time you rearrange your collection you will have a lot of moving of specimens if you keep them in boxes as big as these, but by using a smaller size of box as a unit in your collection you can reduce the work of rearrangement considerably.

Store-boxes may be either single or double-sided: that is, they may have specimens in the bottom only, or in the lid as well (Plate XII). The pinning material is cork, or one of the synthetic materials ('peat' or 'moll'), and is covered with white paper. The important things to look for are strength and rigidity: wood that seems well seasoned and with a good grain, so that it is unlikely to warp out of shape; and a lid that closes firmly enough to keep out insect pests, but not so tightly that it opens explosively and blows all the specimens to bits.

In the front wall is generally a small cell for holding naphthalene or paradichlorobenzene (shown open in fig. 71). The depth of the box is generally about one-and-a-half inches each side, if double-sided, including the soft lining material. Extra deep boxes are available, but are seldom needed, except for very large beetles, or the largest Orthoptera, insects which are thick as well as long.

See that the lining material is soft enough to take a long fine pin without bending it, yet firm enough to hold it securely. A *gentle* pressure with the fingers will show if the material is unduly spongy: some of the molls with large particles and big air-spaces

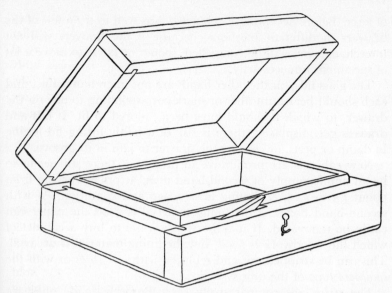

Figure 71. An entomological store-box, which may be used either for general storage, or as part of an arranged collection.

between them crumble easily, and this causes the paper to tear, especially along the edges, and in a few years' time the box fills with fine dust.

New boxes cost from £1 to £2 each, according to size. Second-hand boxes can be bought from dealers much more cheaply, since they often buy in old collections just to get the boxes. You can do the same, if you come across them in the sale-room, or at country auctions. Second-hand boxes should be examined carefully to make sure that they are still pest-proof, and that the lining material has neither hardened nor crumbled with age. If this material seems to be firm, it does not matter if the paper is full of pin-holes, and stained or spotted, since the box can easily be relined with white ceiling-paper.

A snag about buying second-hand boxes is that it is difficult to get them uniform in size and appearance.

Cabinets consist of a number of glass-topped drawers, each sliding on a pair of runners, so that any drawer can be pulled out without disturbing the drawers above and below it. These drawers are made to a high degree of perfection, and should be completely interchangeable without sticking, or requiring the use of force. Before accepting a cabinet it is as well to try a few of the drawers in different positions, because if the drawers will not interchange you will be compelled, sooner or later, to move a lot of specimens unnecessarily.

The glass lids, on the other hand, are not interchangeable, and each should bear a number or mark corresponding to one on the drawer, to which it should have been tailored to fit. If lids and drawers get misplaced, there is risk of a badly fitting lid letting in damp or pests, or causing the drawer to jam in its groove.

New cabinets are prohibitive in price, but there still seems to be an ample supply of second-hand ones, at prices varying from about £5 to £25, according to size, age and condition. As with second-hand boxes, if the lining material is good the paper can easily be renovated. It may be worth while to buy a cabinet of which the woodwork is good, but the lining material is decayed. This can be stripped out and replaced with *cork strips* or with the *cardboard trays* of the unit system.

The strips are comparatively easy. Properly made ones are edged with wood at each side to obviate crumbling and curling of the soft material, and to make a neater fit, but this is not strictly necessary. A workable alternative can be made by cutting up a sheet of cork or moll and wrapping each strip in lining-paper, finishing it off neatly and smoothly with a rubber adhesive. The number and breadth of the strips obviously depends on the size of the drawer, and of the specimens to be put in it: if they are butterflies, or dragonflies, or cicadas, all of nearly the same size, each strip can be made broad enough to take a single column of specimens; for smaller and more varied insects you will want to get several insects abreast on each strip (fig. 72.)

The original lining material of the drawer is cleaned out completely, together with all the glue that was holding it. The strips are then laid side by side to fill the bottom of the drawer, and held in position by a narrow beading screwed to the front and back wall of the drawer.

The advantage of the strip system is that whole columns of specimens can be moved about during rearrangement, not only saving time, but reducing the wear and tear on the specimens.

Drawers for butterflies may have glass bottoms as well as glass tops, so that both sides of the specimen can be examined. The pinning material is then a very narrow strip of soft wood, broad enough only to take the pin. These drawers are heavy, as well as expensive.

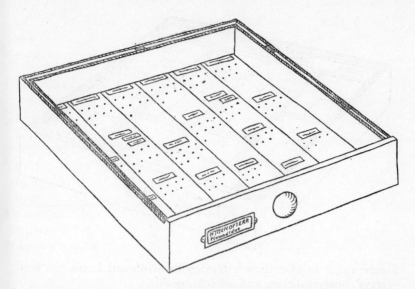

Figure 72. A cabinet drawer, with the bottom divided into interchangeable strips. Note also the double walls, which give an air-tight and pest-proof fit for the glass lid (which is not shown).

Unit-trays are a much more expensive item, because they have to be machine-made, to exact outside dimensions. The units are chosen so that the drawer can always be exactly filled with them, and each tray has its own lining of peat or moll, like a miniature drawer. This is the most modern way of keeping a collection, and has great flexibility. Not more than one species is put into one tray, but long series of specimens of one species may extend into a series of trays. Rearrangement, of course, is a simple matter of moving the trays about, and for routine examination of specimens it is necessary only to take out a tray and put it under the binocular microscope. Here the wear and tear on the specimen is even less than it is in the strip system (fig. 73).

Unfortunately at the present time the cost of this system is prohibitive for all except the bigger institutions, and the advantages of unit-trays are most apparent in a major collection.

The question whether to keep one's permanent collection in store-boxes or in cabinets is primarily one of cost. Apart from this, however, both have their pros and cons as follows:

Store-Boxes. Advantages: collection can be added to indefinitely, a box at a time; it is easy to insert an extra box at any point to

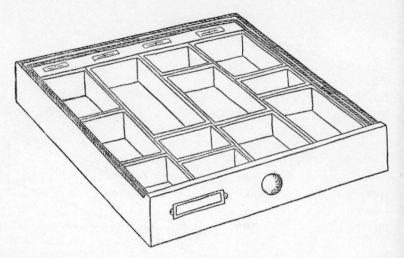

Figure 73. A cabinet drawer filled with cardboard boxes, or 'unit-trays', of several sizes, and interchangeable.

relieve congestion; rearrangement of the boxes into a different order is easy; the only accommodation needed is a set of shelves, or even an improvised arrangement of blocks and planks; double-sided boxes save a lot of space; well-made boxes are pest-proof.

Drawbacks: specimens cannot be examined without opening the box, and this causes wear of the specimens, through shock and sudden draught; loose specimens, labels and pins are not seen if the box is not opened, and may move about and damage others; with double boxes there is danger that pins on the two sides may interfere with each other; boxes are generally treated more roughly than drawers, and if stacked on edge they may be allowed to topple over.

Cabinets. Advantages: each drawer can be handled without disturbing the others; the specimens are visible without taking off the lid, saving both time and wear and tear; a collection in drawers has a much better appearance; and, because it is visible, there is less temptation to neglect and overcrowd sections of it.

Drawbacks: rearranging the collection is a bigger undertaking, especially if the cabinet is not a first-class one, and the drawers are not fully interchangeable, and if the drawers have solid bottoms; a cabinet-drawer and its glass lid are more cumbersome than a store-box, and take up a lot of table space while they are being opened; the cabinet is an article of furniture, which takes up space in a room, and may not match the rest of the furniture.

A compromise may be sought by using single-sided store-boxes with glass tops, as is the practice in some of the biggest museums. These boxes may be stacked either vertically on shelves, like ordinary store-boxes, or horizontally like drawers. They are not as pest-proof, nor as durable as either ordinary store-boxes or drawers, but they make a convenient system.

Labelling of boxes and drawers

We have dealt already with the labelling of each individual specimen, and stressed the importance of preserving intact all the labels that may be given successively to a specimen, so that the information on them is not lost.

The labelling of boxes and drawers serves a different purpose. It is not to preserve data, but to act as a guide and an index to the collection. This labelling is consequently much more flexible, and there should be no hesitation in scrapping it and renewing it whenever it gets out of date.

A collection worthy of the name should be arranged according to some system. The expression 'a systematic arrangement' is generally used in a narrow sense to mean an arrangement in Order, Families, Genera and Species, on the lines indicated in Chapter VIII. This is commonly the most useful plan, but it is not the only one. A biological arrangement may show the insects grouped into plant-feeders, predaceous forms, and so on; or an ecological collection may bring together the insects of a hedgerow, a chalk down or water-meadow, or those living under bark, or breeding in a tree-hole. Such collections are particularly useful for exhibition or demonstration purposes.

The labelling of such collections is part of the general display, and may form a big part of it. Typed or printed explanatory labels, diagrams and photographs may be appropriate, as well as eye-catching devices such as arrows, coloured pointers, and so on. This is an exercise in montage and décor rather than in curating, and goes beyond the scope of this book; there is a section about it in Borror and Delong's book.

Collections arranged on biological, ecological or similar lines rank as exhibits, rather than as primary collections. Their value depends upon the correct identification and classification of the insects included in them, and these in turn call for access to a true 'systematic' or taxonomic collection.

I

Obviously the outside of boxes or cabinet drawers will have a general label, either stuck on, or fitted into a little frame: the latter is more usual on cabinet drawers. The label should bear the name of the Order of insects in capitals; the family; and usually either the genus or genera included, or some other indication of the scope of the contents. An example is shown in fig. 72.

Inside the drawer, the usual practice is to cut rectangular labels and fix them to the bottom of the drawer with short pins. Very short, white pins are sometimes used, but these are soft and easily bend. Less conspicuous are short, headless pins, or the points cut from ordinary white pins of No. 11 or a similar size. It is useful to cut a number of these and keep them ready in a corked glass tube. Any strong wire-cutters may be used (see above, under 'staging').

Names of families and genera, and intermediate categories such as sub-families and tribes, are put *above* the specimens to which they refer: names of species are placed *below* (see fig. 74). Where more than one name is in use for a genus or species (*synonyms*, p. 206) the oldest one generally has priority in use, and the other labels are placed below it, and slightly to the right, to indicate that they are not in valid use.

These internal labels may be written, typed or printed, but whichever method is used, be consistent and be neat. It makes a great difference to the appearance of the collection. Cut the labels carefully, with straight edges, and close to the print all round, as it is difficult to estimate a wider margin accurately. Bend the ends of the label slightly downwards before pinning, so that they do not curl away from the lining paper.

In groups such as British Butterflies, where the names are fairly well settled, it is possible to buy printed *Label Lists*, on one side of the paper only, and ready for cutting out for use in the collection. To have such a list printed specially for less popular groups would be very expensive, of course, because of the amount of setting involved, but it is sometimes possible to cut out names from old catalogues or other works, provided that the paper is opaque, so the print on the back does not show through, and provided that the paper is a good white colour.

Protection against pests, mould and grease

Most cabinet drawers and store-boxes have a compartment at the front for preservative. If this is not obvious, look for a small wooden insertion, which tilts and opens into a cavity in the wall of the box, as is visible in fig. 71. There should also be a piece of

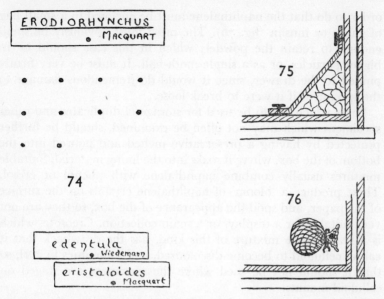

Figures 74–76. Details of a collection-drawer, or box. 74, how a species is labelled, with the name of the genus at the top of the strip or column, and the name of the species, and its synonyms, if any, below: position of specimens shown by pin-holes; 75, preservative held in the corner of the drawer by a piece of card; or, 76, in a muslin bag pinned into place.

gauze or mesh in the wall of the box or drawer, through which the fumes of the preservative can escape into the interior.

The most convenient general preservative is flake naphthalene, bought by the pound from chemists. This is a white, crystalline, flaky solid, which needs to be broken quite finely to pack in the small cell. Avoid loose lumps in the box, where they may damage the insects by shaking about when the box is stood on end.

The naphthalene does not melt at ordinary temperatures, but sublimes slowly, changing straight from a solid into a vapour. Paradichlorobenzene is a similar solid, with a smell that is different from the rather objectionable 'moth-ball' smell of naphthalene. It is more expensive than naphthalene, and costs about three shillings a pound.

If your box or drawer has no cell, a small compartment may be made in one corner by sticking a piece of card across as shown in fig. 75. This does not allow the box to be stood on end, and in order to do that the naphthalene must be enclosed in a small bag of gauze or muslin (fig. 76). The mesh must obviously be small enough to retain the powder, which in this case should be in bigger particles, or as a single moth-ball. It must be very firmly pinned to the drawer, since it would do tremendous damage to the specimens if it were to break loose.

Boxes which are to be used for storage of duplicates and other specimens which may not often be examined, should be further protected by having a preservative melted and poured into the bottom of the box, where it soaks into the lining material. Suitable mixtures usually combine naphthalene with phenol or cresol. These produce a 'bloom' of naphthalene crystals on the surface of the paper, and spoil the appearance of the box, so they are not very suitable for a display, or a main collection. Creosote, which is a ready-made mixture of this kind, has the drawback that it causes celluloid to become discoloured, and sometimes to curl, so that it should not be used where the specimens are staged on celluloid mounts.

Mould can be removed by cleaning the specimen in a solution of glacial phenol in benzene in the ratio 1:10 or in dilute formaldehyde.

Grease oozing out on to the surface of a specimen often destroys all the surface markings. It can often be dissolved out by pinning the insect into the cork of a tube of benzene and turning the tube upside down, or dropping the pinned specimen on to the surface of benzene in a bigger jar (figs. 47, 48). Leave for 24 hours to several days according to size, remove and allow to dry naturally. A dry-cleaning method is to put a layer of fuller's earth, about half an inch deep in a saucer, put the pinned insect in this and then shake more fuller's earth over it. Leave for 2–3 weeks and then blow the fine earth off the specimen.

SPIRIT COLLECTIONS

Larvæ and nymphs of most insects, and the adults of those that are soft-bodied, are best stored permanently in a liquid. The groups to which this rule applies are indicated in Chapter IX. The best liquid for general use is spirit: 75–80% ethyl alcohol. Some workers prefer other liquids, notably chloral hydrate and Pampel's fluid (see List of Formulæ) for the early stages of preservation, but even so the larvæ are generally transferred to plain alcohol for permanent storage. Formalin is unnecessary, and should be avoided: it has a strong hardening effect, and is trouble-some to the eyes and nose when the specimen is being examined under the microscope.

The most readily obtainable cheap form of spirit is methylated spirit, and for small collections this may be quite satisfactory. It has the drawbacks of being coloured, and of turning milky when water is added to it. By applying to your local Excise Officer, you can get a permit to buy industrial methylated spirit, which is without these disadvantages. This must be diluted with one part of water to five parts of spirit to give the right strength for permanent storage of insects.

Absolute alcohol, pure C_2H_5OH, is much more costly, and is bought in very small quantities as a pharmaceutical preparation. It has been rendered free from water at great trouble and expense, and should never be diluted to make a lower grade spirit. It is normally used as a dehydrating agent, for making slide-mounts, or in the dry preservation of larvæ.

Storage of Spirit Collections

The collection unit is normally a tube, and the size that is chosen for this depends on the size and scope of the collection. Van Emden (1942), for a private collection, finds that small, round-ended tubes, of $1 \times \frac{1}{8}$ in. inside measure are the most useful, with intermediate sizes up to $1\frac{1}{4} \times \frac{1}{4}$ in. The smaller the tube, the more difficult it is to write labels, but on the other hand fewer container-jars are needed, and the collection as a whole takes up less space (fig. 77).

When the specimens are few, or are relatively big, they may be given a tube each, but generally it will be necessary to keep a batch of specimens in each tube. Naturally these should all have been collected together, or under the same circumstances, or in some other way be conveniently lumped together. A small label is written, either in pencil or Indian ink, as we have discussed above under 'labelling'. Since these are often difficult to decipher quickly, the sorting of tubes of spirit material can be a nuisance. Van Emden recommends the use of round labels, numbered serially, which fit tightly into the bottom of each tube. If the tubes are stored bottom upwards these numbers are visible (fig. 77), and a diary or card-index can be kept as a quick index to the numbers.

It is very important to restrict movement of the specimens, otherwise they will soon break up. Having put in the bottom label,

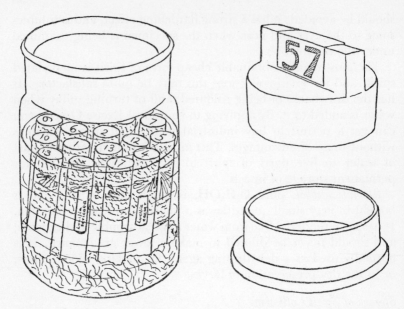

Figure 77. A spirit collection. The specimens are stored in small tubes, inverted in spirit in a larger jar. There is cotton wool at the bottom of the jar to prevent breakage, and each tube has a numbered label visible through its bottom. On the right are two types of glass stopper, the upper with a ridge which can bear a numbered label.

fill the tube nearly to the top with spirit, and then push in a small wad of cotton wool which has already been dipped in spirit: if you put it in dry it will absorb most of the liquid. Push the wad down until it just confines the specimens without crushing them, but make sure that there is enough cotton wool to avoid the risk of its falling out when the tube is turned upside down.

If the tubes are long enough, it is possible to keep two batches of insects in each tube, though with some risk of confusion between the two.

The tubes are stored in jars, which have the straight side-wall a little higher than the length of the tube, and with a close-fitting lid. Laboratory jars with the lids ground in are excellent, but expensive. Various kinds of preserving jar may be used, but those with a rounded shoulder at the top are less convenient, because the tubes may jam beneath it. The broad, low kind of glass jar in which tongue and such cooked meats used to be sold is very handy, and usually has a tightly-fitting glass lid, but is not as common as it used to be. Van Emden (1942) recommends 'a 16-oz., extra wide-mouthed, flat-stoppered bottle', such as that obtainable from R. B. Turner and Co., 9 Eagle Street, London, W.C.1.

The bottom of the jar should be covered, either with two layers of blotting-paper, or a shallow layer of cotton wool, so that the tubes do not strike against the glass bottom of the jar. Alcohol is poured in to saturate the cotton wool, and to stand about one inch above it. The small tubes are then put in open end downwards. Put them in carefully, making sure that the plug of cotton wool does not fall out, and that the tubes are not knocked against each other, nor jammed tightly together. A small crack may not be noticed at the time, and later on all the specimens from that tube may be found loose in the big jar.

The arrangement that allows easiest reference is to put tubes only round the outside of the jar, with their labels visible; the middle of the jar is packed with cotton wool. Any particular tube can be located and taken out without disturbing the others, or looking into more than one jar. For a collection of any size, however, this is an extravagant allowance of jar space, and tubes usually have to be put into the middle of the jar as well.

In this event the round labels at the ends of the tubes are a great help. Van Emden recommends a further refinement in the form of a cross of wood or celluloid, which divides the jar into four compartments. The tubes can then be arranged round the sides of these, and by following a consistent plan the tubes can be kept in a systematic arrangement comparable with the one followed in the dry collection.

The spirit collection should be housed in a cool, dark cupboard. While it is not dangerously volatile, like petrol or benzene, 80% alcohol is certainly inflammable, and precautions should be taken against accidental ignition, if it is spilled, or leaks from a cracked jar. A tin of fire-extinguishing fluid (usually carbon tetrachloride) can be bought for a shilling or two at a shop that sells car or cycle accessories, and is useful to have about the house in any case. Failing this, a small, thick blanket or rug should be handy to smother any accidental blaze at once.

The spirit collection should be watched to see that no tube ever dries up. The risk of this is reduced by putting the tubes mouth downwards, but if you keep your spirit collection in a cupboard in the chimney corner, or above the airing cupboard, you will need to top up the glass jars fairly often.

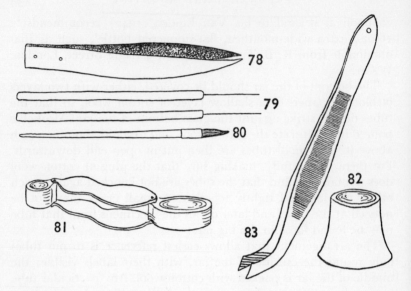

Figures 78–83. Equipment for examining and dissecting insects. 78, fine forceps; 79, pair of dissecting needles; 80, a small camel-hair brush; 81, a double pocket-lens; 82, a watchmaker's glass; 83, pinning forceps.

If specimens in spirit have been allowed accidentally to dry up they can often be restored by putting them in a weak concentration (2%) of cold caustic potash for a day or in a modern detergent, such as 'Tide', and then transferring them first to 40% alcohol, 70%, and finally 80% (see dehydration, below).

DISSECTING, AND MAKING SLIDE MOUNTS

Dissection of insects is a subject too big to be dealt with adequately in this book. Dissection of the soft tissues, together with section-cutting and examination of cell-structure, all require careful fixation of the tissues at the time of death, so that their structure is not changed by decomposition.

Merely to preserve the specimens in spirit seldom leaves the internal organs in a suitable state for dissection. Apart from post-mortem changes, the tissues are liable to become brittle, and to break up when they are dissected. One of the fixatives listed at the end of this book should be used if specimens are to be preserved for later internal examination.

Dissection of the external organs, or of any of the chitinised parts of the body of an insect, is in some ways a simpler matter. In order to name and classify many groups of insects it is desirable, or even essential to be able to make mounts of the mouth-parts or of the structures at the tip of the abdomen ('terminalia', or 'genitalia'), and a simple technique is useful. 'Dissection' is rather a grand term for what generally is no more than a gentle pulling apart of the parts concerned, using a pair of mounted needles, or just a pair of fine, long entomological pins, held in the hands. The critical part of the job is preparing the specimen, so that it is soft and transparent, and easily manipulated. This is exactly the same treatment that is needed to prepare a whole specimen for making into a slide mount, as we shall now describe.

In a slide mount for use with the monocular microscope the specimen is held between the glass slide and a thin glass cover-slip, and the space surrounding it is filled up with a mounting fluid. The purpose of this fluid is to make the mount completely transparent, and to get rid of confusing reflections from the surface of the specimen. Consequently, the fluid must wet the specimen easily, so that it makes contact with all the surface of the insect, and does not leave a thin layer of air. The commonest mounting fluid is Canada balsam, a resin, and to get this to penetrate completely into an insect specimen the latter must first be impregnated with an oily liquid that mixes readily with the balsam. Clove oil, cedar-wood oil and xylol are commonly used for this purpose, but as none of these will mix with water, the specimen must first be dehydrated, or have every trace of water removed.

The sequence of events, therefore, is as follows: since we have already agreed to limit ourselves to a study of the hardened or chitinised parts of the insect, we start by destroying all the soft, internal tissues, leaving the rest now soft and transparent; these are stained or bleached as may be necessary; dehydrated; cleared in oil; and immersed in Canada balsam on a slide to make a permanent mount.

Caustic potash (10% KOH in water) is used both to soften the specimen and to destroy the soft internal tissues, but not the chitinised parts of the body, nor the membranous cuticle in between them. By its use, therefore, we can make a whole insect into a soft, transparent skin, or reduce the mouth-parts or genitalia to the hard organs themselves, without the muscles and other related soft tissues. The specimen may be left in the cold potash overnight, and this is desirable for fragile insects or very small ones, which may disintegrate, or simply be lost, if they are boiled. Bigger and more substantial specimens may be boiled for about five minutes, and should have a small cut made in the skin underneath the base of the abdomen, to allow the potash to penetrate quickly.

The simplest way of boiling a single specimen is in an ordinary test-tube, over a Bunsen burner or a spirit lamp. Hold the tube in a wooden holder, or one made from folded paper (fig. 84). Always hold the tube so that neither the top nor the bottom points towards you, because hot potash is very unpleasant if it splashes about. Apply the flame near the top of the liquid and keep the tube moving gently just above the flame, trying to keep it boiling gently without bumping and splashing up the tube. This is not difficult to do the first time you boil it, because the dissolved air helps the bubbles to form; but if you have boiled your potash once and allowed it to stop boiling, be very careful how you heat it up again, or it may boil suddenly and shoot out of the tube. It helps if you drop in a few grains of dry sand before reheating.

A safer method is to put the specimen in a small dish and heat the dish on a tray of sand, made from a tin lid. If the dish should break, the potash will be absorbed by the sand. Several specimens may be boiled at once by putting each one in a small glass tube, with potash, and then standing the tubes in a glass beaker, or a metal mug. Enough water is placed in the beaker or mug to boil quietly without bubbling over. Using a water-bath in this way, there is little danger of sudden boiling of the potash, but of course the process takes much longer from the time of starting, although this is offset by having several specimens prepared at the same time.

There is no certain way of knowing how long to boil specimens, but experience will be a guide if you keep to one group of insects. If the specimen is fairly fresh the potash will probably turn brown as the tissues dissolve, and naturally you will keep on boiling as long as the liquid gets darker. If the specimen at first floats on the surface, you should periodically take away the flame, and let the liquid settle; if the specimen does not sink to the bottom, boil again until it does so. If the specimen refuses to sink it usually means that the potash is not penetrating, and you should make a small cut in it with a fine pin, as mentioned above.

The next step is to rinse away the potash as much as possible with tap water, taking great care not to lose the specimen in doing so. One way is to draw off the potash with a glass pipette (or an

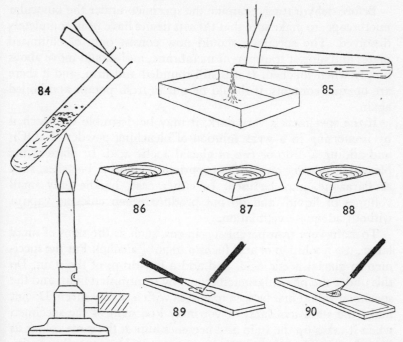

Figures 84–90. Making a slide-mount. 84, boiling in caustic potash; the test-tube is held in a holder made from twisted paper, and is heated carefully, near the *top* of the liquid; 85, pouring into a white dish, so that the specimen can be picked out with forceps or a brush; 86, rinsing in water; 87, dehydrating in glacial acetic acid; 88, clearing in clove oil; 89, dissecting in a little clove oil on the slide; 90, adding a drop of Canada balsam, and gently lowering the cover-slip with the help of a needle.

eye-dropper), and replace it with clean water, repeating this several times. Another is to pour the contents of the tube out on to a porcelain dish, or into a clean sink (with the stopper in place!), pick up the specimen with forceps, and put it into water in a fresh dish.

The dehydrating and clearing are best done in a small dish such as a 'solid watch-glass' (figs. 86–88), which cannot tip over. Put glacial acetic acid in one and clove oil in another, and cover each with a glass cover. Transfer the specimen with fine forceps, but try to avoid taking over a big drop of liquid each time. You may drop the specimen for a moment on to blotting-paper when transferring it.

Before dehydrating, examine the specimen under the binocular microscope, to make sure that the soft tissues have been completely dissolved. The specimen should now consist only of chitinised plates and almost transparent membrane, and should move about limply when touched. If it is still rounded and firm, and if there are opaque contents, it should be put in fresh potash and boiled again.

If the specimen is very dark, it may be desirable to bleach it by immersing in a weak solution of bleaching powder (NaOCl) and adding a drop or two of glacial acetic acid. In place of the bleaching powder one of the proprietary chlorine bleaches, such as Parazone, may be used. In either case, handle only small volumes of liquid, and do not produce much chlorine vapour without adequate ventilation.

To stain very transparent specimens, such as the skins of small larvæ, use a solution of acid fuchsin in 20% alcohol. Put the specimen in glacial acetic acid, and add a few drops of the stain. Do this under the binocular microscope, by transmitted light, and the specimen will at first be seen to glisten with a silvery sheen. Do not make the stain too dark, or you may lose sight of the specimen when it takes up the stain and becomes almost the same colour as the solution. The safest method is to use only a very small quantity of stain, and then to blot it away with a small piece of blotting-paper, watching out carefully for the stained specimen.

Whether stained, or bleached, or not, the specimen is now put in glacial acetic acid for about five minutes, to remove all the water from it. This drastic method can be used for preparations which contain only chitinised structures, in place of the more usual progress through alcohols of gradually increasing strength that is normally necessary for making slides of soft tissues. After about five minutes the specimen may be transferred to clove oil or cedar-wood oil, and again examined under the binocular microscope. If the water has not been removed completely patches of a milky colour will appear in the specimen; it should then be returned to the acetic acid for a further five minutes, when on transferring again to the oil it should remain clear and become increasingly transparent.

Some entomologists dislike clove oil as a clearing agent, because they say that it makes the specimens brittle; certainly the insects should not be left to stand in it, but should be mounted as soon as they are clear. Cedar-wood oil may be preferred. Xylol is not very satisfactory for small preparations, as it evaporates quickly, and does not allow enough time for dissection and manipulation of the parts. It is a good idea to do the final dissection and arrangement on the slide, in the clearing agent, so that the small parts are not lost (fig. 89). For example, when mounting mouth-parts, I cut off the head, and boil it whole, dehydrating and clearing without further dissection; then I put it in a drop of clove oil on the slide, and pull it apart with two long pins under the binocular microscope. I keep only the parts I want to study, and throw away the rest of the head. If you try to keep the more bulky parts of the head, they make the mount thick, and the mouth-parts have room to turn over into positions in which it is difficult to examine and draw them. In very large insects it may be possible to cut off the mouth-parts and leave the rest of the head intact on the body but it is usually necessary to relax the insect before doing this, and there is danger of losing some of the smaller mouth-parts.

When the specimen has been displayed as you want to see it, the clove oil is gently mopped away with a scrap of blotting-paper, and then a little Canada balsam is dropped on to the specimen from a glass rod. This final step in mounting is very important in getting the specimen permanently arranged in a good position for study and for being photographed. The balsam should be just liquid enough to run, and no more; it should not be so tacky that when you take the glass rod away the specimen is lifted too, nor yet so liquid that it spreads over a big area of the slide. Probably the balsam as it is bought will be about right, but it has already been diluted with xylol, and as the xylol gradually evaporates the balsam becomes stiffer. Restore it to the right condition by adding a little xylol, but always add less than you think may be necessary. If possible leave it to mix by diffusion, because it is difficult to get a good mixture by stirring, and usually fills the balsam with small air-bubbles, which spoil a slide mount.

You should have the cover-slip already selected, gently polished, and close at hand. Choose one that is not a great deal bigger than the specimen, and use a corresponding amount of balsam. Then lower the cover-slip gently down, using a pin to support one edge (fig. 90). Do not drop the cover-slip on flat with the fingers, because this will trap air-bubbles, which always seem to move to the most important parts of the specimen. Cover the balsam as soon as it is reasonably possible, or it may begin to form a 'skin' on its surface, which will not wet the cover-slip. If you think this may have happened, wet the underside of the cover-slip with clove oil before putting it on.

Slide mounts of *wings* can be made more simply and quickly. It is not necessary to treat them with potash, which often makes them shrivel. Before boiling up a whole insect it is often better to detach the wings, and put them straight into xylol, which wets them more quickly and evenly than an oil. If there is any trace of milkiness the wing may be transferred to glacial acetic acid for a few minutes; otherwise as soon as it is wetted it can be mounted in balsam. There is usually a little air trapped in the bigger veins, but this may be disregarded. It often diffuses out gradually as the mount ages, but if it is essential to get rid of the air because it obstructs something one wants to see, then the wing in xylol may be warmed gently on a water-bath. The xylol is very inflammable, so take care to use small quantities only and keep the flame low.

Do not forget to label the slide as soon as it is made, with a white paper label stuck across one end. These labels can be bought ready-made on sticky paper. Make the label a detailed one, so that it will be easier to identify the specimen if the slide gets separated from the rest of the insect.

Canada balsam takes several weeks to harden naturally and in the meantime the slide must be kept horizontal, not stored on edge. Hardening can be hastened if the slide is warmed over a *gentle* heat, such as an electric bulb, but take care not to heat it so much that bubbles form.

Full-sized microscope slides are useful for detailed work under the monocular microscope, including demonstration and photography. From the collector's and curator's point of view it is undesirable to be left with headless or tail-less specimens, and to have the detached parts on slides elsewhere, and it is only rarely convenient to mount the slide in the main collection along with pinned material. This can be avoided by making a small mount which attaches to the same pin as the dried specimen.

One way is to cut a small strip of card of Bristol board, as if for staging, and to stick a cover-slip on to the end of it by means of balsa cement or other quick-drying medium. This can be done while the specimen is being cleared and dissected and the cement will be hard by the time the specimen is ready for final mounting. Then arrange the specimen on the cover-slip, run on the balsam, and finish off with another cover-slip on top, just as you did on a slide. This small mount can easily be examined with the binocular microscope, and for monocular inspection it can be removed from the pin and laid on a blank slide (figs. 91, 92).

For bigger insects it may not be necessary to use a cover-slip,

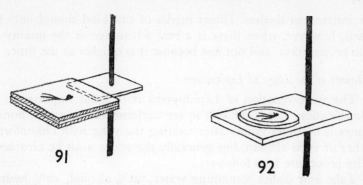

91   **92**

Figures 91, 92. Two ways of mounting parts dissected from a pinned insect. 91, between coverslips cemented together with balsam, and stuck to a card mount with a quick-drying cement; 92, in a 'cell' made by cutting a hole in the card mount, and sticking a cover-slip above and below, with balsam.

and the genitalia or mouth-parts may be stuck directly on to the special card stage with balsam, and examined as a solid object.

Direct Mounting

Small, soft-bodied insects may be mounted direct in one of the compound media, such as de Faures, Gum Chloral, Polyvinyl-lactophenol, or Shellac Gel (see section on Formulæ, p. 303). For these media there is no treatment in potash, nor dehydrating, and the specimens may be transferred direct from spirit, or put into the medium while they are still alive.

These media are very convenient for the quick examination of a large number of very small insects, and workers on very transparent insects, such as Collembola or lice, find them preferable to balsam because the refractive index can be varied, by experience of the group, to make the specimens show up more clearly. They do not give such a hard and durable permanent mount as balsam does, and if used for a collection intended to be permanent, the cover-slip should be circular, and should be 'ringed'. To do this needs a ringing-base, a rotating stand on which the slide can be spun while a brush charged with ringing paint is held against the edge of the cover-slip. This forms a hard and protecting rim, and prevents the medium from shrinking away from the edge and admitting air beneath the cover-slip.

Ringed mounts are very pretty if they are done skilfully, and necessary apparatus can be bought from natural history suppliers or instrument dealers. Direct media of this kind should only be used, however, when there is a real advantage in the quality of the preparation, and not just because it is quicker at the time.

Mounts of the wings of Lepidoptera

The wing-venation of Lepidoptera is of great importance in classification, but is difficult to see underneath the scales. Sometimes it becomes visible after wetting the wing with chloroform, ether or even alcohol, but generally the scales must be bleached. The procedure is as follows:

Take four dishes containing water, 90% alcohol, 10% hydrochloric acid and finally a solution of bleaching powder (NaOCl) in water. Some authorities add common salt (NaCl) to the last in about equal quantity, or one may use one of the compound bleaches referred to above.

Wet the wing in the alcohol, then dip into the acid for a few seconds. Transfer to the bleach for a few minutes, until the wing veins are visible. If action is slow, dip the wing in acid again. Rinse the wing thoroughly in water, and it is ready for mounting. It may be mounted dry by placing on a slide, allowing to dry and then covering with a cover-slip supported by a circular mask so that it does not press down on the wing.

Alternatively the wing may be mounted direct in Euparal, or dehydrated through a series of alcohols, to absolute alcohol, clove oil and Canada balsam.

VI

EXAMINING INSECTS IN A COLLECTION

A good deal of observation of insects, both living ones and those preserved in a collection, can be carried out with the naked eye. With experience, and practice, it is astonishing what minute details can be seen. Moreover, the naked eye sees the whole insect, and will often notice a characteristic shape, or the proportion of different parts—breadth of head, shape of abdomen, length and proportions of wings or legs—that is lost if only a part of the insect is examined at high magnification.

This is particularly true of the living insect. Most insects, like people, have a characteristic stance or movement, a trick of waving the antennæ or legs, that anyone can learn to recognise. This aspect of the identification of insects is touched on again in Chapter X, but it is important not to despise the naked eye or to think that high-powered and expensive instruments will, by themselves, guarantee better results. As in most activities, the tools are not a substitute for skill and practice.

None the less, even with the biggest insects, it is sometimes necessary to get an enlarged view of some small detail, while a great many insects are so small that they cannot be studied at all without some means of magnification.

HAND-LENS

Every entomologist needs a hand-lens, whether or not he has more complicated equipment. A single lens like the old-fashioned 'reading-glass', is useful for looking at bigger insects in which the characters are superficial, such as butterflies. It gives a very low magnification, but has the advantage of working at a safe distance from the specimen, so that there is little risk of accidentally touching it. It can also be used on glass-topped drawers and boxes without having to remove the lid, and is particularly useful for the rapid sorting of a large collection, where only superficial inspection is needed.

Simple lenses of this type can be bought, unmounted, at surplus supply stores for a shilling or two: care should be taken to choose one with a ground edge, so that it can be carried in the pocket, and handled, without cutting the fingers. Single lenses can be bought from instrument firms, either mounted for use in the hand, or on a tripod or swing mount. With the last two mounts, both hands are left free to manipulate the specimens.

A variant of the simple lens is the *watchmaker's lens* (fig. 82), mounted in a little, cup-shaped, plastic holder which can be gripped in the eye like a monocle. This also leaves both hands free, and in addition the lens itself is mobile, but some people find it difficult to learn how to keep it in position. It is made to work much closer to the specimen than the bigger lenses, and so compels the user either to lean over the specimens, or to hold them up to the eye, and it is sometimes difficult to get enough light on to the specimen. The watchmaker's lens is cheap, and can be had for as little as 3/6.

For all-round use it is difficult to improve on *a folding pocket lens* (Plate X; fig. 81) giving a magnification of × 10, or × 15. These range in price from six or seven shillings to about £3, and it is well worth getting the best one can afford. The cheapest forms, in shallow plastic mounts, are little better than the reading-glass, and to get really good definition at this magnification requires either a Coddington lens, or a cemented doublet, each of which is thick in proportion to its diameter. A good hand-lens is therefore a small, thick one, in a chromium-plated brass mount, and will last a lifetime if care is taken not to lose it.

Such a lens, skilfully used, will show as much detail as a low-powered microscope, with the advantage that it can be carried about, and is always available, without any preparation. Some professional entomologists do most of their work with a hand-lens, and have a beautiful double-mounted one, giving one glass of × 15 and one of × 20. These work extremely close to the specimen, as well as to the eye. Apart from the risk of breakage, these very powerful lenses cannot be used without taking off the glass lid of a box. For all-round usefulness it is better to be contented with × 10.

When choosing a hand-lens, look not at a specimen, but at a flat piece of print, such as a printed card or label. See that the field of focus is reasonably flat—that is to say, that letters near the edge of the field of view can be seen in sharp focus at the same time as a letter in the middle. See that the letters are not distorted out of shape near the edge of the field, and that those in the middle have not got coloured edges; a slight 'rainbow' effect will probably be seen at the edges, but it should not be distractingly obvious.

A problem when using a hand-lens is to get enough light on the object without the shadow of one's head getting in the way. With daylight, stand sideways to the window: in artificial light one often needs to stand uncomfortably close to a hot lamp. A 'bulls-eye' lens of the type used with a microscope will enable one to work further from the light (see below, under Lighting).

BINOCULAR MICROSCOPES

This term is used for microscopes that have two objectives (i.e. the lenses close to the object), as well as two eye-pieces, and which are suitable for looking at solid objects, such as dried insect specimens, by reflected light. It excludes those instruments, used chiefly in medical laboratories, which have two eye-pieces, but only one objective, and are used for looking at glass slides. Such a binocular microscope as is shown in Plate XIV is called a Greenough Pattern instrument.

Besides allowing much higher magnifications to be used, binocular microscopes have three big advantages over the hand-lens: the microscope can be left at a set position of focus, and the specimen can be manipulated with both hands; both the microscope and the specimen can be fixed in position, in correct focus, of course, and both hands are then free for drawing, making notes, or dissecting; and, biggest advantage of all, the use of both eyes, when applied to such a small object, gives a pronounced stereoscopic effect, which makes the different parts of the structure stand out, whereas a monocular microscope or a single lens tends to merge details into the background.

In the cheapest binocular microscopes, the objectives are mounted, in their pairs, in a sliding removable mount, so that they can be interchanged to get different degrees of magnification. The eye-pieces fit into vertical tubes (i.e. tubes that do not tilt towards the operator, though of course they converge towards each other), and are also interchangeable. The eye-pieces can be moved nearer together or further apart, and the whole optical apparatus moves up and down for focusing, by a simple rack and pinion.

There is a good clearance of several inches between the objective lenses and the flat surface of the stage, allowing insects of any size to be put there, while the working distance of the objectives when in focus should be about 1–2 in., to allow ample room for manipulation or dissection of the specimen. The glass stage may rest on the table, or be mounted on a 'foot' which allows the object to be seen against a bright background of ground—or opal —glass (Plate XIV): this is particularly useful for examining wings.

Such a microscope may give a range of magnifications from about × 7 to about × 120, using various combinations of objectives and eye-pieces. It is desirable that the magnification should come as much as possible from the objective, because that lens is accepting light from the specimen itself, and has only its own errors to contend with: the eye-piece, on the other hand, is working on the image made by the first lens, and if you magnify this image excessively you don't make it better; on the contrary, the distortions of the first lens become more obvious.

It is also good practice always to use the *lowest* magnification that will show what you want, and not the highest that can be got. The illumination at low magnification is correspondingly greater, the resolution of the lens better, distortion and colour fringes less evident, and the portion of the specimen being examined can be seen in better relation to the whole.

The cheapest Greenough pattern binocular microscope costs about £45, and prices go up from this, according to the optical equipment, and the mechanical refinement. Second-hand instruments can be had, but when buying these one needs to take extra care to see that they have been properly adjusted, as discussed below.

More complicated, and consequently more expensive models may have some of the following features.

Independently adjustable eye-pieces. Few people's eyes are perfectly matched, and then the two images are not equally sharp at the same moment. The eyes try to correct this by varying their accommodation, and the user may not be aware of what is going on until he feels the strain, or gets a headache. Nearly all binocular microscopes have some way of raising or lowering one eye-piece independently of the other. Always make a point of finding this adjustment, and using it. To do this, put a printed card under the microscope, hold a smaller piece of card over the adjustable eye-piece, and focus sharply on the print with the one eye; do not close the disengaged eye, but keep it open and relaxed like the other. Then move the small card to the other eye-piece, and, without touching the focusing knob, make the image sharp by turning or sliding the adjustable eye-piece, according to its design. This check should be made at intervals when the microscope is in use, and it will often be found to give a surprising improvement in clarity. Note on which side the adjustable eye-piece goes, and remember to keep it on the correct side, especially when interchanging different pairs of eye-pieces. There is no rule as to whether it should be on the right or the left, since this depends on the needs of the user, but once adjusted, it must not be altered.

Turret nose-piece. This is a multiple mounting to carry two, or three pairs of objectives, so that these can be quickly interchanged. Even if you expect to work most of the time on insects of uniform size, it is still most convenient to be able to turn quickly to a higher magnification to examine a detail, and then swing back again for a general view. There are three general types of movement: a horizontal sliding, as in the Leitz (Plate XIV); a barrel-shaped drum which rotates about a horizontal axis, as in the Bausch and Lomb; and a circular mount rotating round a vertical axis, as in the Watson, the Cooke, Troughton and Sims, and the Baker. The pairs of objectives themselves generally clip or slip into the mount, and the makers offer a selection to suit the needs of the buyer. The only difference in practice between the three types of fitting is in the extent to which the objectives that are not in use may get in the way, or throw shadows on to the specimen. This is a matter for individual testing before purchase.

Inclined eye-pieces. The tubes carrying the eye-pieces may be tilted towards the operator (Plate XIV), so that he can sit comfortably erect, without having to lean forward. They are an advantage if long hours are to be spent at the microscope, but they complicate slightly the optical design, and sometimes result in a loss of quality. This need not occur, and indeed some magnificent instruments have inclined eye-pieces, but it is advisable to see a prospective purchase alongside a similar model with vertical eye-pieces, to make sure that quality has not been sacrificed to convenience. Inclined eye-pieces also make it slightly more difficult to use a camera lucida as an aid to drawing (see below).

Wide-angle eye-pieces (*wide field*). These are designed to accept a bigger cone of light than standard eye-pieces, and show you more of the object at one time. The lenses are bigger, and consequently it is easier to bring one's eyes quickly into line, especially for someone who has to wear glasses while using the microscope. Generally speaking, if glasses are worn merely for correction of accommodation (focusing) they need not be worn when using a microscope, because the lens system will do the work, but if glasses are needed to correct astigmatism or other aberrations they must be kept on all the time. In the latter case, it is sometimes difficult to get the eye close enough to the eye-piece to receive the narrow pencil of rays, and the wide-field eye-piece is a great help. For anyone, glasses or not, the wide-field set is very restful to use, but is limited in magnification, and you may find that you have to buy extra objectives to get the desired results.

Testing a binocular microscope

Adjusting a microscope, either optically or mechanically, is not a job for the amateur, and should always be done by a reputable firm of instrument makers or repairers. It is essential, however, to be able to tell when a microscope needs attention, not only at the time of purchase, but also during the working life of the instrument. Faults in a binocular are more serious than they are in a monocular, because if the two eyes cannot see their respective images equally clearly, and combine them into one, eye-strain will be caused. The eyes have astonishing powers of adaptation, and if the microscope is in regular use it can go a long way out of adjustment without the fact being realised. For this reason the following simple tests should be carried out at frequent intervals, and always after the instrument has been involved in a removal, or a journey, or has been lent to someone other than its regular owner.

1. See that all lens surfaces are clean. Use only a soft tissue for cleaning, such as is supplied for cleaning spectacles, or camera lenses. Do *not* scrub with a coarse rag, or a freshly starched handkerchief, because optical glass is often very soft and easily scratched. Incidentally, small scratches on a lens, or even bubbles in the glass, are not seen as such when the microscope is being used, but they scatter light, and help to give a grey, misty appearance to the image.

If the lenses are covered with a grey film from long neglect, it is best to have them expertly cleaned, but failing this, it is possible to improve them by using cotton wool slightly moistened with 80% alcohol, the spirit used for preserving insects. Do not swab the lens, and make it so wet that surplus spirit can percolate into the mount, and on no account use water: if you get a fine mist of condensation on an inner surface of the lens it will be difficult to get rid of it. Eye-pieces usually unscrew easily into two components, but objectives generally have cemented, or at least closely mounted components. When using spirit, take care that it does not wash off the black coating that is put inside the tube to absorb scattered light; if this black is worn and shiny it can be touched up with 'dead black', a spirit preparation sold at photographic shops for treating the insides of cameras. If you get Canada balsam on to the objective through touching it on to a wet slide, do not try either to scrape it off, or to dissolve it. Spirit will not soften balsam, and if xylol is used it may attack the cement used in assembling the lens. Such a lens must be expertly cleaned and reset, so take great care not to get balsam on the lens.

Look into the main body of the binocular, and see if the exposed surfaces of the prisms are dusty. A little *gentle* attention with a tissue may improve them, but great care is needed not to move the prisms in their mounting. In some binoculars the prisms are held only by friction grips, and any movement will put the images hopelessly out of alignment. Perhaps the best thing is to use a gadget with a rubber bulb and nozzle, which is sold for blowing the dust out of cameras in the same way, but if inaccessible surfaces are dirty it is again a matter for the expert.

2. When the lenses and prisms are clean, set the adjustable eye-piece as described above. If the full adjustment of the eye-piece is insufficient, try changing the eye-pieces round to the other tube, but if it is still impossible to see both images sharp at once, do not accept the instrument until it has been reconditioned.

3. Having got the centres of the two fields sharp, compare the two images. Do the centres correspond—i.e. is the same object in the middle of each field? Do the edges agree; if you drew the picture as seen in each eye-piece separately would the two drawings correspond very closely? They are never exactly the same because the two objectives are looking from slightly different directions, just as one's two eyes do not see exactly the same picture in ordinary vision.

Finally, open and close each eye separately and alternately, in fairly quick succession, and see if you get an impression that the print jumps from side to side, or up and down. If it does the two fields are not properly coincident. The best test slide for this purpose consists of a bull's-eye of concentric rings. This is easily centred in one field by ensuring that a complete ring just touches the edge of the field, and then it shows immediately whether the other field is also centred, and if not, in what direction it is out. The centre point of the ring-slide must be exactly vertically below the centre line of the microscope, and so equidistant from the two objectives.

If the fields are out of line, test each pair of objectives in turn, and so find out whether the error is in one pair only, or whether it affects them all; in the latter case it is likely that the prisms are displaced. Each objective is provided with three screws for centring, but if possible it is better to have the instrument expertly adjusted than to try to do it one's self.

Always protect the binocular microscope carefully against sudden bumps: do not bang it down on the table, nor hit any part of it against the case when putting it away, and when using it, do not be so absorbed in looking down the eye-piece that you hit the objectives with a specimen-box, or with anything else.

MONOCULAR MICROSCOPES

These are suitable principally for looking at transparent mounts, by transmitted light, and they are normally fitted with a stage designed to take the standard glass slide, 3×1 in. Such slides can be examined also with a binocular microscope, using transmitted light, but the relatively low magnification, the oblique viewpoint, and above all the difficulty of directing the light equally into two tubes that are not parallel, all make the binocular less suitable for such work.

Similarly, a monocular microscope *can* be used for looking at solid objects by reflected light, but there is seldom much clearance below the objective (because it generally has a higher power, and consequently a shorter focal length than is used on a binocular), and the lack of stereoscopic vision is a serious defect with a solid object.

Thus for serious study one needs a binocular for use on solid objects at relatively low powers, and a monocular for use on transparent slide mounts, with the option of much higher magnifications if desired.

Simple monocular microscopes, giving a magnification of about ×40, can be had for as little as 35/-, but naturally these are not instruments of great precision. The light is supplied by a small mirror beneath the stage, and focusing is by sliding the optical apparatus inside a tubular mount. Refinements in the more expensive models (which exceed £100) include rack-and-pinion focusing; separate knobs for coarse and fine focusing; a rotating nose-piece carrying three alternative objectives; a sub-stage condenser, with iris diaphragm and colour filters, all moved by rack-and-pinion to give accurate control of lighting; and a mechanical stage, a slide-holder which is moved in two directions by slow-motion screws fitted with vernier scales, so that once a detail of the object has been located, the specimen can be moved about, and easily returned to its original position in the field (Plate XV, M).

The most usual optical equipment consists of two eye-pieces, ×6 and ×10, respectively, and two objectives of $\frac{2}{3}$-in. (×10) and $\frac{1}{6}$-in. (×40). The precise magnification depends on the separation of the objective and eye-piece. This is usually fixed in a binocular, but most monoculars have a draw-tube, by which the length of the tube can be increased like a telescope. That is why the specification usually gives the focal length of the objective rather than its nominal magnification. This equipment gives total magnifications ranging from 60 to 400, which is sufficient for most general work. For occasional use an eye-piece of higher magnification (×15 or ×20) will give a correspondingly bigger image, but, as we have seen above, it is bad practice to rely upon the eye-piece to provide extra magnification. For regular use it is better to increase the power of the objective, using the $\frac{1}{12}$-in. oil immersion lens. This is so-called because it is designed to work, not in air, but in a drop of special oil which is run in between the lens and the cover-slip of the slide. Such a lens gives slightly more than double the magnification of the normal $\frac{1}{6}$-in. objective, and with a ×10 eye-piece will give a total of ×1,000.

Conversely, it is sometimes desirable to have an objective of lower power (i.e. longer focus) than $\frac{2}{3}$-in. If the wings of a medium-sized insect are mounted on a slide they will probably be bigger than the field of view of a $\frac{2}{3}$-in. objective, and this is a nuisance if they are to be drawn or photographed. A 1-in. or $1\frac{1}{2}$-in. objective will probably cover the whole wing (see Chapter VII).

Testing a monocular microscope

This is much simpler than testing a binocular, since there are none of the problems of matching two images. There are no prisms to get out of adjustment, and in the optical part of the instrument there is nothing to go wrong so long as the lenses are not cracked, nor their cement perished, and they are still firm in their mounts. The lenses are cleaned like those of the binocular.

When buying a monocular microscope, the main points to watch are the range of lenses supplied, and the general state of the instrument, especially that the focusing works smoothly and positively; that is, it should move easily, should change direction without any free movement of the knob ('back-lash'), and should be quite free from any tendency to creep downwards under its own weight. The last is most important, because it is liable to bring the objective down on to the cover-slip of the slide, and damage both. Faults in the rack-and-pinion focusing are very troublesome and difficult to cure, so when buying a monocular microscope pay as much attention to this as to the optical qualities (the same is true, in principle, of a binocular, but the working distances are less minute, and there is no fine focusing gear to complicate matters).

The making of slide mounts for use with a monocular has been discussed in Chapter V, above.

LIGHTING FOR MICROSCOPY

Success with any microscope depends upon good lighting of the object. This sounds trite, but it is often not realised that the lighting can be as critical as the focus, and that a small change in the lighting may bring about an astonishing improvement in the quality of the image. The binocular microscope, with its solid object, and the monocular microscope with its transparent slide, present different lighting problems.

(a) Solid objects

There are differences of opinion about the best lighting for solid objects, such as whole insects. Some people like a strong beam of light from one direction, claiming that it throws small structures into stronger relief; others say that the shadows are confusing, and obscure the surface detail, while fine hairs and downy coverings are made to glisten in unnatural colours. The only solution is to experiment and to see which is best for one's own requirements, and the insects one works with.

An ordinary table-lamp, of the office kind, can be used, preferably with a flexible mounting so that it can be pushed down close to the stage of the microscope, where the light shines on the object and not into the eyes of the operator. This gives one-sided lighting, though it is not intensely concentrated, and to relieve the shadows a small piece of mirror, or a white card, can be propped up on the side facing the lamp. The shade of the lamp gets hot, and it is uncomfortable to have to work long with a current of hot air rising round one's forehead.

The lamp can be placed further away if the light is focused with a bull's-eye, a rather thick kind of lens on a swivelling mount. This gives a fairly large spot of light, not intensely concentrated, and is a favourite form of lighting with many workers. The bull's-eye can be used with daylight from a window, but *not*, please note, with *sunlight*, when it will act as a burning-glass and destroy the specimen.

A *spotlight* of some kind is a great help. There are several kinds on the market, mostly using small bulbs which work on a low voltage of 6–12, consuming about 30 watts. They can be run off a car battery, but it is more usual to operate them from the mains, through a suitable transformer.

Some microscopes have a spotlight attachment clipped on to the nose-piece, at the side away from the operator. Once the beam has been adjusted it remains automatically directed at the point of focus of the objective, since the spotlight goes up and down with the nose-piece. Such a spotlight is necessarily small, and the beam is often neither very intense nor very sharply focused. Moreover, it must necessarily always come from the same direction.

The best spotlight is a separate one, on its own stand, which can be moved about independently of the microscope. A typical one is made by Baker (Plate XIV), and has a lamp-house on a vertical rod, so that it moves up and down and pivots in any direction. The bulb is a sturdy one with full-size, centre contact, screw fitting, consuming 5 amps at 6 volts. The filament is a tightly-wound spiral, and approximates to a point source of light, in a clear glass. The light is concentrated by a lens of about 2-in. diameter, which has a considerable focusing movement, so that an intense beam can be focused on to the specimen from any side, and from any convenient distance. By varying the focus one can have either a very small, intense spot, or a bigger circle of more diffuse light. The colour of the light can be varied by using filters in the mount provided (on newer models than the one illustrated).

Because of the tightly-wound filament, these spotlight bulbs generate a great heat, and although the lamp-house is efficiently ventilated, the bulb has only a limited life. It is necessary, therefore, to budget for periodic replacements at about 7/6 each. The life of the bulb is greatly lengthened if a switch is fitted, and the lamp is regularly switched off except when it is actually needed.

(b) Transparent slides.

Here the ideal is to provide a beam of parallel rays vertically upwards through the slide. The cheapest monoculars have a concave mirror pivoted underneath, and this is quite satisfactory for daylight, reflecting the light from the sky. If a lamp is used, the rays received are already convergent instead of parallel, and it is preferable to have a plane mirror.

The total light reaching the objective by this means is small, because the reflected light is not greatly concentrated as it goes through the object. All the better instruments have a sub-stage condenser, which collects light from an area of about three square inches, and directs all this through the small area that is the field of view of the objective, thus considerably increasing the brightness of the image. The condenser can be moved up and down, usually by rack-and-pinion, and this has a great effect on the nature of the image seen. Moved up close to the slide, the condenser gives a greater all-over brilliance, with the planes of the object sharply separated, so that it is possible to pick out a small part of the structure of the object and focus on that selectively: on the other hand contrast is poor, and it is easy to miss structures altogether. Racking the condenser down, away from the slide, reduces brilliance, but increases contrast and depth of focus, and so brings a maximum of detail into view; because of the lack of stereoscopic effect in a single image, it is difficult sometimes to separate structures that are superimposed. The sub-stage condenser of the monocular microscope should be utilised to get the most out of a slide, and it should be racked up and down to see which position gives the most information about the specimen. After the specimen has been placed in position and focused, there is only one position of the condenser that is 'correct' according to optical theory, but we are not concerned with correctness, but with seeing all we want to see.

The sub-stage is also often provided with an iris diaphragm, which cuts down the amount of light when a knob is moved. The iris should be closed, and then accurately centred by means of the screws provided. In normal practice it should be left wide open, and it is needed only exceptionally when the light supply is excessively strong.

The colour of the lighting can be controlled by putting glass filters in the holder provided, also in the sub-stage, and this is very useful in photography of slide preparations (see Chapter VII).

Instead of a sub-stage condenser, some modern microscopes are provided with a translucent stage of ground glass or opal glass, which is lighted from below by a built-in electric lamp. This gives diffused lighting, which has certain advantages over the parallel rays of a condenser. The diffused lighting gives less contrast, and is apt to lose the detail of very transparent objects. On the other hand it is kinder to the eyes, and does not throw dust and debris into a strong relief, so that it is more suitable for photography.

THE PHASE CONTRAST ATTACHMENT

When a colourless, transparent object, such as the cleared skin of an insect larva, is examined as a slide mount, it is often difficult to study, because there is very little variation in tone or colour between different parts of the object. The Phase Contrast Apparatus is a device which increases the contrast between different parts of the image by setting up optical interference between rays that have taken different paths between the lenses of the microscope system.

A microscope that is bought already equipped with this apparatus can be used for normal viewing as well (see below), or the Phase Contrast Apparatus can be bought as a separate outfit in its own box, and can be fitted to almost any standard monocular microscope, including those previously mentioned which have a single objective, but two eye-pieces.

The Apparatus consists of a *condenser unit*, one or more *phase contrast objectives*, and a *viewing microscope* (figs. 93–96). The condenser unit replaces the ordinary sub-stage condenser, and carries below the lens a *sub-stage diaphragm*, which is seen as a sheet of black glass with a cross of clear glass. The latter can be centred

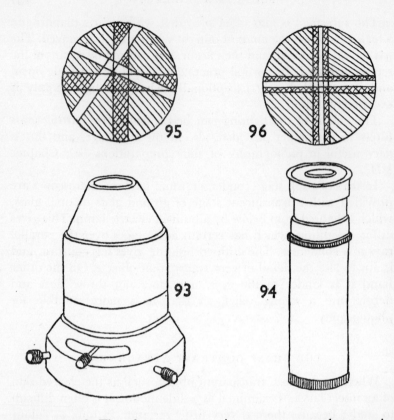

Figures 93–96. The phase contrast microscope. 93, condenser unit; 94, viewing microscope; 95, the white and black crosses, before adjustment; 96, the crosses superimposed, when the microscope is adjusted. (Baker model.)

by means of the knobs A, B, and turned through rather more than ninety degrees by the lever C.

The special phase contrast objectives are normal $\frac{2}{3}$-in. and $\frac{1}{6}$-in. objectives in appearance and fitting, but inside the mount, exactly at the point of optical focus of the lens, is fitted a *phase plate*. This is a sheet of plane glass upon which is engraved another cross, cut down into the glass to a depth that is carefully calculated according to the refractive index of the glass. Light passing through this area of thinner glass is thrown out of phase (i.e. out of step) with the light passing through the rest of the glass plate by an amount equal to one-quarter of the wavelength of green light. When the objective is held up to the light this plate appears as a black cross.

The viewing microscope is used only during adjustment, and is not part of the working equipment.

The condenser is put into position in place of the normal sub-stage condenser, a slide is put on the stage, and the image is roughly focused. The mirror and condenser are adjusted and centred in the usual way, to get the best lighting possible of the very transparent object. The eye-piece is now taken out and, looking down the tube, the white and black crosses can be seen together, usually askew, as in fig. 95. To get the apparatus to work these crosses have to be exactly superimposed, and this is difficult as they are so small. The viewing microscope is now put into the top of the tube, and pulled out, telescope-like, until the two crosses can be seen in sharp focus, and greatly magnified. By manipulating knobs A, B and lever C of the condenser unit, the white cross can be turned and moved until it exactly fits on top of the black cross (fig. 96).

The viewing microscope having served its purpose, it is now removed, and the normal eye-piece replaced. The microscope is re-focused as necessary, and it is found that the transparent tissues show up with much greater contrast. If lever C is gently moved, it will be found phase contrast is lost, so that the object can be seen with or without phase contrast, as required. There is a sharp optimum position of lever C, so that the change-over can be made quickly, and there is no need to take off the Phase Contrast Apparatus in order to resume normal work. When changing to another objective, however, it is necessary to re-align the crosses.

The full theory of phase contrast is a matter for a text-book of optics, but it can be explained in principle. The only light that reaches the condenser, and is then passed through the object, is that of the clear cross on the sub-stage diaphragm. The apparatus is carefully adjusted so that the image of this cross formed by the objective is made to fall exactly upon the engraved cross on the phase plate. Consequently, when there is nothing on the stage of the microscope, and the rays of light are not deflected on the way, all the light from the condenser must pass through the inner glass of the engraved cross.

If a transparent object is now put into the path of the rays (i.e. a slide is put on the stage), then some of the rays are deflected to a slightly different path, and these no longer pass through the engraved cross, but through the thicker glass of the rest of the plate. As a result these rays are retarded by an amount that, as we have already said, will put them out of step (or out of phase) with the other light by one-quarter of a wavelength. When the various pencils of light are reassembled by the eye-piece into an image, those which are out of phase interfere with each other, and show up as a dark patch.

Thus the very slight refractions produced by a nearly invisible object are converted into pronounced differences in light and shade, and contrast is greatly increased.

The apparatus described is made by C. Baker, of London, but Phase Contrast Apparatus is made by most manufacturers of microscopes.

HOLDING AND MANIPULATING THE SPECIMEN

Slide mounts are easy to hold and manipulate. Both monocular and binocular microscopes are normally equipped with a pair of spring clips for holding slides, and the only precaution necessary in using them is to see that the clip is not allowed to rest on the cover-slip, which would break under the pressure, or the mountant would squeeze out.

The mechanical stage has already been mentioned. This allows the slide to be moved slowly in two directions at right angles, so that by a combined movement, any part of the object can be brought into the centre of the field. Besides its delicacy of movement, this apparatus has the advantage that the position of any object on the slide can be recorded by making a note of the readings of the two vernier scales when that object is in the centre of the field of view. This is a great help when comparing one slide with another, at high magnifications, because it is then easy to find the same detail again quickly, without having to search all over the slide for it.

It should be remembered that the monocular microscope gives an inverted image, so that the slide must be moved in a direction opposite to that in which you want the image to move. The mechanical stage helps in this respect, too, because the movement is so slow, and if you start off in the wrong direction it is possible to retrace the movement exactly.

A mechanical stage is sold separately, as an accessory, and clamps on to the stage of almost any microscope. If you buy a monocular microscope of good quality, and use it often, a mechanical stage is a good investment (Plate XV, M).

XI. Ready for pinning. *Left*, strips of polyporus; *top*, tubes with pins; *right*, pocket lens; *front*, pinning forceps. *Centre*, four useful sizes of pins.

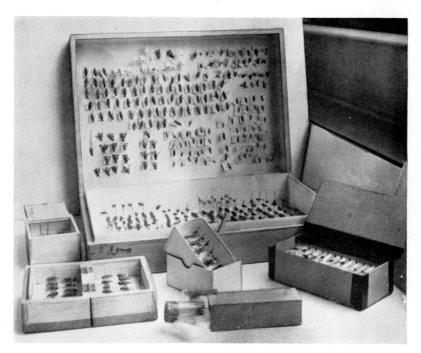

XII. Six different containers for pinned insects.

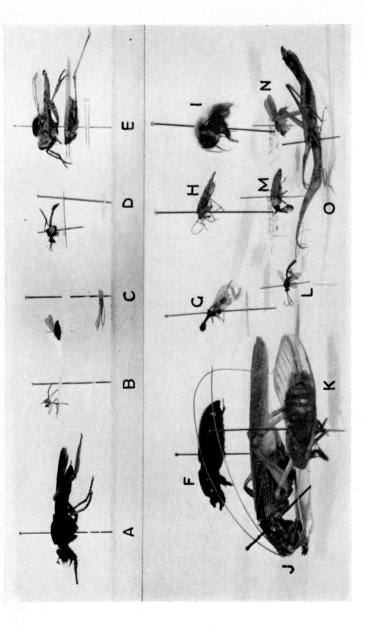

XIII. Methods of pinning, and faults to avoid. A–E, Diptera: A, pinned direct; B, on minuten (bent!); staged on cardboard; C, on polyporus; D, on celluloid; E, pinned direct, with prey below (grasshopper); F, M, Coleoptera; G, Megaloptera; H, Mecoptera; I, L, Hymenoptera; J, O, Orthoptera; K, Homoptera; N, Diptera. I. G. H, bad angle of pin or drooping specimens. O, pair of insects taken *in copula*.

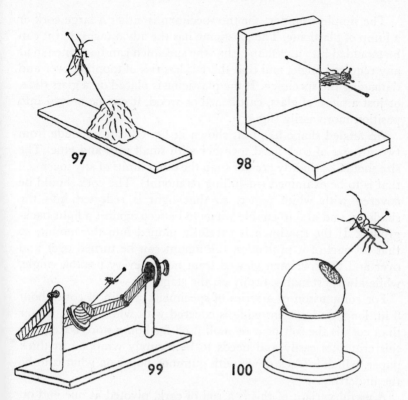

Figures 97–100. Ways of holding an insect under the binocular microscope. 97, in a lump of plasticine on a slide; 98, an L-shaped cork-
holder; 99, a universal mounting, of which a number of patented
designs exist; 100, a simple ball-and-socket arrangement.

Binocular microscopes, because of the additional reflections
through the prisms, give an image that is not only right way up,
but is also correct from left to right. Movement of the image,
therefore, is in the same direction as movement of the object,
though of course movement is exaggerated according to the degree
of magnification. It is perfectly possible just to hold an object by
hand under the binocular microscope, having first set the focus
high so as to leave plenty of space for manœuvring below the
objective lenses. This is an excellent practice for quick comparison
of specimens, at low magnifications: at higher magnifications
involuntary movement of the hands spoils the definition of
details.

L

The simplest support for the specimen is either a large cork or a lump of plasticine. The plasticine has the advantages that it can be moulded into any shape, that the specimen can be pinned in at any required angle, and that there is less risk of toppling over and damaging the specimen. If the plasticine is placed on a glass slide, or just a piece of glass, cardboard or wood, it can be moved into position more easily (fig. 97).

An angled shape like that shown in fig. 98 can be made from two squares of cork fixed together with small pins and glue. The size should be slightly greater than the outer limits of any specimen that is to be examined (including its mount). The cork should be covered with white paper, so that light is reflected into the shadows, and also to enable wings to be seen against a light background. If the specimen is carefully pinned into the mount, so that no part of it protrudes, the mount can be turned over and over and the specimen viewed from nearly every possible angle, while always standing firmly on the stage.

For comparison of a series of specimens, a strip of cork about 8 in. long, and 1–2 in. wide is covered with white paper. Better than cork is the soft peat or moll used for lining store-boxes, but this crumbles easily and needs to be securely wrapped in thick paper, which is stuck down with gummed paper on what is to be the underside.

A useful variant of this is a rod of cork, pivoted at one end on to a bar, along which it slides. This allows movements in all directions, but practice is needed before it can be used smoothly while keeping the eyes applied to the microscope.

The best support of all for use with the binocular microscope is some form of universal joint, or ball-and-socket. Two forms are shown in the illustrations. The simplest to make is to take a sphere of brass or other soft metal and drill into it a hole $\frac{1}{8}$-in. in diameter, which is filled in with plasticine. The ball is then rested in any kind of cup-shaped mount, such as a short length of tube soldered vertically on to a small brass plate (fig. 100). The insect is pinned into the plasticine, and can be examined from any angle by rotating the ball, which will be heavy enough to hold the specimen wherever it is set, without toppling over. The problem here is to get a ball of soft metal, because most such balls are made for casters, door catches and so on, and must necessarily be made from a hard metal.

A little gadget with two directions of rotation (fig. 99) is apt to

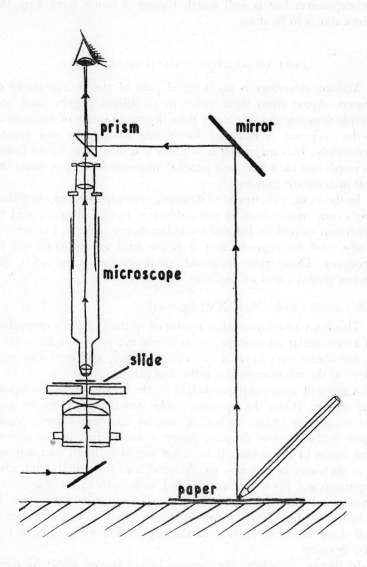

Figure 101. Principle of the camera lucida attachment for drawing with the microscope.

be expensive, but is well worth having if much work with the binocular is to be done.

AIDS TO DRAWING WITH MICROSCOPE

Making drawings is an integral part of the serious study of insects. Apart from their value in published papers—and one simple drawing can be clearer than dozens of words of description —the very act of drawing forces one to observe and record accurately. It is surprising how often you may describe an insect in words and then find your general impressions will not stand the test of accurate drawing.

In the same way, freehand drawing, though a help in clarifying one's own impressions, is still subject to optical illusion, and to confusion caused by the sudden enlargement of scale. For serious study, and for reproduction it is essential to use some aid to accuracy. Those most commonly used are the *camera lucida*, the *squared eye-piece*, and *the projection apparatus*.

The Camera Lucida (Plate XV; fig. 101)

This is an attachment that screws on to the eye-piece mounting of a monocular microscope, or on to one eye-piece of a binocular. A horizontal arm bears a swivelling mirror, and over the eye-piece of the microscope is a reflecting prism.

A piece of drawing-paper is laid on the bench, vertically below the mirror. When the operator looks into the eye-piece he sees the magnified image, as before, but he now sees superimposed upon it the sheet of drawing-paper, reflected first in the mirror and again in the prism. If he takes pencil in hand and applies it to the paper he can now see his hand, and the pencil point, also superimposed upon the image, and so he can easily trace over those details that he wishes to draw. Having drawn as much as is in the field of view, he can then move both object and sketch and draw the next portion of the object in continuation of the first drawing.

In theory, therefore, the camera lucida is easy and foolproof. It has, however, a number of irritating peculiarities. The biggest difficulty is to match the brightness of the two fields of view, otherwise you may be able to see the pencil, but not the insect, or vice versa. Coloured screens are provided for one, or both beams of light, so that the brighter may be dimmed to match the other. Even so there is often a sharp change in intensity of one field if you move the head slightly. I used to have much trouble of this sort until someone told me that when I looked down the microscope with my left eye, my nose cut off the light from the mirror.

Sometimes there is a problem of parallax, the two images appearing to move in relation to each other when the head is moved. This can be partly corrected by adjusting the focus of the microscope, and care should be taken to eliminate parallax as much as possible before beginning to draw. If the microscope is not of high quality, and the image is distorted towards its edges, it will not be possible to join up one drawing with the next and, indeed, failure to do this may draw attention to distortions that had not previously been noticed.

A difficulty that faces all beginners with the camera lucida is that of controlling the scale of the drawing. It is distinctly discouraging to have drawn happily for some time and then to look up and find either a tiny thumbnail sketch, or a gargantuan figure running off the paper in all directions. The scale of the drawing is controlled by the distance of the paper from the mirror, and one who uses the instruments regularly will have discovered a standard arrangement that gives him a drawing of a convenient size. It is the occasional user who is to be seen trying to work with his paper up on a pile of books, or down on the floor.

Finally, the drawing can be accurate only if the plane of the paper is parallel to the focal plane of the microscope, and this is most easily attained by having the microscope standing vertically and the paper flat on the bench. This is not difficult with a monocular microscope, and a few binoculars also have vertical eye-piece tubes. In most binoculars the eye-pieces converge towards each other, as well as often inclining towards the user. For strict accuracy the paper should be on a board which is tilted to the same angle, but the error is not always enough to be worth the trouble. It can be checked by making a drawing on such a board, and one flat on the bench and comparing the results.

The Squared Eye-piece

This is a circle of plane-glass, just smaller than the diameter of the eye-piece itself, and upon which is engraved a block of squares, usually 5 × 5. It is put into the eye-piece by unscrewing one of the component lenses and fixing the glass disc against the 'stop', the black ring that gives a sharp edge to the field of view. This stop is always placed at a point where the rays converge into an image, and so if the graticule (the block of 25 squares) is fixed at this point it will automatically be in sharp focus at the same time as the object.

Most microscopes have a huyghenian eye-piece, with the stop midway between the two components. The upper lens is unscrewed, and the glass disc dropped in to lie on the stop, with the engraved side downwards; if it is put in the other way up the graticule will be above the plane of the stop by the thickness of the glass. Three small pieces of plasticine will fix the disc in position. The upper lens is then replaced.

At first a little practice is needed to be able to see the graticule and the image in sharp focus together. When using a microscope one should always have the eye relaxed, and get sharpness entirely by focusing the instrument, not by focusing one's eye. By making the microscope do the work in this way it can be used for long periods without eye-strain. If there is difficulty in seeing the graticule it usually means that the eye is not being relaxed.

Now take the paper or Bristol board on which the drawing is to be made, and rule on it a set of 25 squares in soft pencil; take care not to score too heavily into the paper so that the squares may still show after rubbing them out. The size of the drawing is very simply controlled by the size of the pencilled squares. Thus, if you want to make a series of drawings to the same *scale*, so as to show the relative sizes of the insects, then the pencilled squares must be the same for all the drawings and, of course, the microscope must be used at the same magnification. On the other hand, if you have a varied assortment of insects and want all the drawings to be the same *size*, you get this result by varying the size of the squares and, if necessary, the magnification of the microscope, for each drawing.

With the squared eye-piece there are no difficulties of lighting or parallax, but there is the problem of what to do about bits of the object that are not all in focus at the same time; even with a wing it is seldom possible to get every part to lie in the same horizontal plane. Obviously you should not draw anything that is badly blurred or distorted. If the objective is quite vertical, then I think you ought to bring every detail to sharp focus, by small movements of the focusing knob, before drawing it. With a binocular microscope, however, the objective is not vertical, and movement of the focusing knob causes the image to move across the graticule. There is no ideal solution of this difficulty, and a compromise must be made.

It should be remembered, however, that the squared eye-piece is not used for making the final detailed drawing, but only for laying out the preliminary sketch, to ensure that shapes and proportions are correct. It is enough, therefore, to indicate approximate positions of all the parts, and to complete the details with an ordinary eye-piece. To avoid having to keep putting in the disc and taking it out again, it is convenient to have it permanently fixed in one eye-piece. In my Leitz binocular I have the squared eye-piece permanently fixed into the $\times 18$ eye-piece, and use this with the $\times 3$ objectives (magnification $\times 54$) for laying out the drawing, changing to the $\times 8$ eye-pieces with $\times 6$ objectives (magnification $\times 48$) for the detailed drawing.

'Micrometer eye-pieces' are similar glass discs engraved with a linear scale, with very fine subdivisions. They are useful for direct measurements of proportions, and so on, but are tedious to use for drawing.

With either the camera lucida or the squared eye-piece the scale of the drawing can be found out by looking at a good engraved scale through the microscope and noting how many squares it occupies. A metal scale is best, and for accuracy the thickness of the engraved lines has to be allowed for by reading from the left side of each line. If you then draw on the sketch a line representing one millimetre, this will still give a true scale however the drawing is reduced by the printer.

Projection apparatus for drawing

The image that is seen in the eye-piece of a microscope, with the eye close to the lens, is a virtual image, that is, the rays enter the eye *as if* they had come from a greatly magnified image at a considerable distance. If the head is moved away the same lens will project a real image, which can be received on a sheet of ground glass (fig. 102). In the case of a binocular microscope, where the object is seen by reflected light, the intensity of this image is too low for practical use, but the much brighter image of a slide seen by transmitted light through the monocular microscope can be used as a guide for tracing.

It is only necessary to surround the eye-piece with something like the body of a camera, complete with ground glass screen. The size of the projected image can be varied within wide limits by

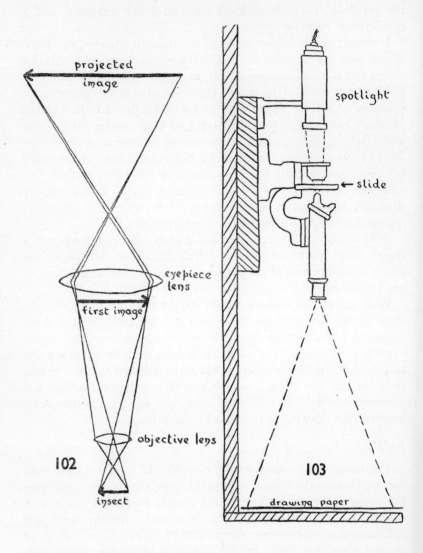

Figures 102, 103. Projection of an image for drawing from the monocular microscope. 102, optical principles; 103, the microscope in use,
turned upside down, and projecting downwards on to a base-board.

varying the distance between the eye-piece and the ground glass, and making a compensating adjustment to the focus of the microscope. The limit in practice is set by the rapidly diminishing brightness of the image, even in transmitted light.

A much more convenient arrangement is possible if a permanent mounting can be built, as in fig. 103; the practical drawback is the size of the apparatus, and its capacity for accumulating dust. The microscope is fixed vertically, with the stage upward and the eye-piece pointing down. A spotlight is fixed to shine directly through the condenser, without any mirror, and the whole fitting, microscope and spotlight, slides up and down in a grooved wooden frame. The image is then projected on to a base-board, upon which the paper is placed. The size of the image is regulated by sliding the microscope up and down, the image is focused and then a drawing made by direct tracing.

A darkened room is advisable, but it is not necessary to have a photographic dark-room, with no trace of light.

MAKING DRAWINGS OF INSECTS

The pencil sketches made by any of the above methods are only a preliminary guide, and are not suitable for any kind of reproduction.

It is true that some kinds of pencil sketch can be reproduced in books, and beautiful examples of such work by Mr. C. O. Hammond can be seen in the volume on *Flies of the British Isles* in Warne's 'Wayside and Woodland' series. To display the subtleties of shading of these drawings a half-tone process must be used, such as is used in making blocks from photographs, and needless to say, the artist's technique must be flawless. Only an accomplished and sophisticated artist can make use of this process, and for ordinary entomological illustration (excluding colour work) the drawing must be made in Indian ink on a white, or near-white surface.

Everyone who intends to study insects should practise drawing in Indian ink, whether he expects to publish his drawings or not. As we have already agreed, the act of drawing is in itself an aid to accurate observation, but much of this accuracy is lost if the drawing is 'roughed in' in an arty way, with the outline and principal features merely indicated. A line drawing in black and white is a severe exercise in economy of means, and forces one to decide firmly whether a detail is, or is not, present. As a discipline alone, it is well worth practising.

Everything in a line block is either black or white. There are no intermediate tones, no grey, and all shading and modelling is possible only by conventional pattern of lines or dots. The first rule, therefore, is that every line or mark of any kind must be made deliberately, and must be not smaller than a certain minimum size. A line block, the metal pattern from which the drawing will be printed, is made by etching out what are to be the white spaces, leaving the black lines as raised ridges of metal. If lines are made too narrow, or dots too small, the thin metal left will break during processing, or during printing. If this should occur, as a result of drawing weak or irregular lines, or covering an area with vague strokes of the pen, the reproduction will be patchy and unpleasant. The appearance of quality in a reproduction of a drawing depends very greatly upon the firmness and regularity of line employed.

To get this line needs good ink, a good pen, and a good surface. Use a waterproof Indian, or carbon ink, made by one of the reputable firms that supply artist's materials—such as Winsor and Newton's 'Mandarin' series—and a mapping pen, or one only slightly larger. Do not use ball-pointed or lettering nibs, because these are likely to give you either monotonously thick and coarse lines, or lines that vary unpredictably in thickness. With a little practice you can make a line as you want it, with a simple nib, just by varying the pressure; if you want to make unusually broad lines, as in drawing wing-veins, it is best to draw two fine lines close together and then fill in the space between them.

The best surface for drawing in ink is Bristol board, a special form of card which has a smooth, polished, very white surface, and which is consistent in colour throughout, not merely prepared on the surface. This gives a clean line, without blurring or running of the ink, and mistakes can be erased by scraping off the surface with a sharp knife or a razor-blade; when smoothly scraped down the surface will take ink again, and so allows the drawing to be corrected.

Bristol board is fairly expensive, and some professional illustrators use paper instead. Leston (1954, *Entomologist* 87, p. 36) recommends Turkey Mill Paper, or 'Bristol Board Paper'. The whiteness of the paper is less important than the amount of absorption by the surface. Even though the ink does not visibly run, it may do so enough to blur the lines, and spoil the clarity of the drawing. The only way to find out is to draw a few lines and see. If the lines remain clear, almost any kind of paper will do.

The fact that a line block can record only black or white has the big advantage that drawings can be pasted together to make a compound figure or plate, and the patchiness of the background, untidy as it may seem to the eye, will not appear in the block. This can be done with Bristol board, more particularly of the thinner kinds, but drawing-paper is easier to cut and mount. Mounting of drawings is mentioned again later in this section.

Entomological illustrations should be simple. Professional artists and talented amateurs sometimes produce beautiful pictures of whole insects, and get their effects by very elaborate systems of shading. Such drawings make a book look attractive, but the illustrations that really help most in identification of insects are the small ones, fragmentary and diagrammatic though they may be. The necessary simplification and selection are a help to the reader as well as to the artist. No one need be afraid to attempt this kind of figure, in which special knowledge of, and interest in, the specimen will more than make up for the slightly more polished line of the professional artist.

There are a few simple principles to be followed. To get the shapes of things as realistic as possible, draw a short piece of a line at one time, keeping the hand and forearm resting comfortably on the table so that the hand has an easy sweep. To draw the next bit of line, move the *paper*, not the hand, to a new position. Notice that what may look like simple lines will nearly always have a number of subtle changes of curvature, and try to reproduce these faithfully, because it is these which make all the difference between a drawing and a mere diagram.

Shading, and effects of roundness, should normally be indicated rather than portrayed, and the simplest methods are often the most successful. It may be enough merely to make the outline slightly thicker on the shaded side, but this must be done neatly if it is to be convincing. Short lines at right angles to the shaded edge are easier to draw. For shading a bigger area there are two standard methods, stippling and line shading (or crosshatching).

Stippling is covering the area with dots, and using variation in size of the dots, and variation in their spacing, to indicate light and shade. Remember what has already been said against making marks that are vague and indefinite, or too small to register properly on the block. The appearance of random dots in a piece of stippling, like so many superficial appearances, is deceptive. Each dot must be made carefully in a well-chosen place, and as far as possible the dots must be similar to each other, so that an even pattern is produced. At the same time it is necessary to avoid placing them either in rows or in regular curves and whorls like a wall-paper design. In general, start with the palest part of the area to be covered, and see how few dots will give the right impression for it; then move to the next palest, placing the dots nearer together. As you progress into the shadows, make the dots bigger as well as closer.

All this sounds formidable, but the basic requirements, apart from practice, are patience and deliberation. Do not hesitate to inspect the pattern and then place a single dot here and there, or enlarge a number of neighbouring dots, till the shading looks convincing. It is possible to erase dots one by one, if necessary, on Bristol board, or to spot them out with white colour if the drawing is on paper; the difficulty is to deal with the space thus created.

In theory, line shading is more difficult than stippling, because it is harder to erase and retouch it. Some authorities will tell you that line shading, like water-colour painting, is a one-way process, because you start with the highlights first, and build up to the shadows, and if you go too far at any point the drawing is ruined; whereas stippling is said to be a reversible process, like painting in oils. Continuing the simile, line shading, like water-colour, is said to be instinctive, and not to be learned unless you have the gift.

The answer to this is to try it and see. Once again the secret is to make short, deliberate strokes as consistently as possible, and to be patient. If you look at any solid object you can see that each surface has at least two principal directions, and if you can make your series of short lines suggest these you will go a long way towards giving an impression of the shape and solid appearance of the object. Line shading becomes cross-hatching when the lines follow more than one principal direction, and so cut across each other. Fig. 135 shows how a curved surface can be shown by successive series of lines, each following a principal curve, yet varying in spacing and density to build up the shading as well as the shape.

While conforming to shape in the direction of the lines, do not forget the principle that areas of both black and white must not become too small. If you have two series of lines crossing each other at a very shallow angle, the white spaces left will be not only long and thin, but irregular as well, since the black lines will not be quite uniformly spaced. When reproduced this will come out irregular and patchy, so try as far as possible to make the different series of lines cross at as big an angle as the shape will allow.

Erasure is easy on Bristol board, by simply scratching out the offending lines with a razor-blade, scalpel, or a sharp knife. Try not to dig a deep pit in the board, but cover an area as evenly as possible. Rub down with an ivory or bone paper-knife, or similar object, to get a smooth surface for re-drawing. A good board should then take the ink again without running. On paper this form of erasure is not possible, so instead, the unwanted line is painted out with an opaque white, such as Process White water-colour. When it is thoroughly dry, it is just possible to draw in a line over it, though it is best to confine this form of erasure to things one wants simply to cut out. If appreciable re-drawing is needed on paper, it is better to start again on a fresh sheet. When Process White has been used the drawing looks terrible, but the patches will not show on the block.

Process White can also be used for showing detail against a black background. Thus, to show pale hairs or bristles the background is painted in, if solid, or covered with stipple or line-shading, then the pale details are painted in white. The drawing of *bristles* is a necessary part of entomological illustration, and should be practised. Whenever possible draw a bristle in one stroke, starting at the base with firm pressure on the nib, and easing off smoothly till the pen leaves the paper altogether at the tip of the bristle. This gives a smoothly-tapered line, with a natural curve to it— try it. Bigger bristles need to be drawn as two converging lines, the space between them then being filled in with ink. For the filling in you may use the same pen, but there is a danger of picking up fibres and smearing outside the lines you have drawn. It is better to use a small paint brush for filling in areas, but remember to wash and wipe it as soon as you have used it; not after the ink has dried.

Every bristle big enough to be drawn as such arises from a pit in the integument of the insect, and this should be shown by drawing a circle round the base of the bristle.

When drawing in Indian ink, keep a fluffless cloth at hand, and wipe the nib very frequently, so that no ink dries on it. In this way you will keep the ink flowing smoothly, and make much better lines.

An excellent article by Buck (1956) discusses drawing at greater length than we can here, and gives special attention to showing sculpturing in beetles. *The Technique of Entomological Drawing in Water-Colour* is described by Wykes (1955).

VII

PHOTOGRAPHING INSECTS

In photographing insects, even more than in collecting and preserving them, we must resist the temptation to buy complicated and expensive equipment for its own sake. Although it is true that much of the fine modern work on living insects is made possible only by the precision-built miniature camera and the high-speed electronic flash, a great deal can be done about photographing preserved insects, even with the simplest camera. Whatever your ambitions, it is a mistake to clutter yourself with unnecessary gadgets, and nearly everything that is needed in addition to the camera can be improvised from simple materials, provided you understand the principles of what you are trying to do.

All kinds of insect photography involve us in the problems of photographing a small object, at close range. Very big insects, such as Goliath beetles, Mantids or big stick-insects, will be bigger than the film we are to use, but generally we want to get a picture of the insect at least as big as natural size, and often enlarged from one to ten times; much more than this if we are dealing with microscopic insects mounted on a slide. While it is possible to make an enlargement from a small negative, this method loses a lot of definition and picture-quality, and consequently the aim should always be to get the image on the negative as big as possible.

We shall consider first how to photograph a single pinned insect, then a slide on the microscope, and finally a living insect.

THE SINGLE PINNED INSECT

If we take this at the normal distance for a portrait, the image of the insect will be very small on the film. As we move closer to the object we have to pull out the bellows of the camera to keep

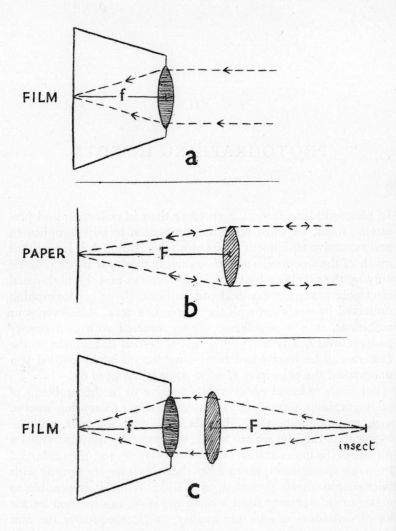

Figure 104. Using a supplementary lens in close-up photography. **a,** camera alone, focused on 'Infinity', receives parallel light and focuses it on the film, at the focal distance, f; **b,** supplementary lens alone will either receive parallel light and bring it to a focus at a distance F, or conversely, will receive light coming from a distance F and pass it on as parallel light; **c,** the two lenses in combination: the supplementary receives light from an insect at a distance F and makes it parallel, so that the camera lens can focus it on to the film.

XIV. A binocular microscope (Leitz) and a spotlight (Baker). The universal holder for the insects came from Flatters and Garnett. Note particularly that there is ample room below the lenses to handle the specimen.

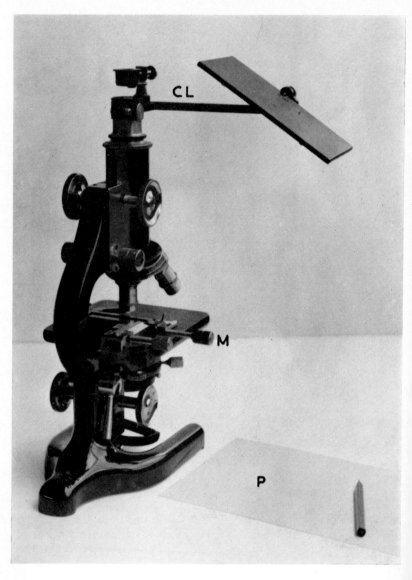

XV. A monocular microscope (Perry), with a camera lucida (CL) and a mechanical stage (M) for moving the slide. Drawing-paper and pencil are at P.

it in focus, and there is an exact relation between the size of the image, the extension of the camera, and the focal length of the lens. If we have a lens of focal length f, and want to use it to produce an image n times as big as the insect, the lens and film must be separated by a distance v, given by the formula $v = (n+1)f$. Thus, to photograph an insect at its natural size $n=1$, and $v = (1+1)f = 2f$; the camera must extend to twice the focal length of the lens. To take a picture six times as big as the specimen we must draw out the bellows to $v = (6+1)f = 7f$.

Obviously we can get this result either by increasing v or making f smaller, and if it is not possible to pull out the bellows very far (as in a simple folding film camera), we can go some way by reducing the focal length of the lens, f, by putting an extra lens ('supplementary', 'close-up' or 'portrait' lens) in front of the ordinary one. If we can open the camera and arrange a focusing screen the effect of the extra lens can be seen, and the image focused sharply. If it is not convenient to do this, there is a trick which can be used, illustrated in fig. 104.

If you take the supplementary lens—a spectacle lens will do— and hold it in front of a piece of paper near the window, you can make it give an image of distant buildings or trees. When this is in focus the distance from the lens to the paper can be measured, and gives you the focal length of the lens (F). In this position the parallel rays from the distance view are being brought to a focus; conversely, if you put an insect at the focus, the rays from it will come out parallel on the other side of the lens. If the camera lens is now put close against the supplementary, as in fig. 104c, and the camera focused on 'infinity', these parallel rays will be sharply focused again on the film.

An example is a spectacle lens of 10 dioptres, which has a focal length of $\frac{1}{10}$ m., or about 4 in. If we focus our folding film camera on infinity, attach the spectacle lens in front of it, and put the insect 4 in. in front of that, we shall get a sharp image on the film. Since an ordinary film camera taking No. 120 size ($3\frac{1}{4} \times 2\frac{1}{4}$ in.) has a lens of about 4 in. focal length, the image will be the same size as the insect.

To do better than this we need a camera which will extend to at least twice the focal length, so that we can get our result by increasing v in the formula. One of the best is one of the old 'studio' or 'hand-and-stand' cameras; the Sanderson type, in teak or mahogany, with a variety of movements, is excellent for the purpose. It does not need an expensive lens, and a simple shutter

M

is adequate, because exposures are likely to be fairly long. The one essential is a long bellows. The focal length will be marked on the lens-mount thus: 'F. = 10.5 cm.'. Pull out the bellows fully and measure the extension, and see that it is at least double this figure.

Such a camera will probably be equipped with dark slides for plates, but modern cut films are very much better than glass plates. They can be put into plate-holders by using cut-film sheaths, which are unfortunately rather expensive. The camera need not be used on a stand, but can be placed on a table or bench, and the specimen pinned into a cork and illuminated by a spotlight, with reflectors, as shown in fig. 108.

If you want more than double or triple extension, it will probably be necessary to fit longer bellows than the original ones, or else to keep the original bellows and to extend the back of the camera by building a wooden box (light-tight, of course) on to it. A very long bellows takes up a lot of room, and it is more convenient to mount it vertically against a wall as in fig. 105, but do not forget that you will want to see the top (i.e. the focusing screen) as well as the lens and object, so start with the specimen on the floor. Focusing may be difficult if you have a long reach between the screen and the focusing-knob, and you may need to improvise some arrangement with a long rod to give remote control. It may be difficult to get the lens panel to focus smoothly and still be rigid, since it was not designed to be used vertically; if so it may be better to have some way of locking the lens-panel after only focusing it coarsely, and make the fine adjustment by moving the *specimen*.

The *exposure* depends greatly on the lighting as well as on the extension, and cannot easily be calculated or measured by meter. It is best to make test exposures at a number of times, say $\frac{1}{2}$, 1 and 2 seconds. If the lighting is kept constant and only the extension is varied, to get different degrees of magnification, the exposure varies according to the formula E^2/F^2, where E is the extension and F is the focal length. Since the insect is dead, the exposure can be as long as may be needed, with the reservation that the longer the exposure, the more risk of loss of definition from vibration. Consequently the intensity of the lighting is less important than its distribution, and its relation to the background.

The *background* is one of the biggest problems in the photography of pinned insects. A white background reflects light into the shadows of the specimen, but if it is placed close to the specimen there are likely to be ugly shadows, which are more noticeable in the finished picture than they are at the time of taking. This is one of the problems of photographing a drawer of insects, where the specimen must necessarily be close to the paper. If you are likely to take many pictures of single pinned specimens it may be worth while to make a plaster background in which the plaster curves smoothly from the vertical face to the horizontal, so that there is no hard line to appear in the photograph.

Strong side-lighting from a spotlight may be used to show up the surface relief of the specimen (e.g. the sculptured surface of many beetles), but for hairy or furry insects strong lighting from one direction is liable to make a confusing pattern of shadows on the insect itself. For these insects two lights at an angle are much better.

At these short ranges the depth of focus of the lens is very short, and the lens should be stopped down to f.16 or smaller. Make test exposures in a series—say $\frac{1}{2}$, 1, 2 and 4 seconds, and develop them carefully. Do not be content with a quick glance in the dark-room, but develop, fix, wash and dry the test negatives properly. You will then have a reliable guide from which you can adjust the lighting, exposure, or contrast as you wish.

Use of miniature cameras. Most modern miniature cameras—i.e. the higher quality 35-mm. cameras, and single lens reflexes generally—have interchangeable lenses, held in position by a bayonet catch in the mount. Extension tubes are available by which the lens can be moved much further away from the film, giving the same result as the use of a long bellows. The twin-lens reflexes usually have fixed lenses, but a bigger image can be obtained in the same way as in the folding film camera, by adding supplementary lenses. On the Rolleiflex, for example, which has normally a minimum lens to object distance of 35 in., the Rolleinar 1 close-up lens allows the object to be brought up to 18 in., and the Rolleinar 2 will focus down to 12 in.; at this distance the image is still only one-quarter the size of the object, but further increase of scale can be got by using two Rolleinars, one above the other, or by using a stronger extra lens, as described earlier. The adverse effect of supplementary lenses on the quality of the image is offset by the use of a small stop, so that only the centre of the lens is in use. The main drawback of twin-lens reflexes for this work, apart from the very limited size of the image, is that the focusing is done by a second lens, and so we must

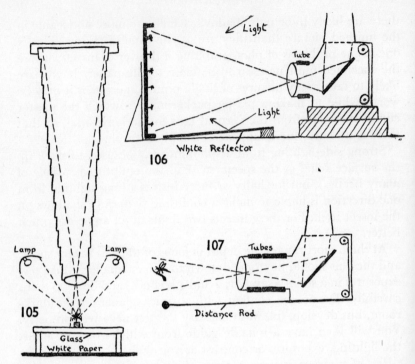

Figures 105–7. Photographing insects. 105, with a long-extension camera, arranged vertically; 106, a collection-drawer photographed with a single-lens reflex camera, using a single extension tube; 107, photographing a single insect, using two or more extension tubes; the distance-rod fixed below the camera makes it possible to get quickly to about the right distance, before quickly focusing on the screen; or, if the depth of focus is sufficient, to take a quick exposure without wasting time in focusing.

either have a matched pair of supplementary lenses, one for the taking lens and one for the finder, or else the supplementary lens must be moved between focusing and taking. The single lens cameras are therefore more convenient to use in photographing insects.

Focusing with the single-lens reflex is particularly easy because the normal reflex focusing screen works equally well whatever the extension of the camera. As in general photography with this type of camera, it is best to focus with the lens at full aperture, and then to stop it down as necessary before taking the picture; it is important not to forget to do this.

The Leica, and similar cameras, are not so easily focused when abnormally extended, because the normal rangefinder does not work any longer. The Leica accessories include a copying-stand, which has four legs sticking out in front of the lens, to make a sort of stool. When this is properly set for the lens and extension in use, the 'stool' can be stood over a document, which will be automatically in focus. This stand can be used to photograph insects in a glass-topped box or a cabinet drawer, provided that you can work out the adjustment necessary for the fact that the pinned insects are below the level of the glass, and so not in the same plane as the tips of the legs. This can be done by a little experiment with the camera open and a piece of tissue paper over the back; there is also yet another accessory that allows the image to be focused on a focusing screen and then the screen slid aside and replaced by the camera.

If you need to photograph specimens in someone else's collection, without the help of the copying stand, it is usually better to support the drawer vertically, and have the camera horizontal on a pile of books or store-boxes, as shown in fig. 106. In this way there is less risk of dropping any of the apparatus on to the drawer. If you must use the camera vertically it can be supported on a tripod with a ball-and-socket joint, or on the old Kodapod, which has a pair of strong jaws to attach it to any support; beware of using this device on soft wood, as the jaws are very powerful.

Films and processing. Use a fine-grain film such as Pan-F, or Panatomic-X. Besides the fineness of grain, which will allow the negative to be enlarged considerably, these films have much greater contrast than the soft, high-speed films. There is no advantage in using high-speed films to shorten the exposure, since the specimen is dead. Develop in either a borax-developer or a true fine grain formula, such as Promicrol or Microdol. Promicrol gives excellent shadow detail, but is rather soft-working unless you increase the times of development over those recommended by the makers.

Filters are not necessary, but a well-designed *lens-hood* should always be used. Its function is not so much to stop stray light from reaching the lens (though it does that), but mainly to restrict the field of view to that which will just cover the film. Anything outside this is merely thrown on to the inside walls of the camera, and in spite of a dead black paint, much scattered light reaches the film, where it causes a general greyness and loss of contrast.

PHOTOGRAPHY USING A MICROSCOPE

The problems are the same whether we focus a solid object through one side of a binocular microscope, or a slide-mount through a monocular, at any rate as they concern the camera; lighting will be discussed later.

We have seen in the previous chapter that the eye-piece of a microscope will project an image that can be received on a screen or drawing-board, and traced. Obviously the same image can be photographed, if we can arrange for it to fall on a film in a suitably dark container. There are two ways of doing this, one using the camera lens and one without it.

The first is suitable for use with a folding-camera, and is similar in principle to the use of a supplementary lens as shown in fig. 104. If the microscope is focused so that the eye can see a sharp image while remaining completely relaxed (as a microscope should be used), then the rays coming out of the eye-piece must be in parallel beams (the image 'at infinity'). If we now focus the camera on infinity, and place it in line with the eye-piece, it should bring these rays successfully to a focus on the film. In practice it is well to check this with an improvised focusing-screen, and make any slight adjustment necessary.

By this method quite good photomicrographs can be taken even with a box camera of fixed focus, but it is particularly necessary to check the focusing, because these cameras are commonly set, not to a focus on 'infinity', but on the 'hyperfocal distance'. This setting brings objects from 8 feet away to infinity into reasonable focus, but its most critical distance is usually 25 feet.

In this arrangement the size of the image obtained on the film is governed by the objective and eye-piece in use, and by the sliding tube of the microscope (monocular); it cannot be varied at the camera end.

The second method, with the camera-lens removed, is the more satisfactory, but it is then necessary to be able to attach the camera on to the eye-piece with a light-tight joint. A miniature camera, particularly a single-lens reflex, is very suitable for this method, because it has a focal-plane shutter, and the lens can be removed while the camera is loaded. Special extension tubes are supplied, one end of which has a bayonet-fitting to go into the camera-body in place of the normal lens, and the other end with an adjustable ring that can be made to grip the tube of the eye-piece. Between these two sections, other tubes of different lengths

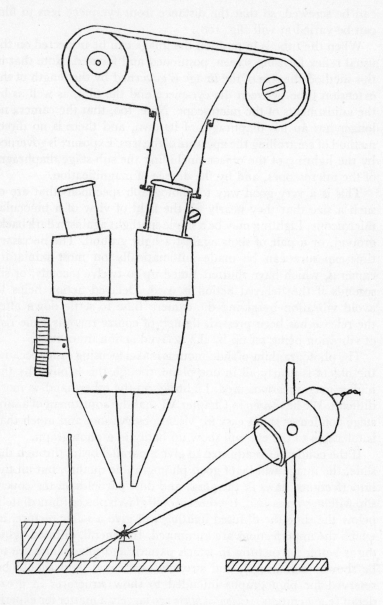

Figure 108. A miniature camera, with extension tubes, mounted on one eye-piece of a binocular microscope.

can be screwed, so that the distance from eye-piece lens to film can be varied at will (fig. 108).

When the tube is in position the image can be inspected on the usual reflex focusing screen, positioned and focused. Note that in this method the size of the image is governed by the length of the extension tube between the eye-piece and the film, as well as by the adjustments of the microscope. Note, too, that the camera no longer has an iris diaphragm of its own, and there is no direct method of controlling the aperture of the lens. Exposure is governed by the lighting of the object (including the sub-stage diaphragm of the microscope), and by the degree of magnification.

This is a very good way to photograph specimens that are of such a size that they nearly fill the field of view of a binocular microscope. Lighting may be a single spotlight against a dark background, or a pair of spots against a light ground. The necessary time-exposure can be made automatically on most miniature cameras, which have shutters timed up to twelve seconds; or six seconds if the delayed action is used. Delayed action helps to avoid vibration by giving the camera time to settle down after the release has been pressed, though of course there is some risk of vibration being set up by the delayed action timer itself.

The photographing of slide-mounts makes focusing easier because the object is nearly all in one plane, though this is offset by the higher magnifications used. Lighting, on the other hand, is more difficult. We have seen in Chapter VI that the adjustment of a sub-stage condenser is not easy for visual observation, and much that is tolerable to the eye will show up badly in a photograph.

If the condenser is adjusted to give a parallel beam through the slide, the image will be of good photographic quality, but all the imperfections, flaws in the glass, and dust particles on the cover-slip will be emphasised. If a sheet of opal glass is placed immediately below the slide the diffused lighting will give a softer picture, in which the imperfections are minimised. In general, diffused lighting is better for pictures in which pattern and tone values are to be shown (e.g. wings), and strongly condensed light should be reserved for photographs intended to show structures in great detail (e.g. genitalia). *Coloured filters* are largely a matter for experiment, but the same principles apply as in general photography out-of-doors: to make an area of a certain colour appear lighter in the finished print, choose a filter of a similar colour; to make this area appear darker in the print, use a filter of complementary colour, according to the following table, which is taken from the Ilford *Manual of Photography:*

MICROFILTERS FOR INCREASING CONTRAST

The Ilford series of nine Microfilters is intended to cover the same range, though the names of the colours do not exactly correspond with the following table.

Colour of object	Complementary filter
Red	Bluish Green
Orange	Violet
Yellow	Blue
Pink	Deep Green
Purple	Light Green
Bluish Green	Red
Green	Pink
Blue	Yellow
Deep Blue	Orange

Need I say that these filters are used only with black-and-white film, and not when photographing in colour?

The filter should be inserted into the holder that is present below the condenser in most monocular microscopes. Since the filter does not come between the object and the image it does not cause any distortion of the image, and so it is not necessary to take trouble to mount the filter in high quality optical glass, as one does for an ordinary camera. The Ilford Microfilters, and the Kodak Wratten series can be bought as simple sheets of coloured gelatine, and fixed into home-made cardboard holders; take great care not to touch the surface of the gelatine.

Very dense areas of chitin may be opaque to any light except the *infra-red*. A photograph by infra-red can be taken by using the special film and filter, but there are two complications. One is that the infra-red filter appears black to ordinary light, and so cannot be put in place while the image is being focused. The second is that infra-red rays come to a focus appreciably nearer to the lens than even the longest rays of visible light (red). The image must be focused using a deep red filter, and then the microscope focused slightly down to bring the objective lens closer to the slide. The distance must be found by making a test exposure, which will serve to check all the other factors, including length of exposure, as well as the focusing.

When using an ordinary monocular microscope for photography it may be more convenient to tilt it on its stand till the barrel is horizontal. On the other hand, the Watson *Holophot* is a ready-made apparatus in which one of their monocular microscopes is used vertically and topped with a reflex camera of special design. With this apparatus the image can be examined directly through a side-tube, or studied on a full-sized reflex focusing screen, and then photographed on cut film. The Holophot is ideal for taking a number of photographs in quick succession, especially if the same setting can be used for all of them.

Use of an enlarger as a projector. A standard vertical enlarger can be used, in the dark-room, to make projection photographs of transparent objects, especially of slide-mounts. The slide is placed in the negative carrier, or if this is not suitable it may be replaced by a sheet of plate-glass and the slide laid on top of that. A projection image is thrown on to the base of the enlarger, and focused on to a piece of card. It is desirable to make a mask of black paper with a hole only a little larger than the object on the slide, so that all extraneous light is cut off; if this is not done the tones of the negative may be degraded and flat.

To make a negative, the piece of paper on the base-plate is replaced with a sheet of cut film. Unless the mount on the slide is very yellow it is convenient to use a slow, orthochromatic film, such as Ilford Fine Grain Ordinary, because this can safely be handled in a red light, and put in position with the enlarger switched on and the red safety cover over the lens. If panchromatic or colour film is used then it must be put in place in absolute darkness; to do this the position for the film must be marked beforehand with drawing-pins, or a bromide paper-holder used.

The use of *colour* film presents no special difficulty in any of these processes, since the exposure can be increased as much as may be necessary. The exposure of colour film needs to be more exactly correct than for black-and-white. The apparent colours of the object, however, depend so much on the light used that a natural appearance is hardly possible, and the colour serves mainly as a means of showing form and pattern more clearly.

PHOTOGRAPHY OF LIVING INSECTS

Dead insects, however skilfully photographed, never look alive, and neither their colour nor their pose seems natural. Strangely enough, a drawing by a first-class entomological illustrator can be more convincing than a photograph, perhaps because the artist puts back into the drawing some of the subtleties of attitude and positioning of the limbs that he has subconsciously noticed in the living insect.

Fortunately the great technical advances of recent years now make possible high-speed photographs of living insects, not only in black-and-white, but also in colour. Whereas a picture of a dead insect often gives little more than a poor reminder of what one saw when it was alive, a coloured picture of the living insect may show more than could be taken in with the naked eye.

Still Photography of Living Insects

In the studio the optical arrangement is the vertical one shown in fig. 105. By a combination of short-focus lens and long-extension bellows, magnifications of up to × 50 are easily obtained. The main problem is to get enough light without injuring the insects. For colour photography, something approaching 1,000 watts will be needed—say four 250-watt floods—and it is necessary to have sheets of heat-proof glass between the lamps and the insect. An alternative heat-filter is made from two sheets of plate-glass arranged as a narrow cell with cold water running between them.

For black-and-white work the intensity of light need not be so great, and one or more ordinary microscope spotlights (see Plate XIV) can be used. 'Reflector Spotlight' bulbs (e.g. Crompton or Osram) fit into normal lamp sockets, and consume 75 watts, but have a mirror silvered on to the base of the lamp, and so concentrate the light into an intense, parallel beam. They also concentrate the heat, so the heat-filter will still be needed. 'Photo-flood' lamps, as used in portrait photography, give a very intense light by overrunning the filament, and in consequence have a short life. They are best used with an arrangement of switches that gives a choice of series or parallel working; the lamps are kept in series, at a low intensity, for all the period of arrangement, and are switched up to full power only for the actual exposure. Not only does this conserve the life of the lamp, but it also protects the insect from the effects of great light and heat.

Light and heat affect the behaviour of insects, and this can be either a handicap or an advantage. Thus nocturnal insects may be made quieter by strong light, but diurnal ones are likely to become more active. A little experiment with your subjects before-hand will show whether you can make use of this influence to get them to keep still, or to begin feeding, as you wish. A sudden, intensely hot and bright beam may make an insect fly away, and this is where the electronic flash scores, by being over so very quickly.

This kind of picture calls for a simple, uniform *background*, without obtrusive shadows, and for this an arrangement such as that shown in fig. 105 is helpful. The insect stands on a sheet of ground glass, and about an inch below this is a sheet of white card, which reflects the top lighting, and gives an even, diffused background.

Still photography by electronic flash. Electronic flash gives magnificent results in the photography of living insects. It can be used either indoors or out, and in fact there is little difference in the photographic technique, since in either case the flash provides all the lighting that is recorded.

The exposure can be made by what is called 'open flash'. The camera shutter is set to 'bulb' (B), and the routine is then: press shutter (opens), and keep pressed; fire flash; release shutter (closes). This method can be used with any camera, even if the camera is not specially equipped for flash. In theory, if the ordinary lighting is kept low it ought not to record on the film at the small aperture in use, but in practice there is much risk of 'ghost' images, odd windows and lights, that appear faintly on the negative because the shutter was held open long enough for them to be recorded. Synchronised flash is much to be preferred, and most modern cameras, even cheap ones, are fitted for this.

In synchronised flash, the camera shutter and the flash-gun are worked from the same cable-release, so that the flash always takes place while the shutter is open, provided of course that the shutter is set to a speed that allows time for this to happen. *Electronic flash* is of very short duration and high intensity. Besides freezing all movement of the insect, it allows the shutter to be set at one of the higher speeds, such as $\frac{1}{250}$ second, thus completely preventing ghost images. The very high intensity permits the use of a small aperture, such as f.22, and the greater depth of focus at this aperture is responsible for much of the brilliant quality of the photographs. *Flash bulbs*, on the other hand, have a duration of about $\frac{1}{50}$ second, and need a bigger aperture of f.11 or f.8. Although the insect as whole may be stationary, its wing-tips or antennæ may be vibrating fast enough to show movement on the negative; and this, together with the softer focus resulting from the bigger aperture give a different quality to the photograph.

It is a matter of taste which one prefers. The perfectly sharp, brilliant picture of crystal clarity is most striking, but some people dislike the appearance of frozen immobility, in human portraits as well as in those of insects. It sometimes seems unnatural, because we ourselves never see living animals so motionless, and in such finely sculptured detail. From an artistic point of view (and the study of insects is an art as well as a science) the softer outlines and suggestion of movement in flash-bulb pictures may actually seem more life-like, at least in black-and-white; full colour is still such a delightful novelty that one needs electronic flash for the full enjoyment of it.

In either case the duration and intensity of the flash is fixed, and cannot be controlled. Exposure of the film is therefore controlled by varying the aperture of the lens.

The *setting* in which the insect is taken needs a little forethought. Indoors an attempt may be made to show part of a plant, or a patch of soil or sand; try to suggest a natural setting, but at all costs avoid an elaborate fake that will look like one of those very dead Victorian wall-cases. Unless the surroundings are part of the picture—as, for example, in showing a stick-insect or a leaf-insect —the insect itself should almost fill the picture, and at this very short range only a fragment of any other object will appear sharp, so that even a metal rod or a wooden block will not necessarily spoil the picture.

Out-of-doors the insect has to be stalked, and the photographer has to act quickly to get a picture at all. Some very fine work of this kind has been done by Edward S. Ross, and his book should be studied, both for the advice, and for the beautiful examples of what can be done. Some of his colour photographs of insects are so perfect that they can be run down in keys, just like an actual specimen; indeed, by showing the full natural colour of the insect they have an advantage over a museum specimen. Not all Mr. Ross's pictures are taken by electronic flash. He shows some taken in sunlight at $\frac{1}{50}$ sec. at f.11 (Plus-X film; double extension), which show excellently the difference between flash pictures and those taken with natural lighting, to which we have referred above.

Ross emphasises that in photographing living insects you have to expect a low percentage of successes, and just go on taking a long series of photographs. There are so many things that can vary that it is only very occasionally you can hope to get all the factors to come right at the same time. All the same there are two things which can mar any kind of photograph, camera movement and wrong focusing, and unless you take care about those you are almost certain to be disappointed.

Camera movement is the greatest single cause of poor quality in photographs of any kind. Many of us know some person who gets sparkling holiday pictures with the cheapest camera, and are puzzled to know how he does it; very often the simple answer is that he holds the camera still. It is especially difficult to hold the camera quite still after you have been stalking a watchful insect, and end up by having to hold the camera in an awkward, cramped position in order to take it at all. But, just as in shooting, those last few seconds can ruin all the careful preparation, and the remedy is the same with a camera as with a gun: keep on practising until you can hold it still without tensing your muscles and trembling, and can squeeze the trigger without jerking.

At the very small aperture of f.22, *focusing* is not as critical as it is in general photography, but it is still necessary to get fairly near to the right distance. Out of doors you cannot hope to alter the focus as you go nearer to the insect and the only way is to pre-set it; this means that you fix the extension of your camera by means of the extension-tubes, and then stand the right distance away from the specimen. As a help in judging this distance you can use one of the tripod fittings, like the Leica copying attachment, referred to above, or you can improvise a simpler one as shown in fig. 107, by fixing a rod to stick out in front of your camera for the right distance. Then you creep up to the insect until the tip of the rod is level with it, centre the specimen in the view-finder, and fire the flash.

I have not given technical details of electronic flash because there is a variety of possible equipment, and the only way to choose it is to go to a reputable photographic shop and ask for a demonstration. Things to be looked at are cost, size and weight. There is no need to look for a specially high-powered model, because you are going to use it close to the subject—which will offset the effect of long extension on the camera—and an aperture smaller than f.22 is not desirable with most modern anastigmat lenses. Many of them are corrected for a best performance at about f.5.6, and it is no longer true, as it used to be, that stopping down always improves the definition. The most important thing about electronic flash is to make sure that it is electrically safe. Its working depends upon the storage of a lethal quantity of electricity in a big condenser, and you should be satisfied that the flash-gun seems to have been carefully made out of good quality materials. Always follow the makers' instructions, and never leave the gun lying about without first discharging it.

Cine-films of living insects

Cine-films in full colour, showing in close-up detail the activities of living insects, have been made with brilliant success in recent years. Some of the most painstaking and beautiful photography is to be seen in some of the films made by or on behalf of the insecticide firms. These are not exactly advertising films, though naturally they are linked with the name of the firm sponsoring them. They are more of the nature of propaganda, to make people more aware of the insect world.

The filming of tropical insects in a truly wild state in their natural setting is a highly professional business, and calls for elaborate organisation, if the right places are to be reached just at the right season, and the insects found and photographed without costly delay and waste of material. Filming insects nearer home, either in the open or indoors, is quite within the scope of any amateur cinematographer, provided that his cine-camera can be adapted by means of extension tubes to work at very close range.

The sub-standard 16-mm. film has an actual picture-space, or 'frame' 10.5 × 7.62 mm., and a still camera of this size would have a lens with a focal length about equal to the diagonal of the frame, i.e. 13 mm. In fact, the normal lens for the 16-mm. cine-camera is 25 mm. (1 in.), so that the cine-image is already about twice the scale of the still picture; the reason for this being that at the cinema we only seldom want to take in a wide view, and are more often interested in one or two figures in close-up. Interchangeable lenses are standard equipment, giving longer focal lengths up to 6-in., with an aperture of f.4.5. A 6-in. lens used at double extension would require the camera to approach to a distance of one foot from the insect in order to get the image the same size as the object, and would need extension tubes to bring the lens out, though not as much as in still photography, because cine-lenses are generally computed to work closer to the film than the theoretical distance.

We have to remember, however, that the actual image on the film cannot be longer than 10 mm., less than half an inch, and few of the insects we want to photograph will be as small as that. Consequently we shall nearly always be taking pictures same size or less, instead of same size or more as we did in still photography. It is possible, therefore, to take cine-films of many insects with a 6-in. lens and otherwise normal equipment, and a very little further extension will do all that we are likely to want.

Having got a suitable camera and lens, the problem is to arrange a subject, to light it—and to have patience. Out of doors the setting usually arranges itself, but it can sometimes be improved without disturbing the specimen. A butterfly sunning itself in one place may go on doing so if you move it to another patch of sunlight that is easier to photograph, or a bug will go on feeding after you have broken away the leaves that were casting ugly shadows across it. But most often you will have to be ready to make a quick check of the light, the distance and the focus, move in close, and shoot before it is too late. The distance-gauge shown in fig. 107 is a help, provided you make sure that it cannot appear in the field of view.

The problems that are present in all out-of-doors cinematography—changing light, excessive contrast, confusing backgrounds, obtrusive objects partly out of focus in the foreground—all these are exaggerated in close-up cinematography of insects, and there is no time to attend to them all, as you would if you were taking a portrait or a posed group. Outdoor photography of insects is more like photographing children, and the sporting element enters into it in the same way.

Photography indoors, in an artificial setting lends itself more to deliberate planning, and to deception. First of all you need a lot of light. In cine-photography you can neither use the high intensity lighting of the electronic flash, nor make up for a weaker light by using a longer exposure. The exposure is fixed by the rate of passage of the film through the camera: the usual rate of 24 frames per second gives an exposure of about $\frac{1}{30}$ second to each picture. Although the lens may have a maximum aperture of f.4.5, it has the depth of focus appropriate to a 6-in. lens, and so when used at close range it will have to be stopped down, probably to f.11. So the only way to get ample exposure is to intensify the lighting.

Several spotlights of 500 watts up to 2 kw. will be needed, and of course must have a power-supply and cables able to handle such a big current as these spots consume. The heat generated is much greater than in still photography, and the insect must be protected against it. A water-cell consists of squares of plate-glass, built up into a hollow cell with the two biggest sides of a diagonal slightly greater than the diameter of the spotlight, and of a thickness of about 2 in. The maximum cooling is obtained by running a stream of water through it, but if the main water is cloudy, or filled with small bubbles, it will cut off the light as well as the heat, and distilled water will have to be used. For top lighting the water can be contained in a glass tray above the insects, so saving the expense of two big sheets of plate-glass. Strictly speaking, of course, since the glass does not come between the insect and the lens, it need not be of the highest optical quality, but if glass of varying thickness is used, such as the glass cell of an accumulator, it is likely to give irregular patches of light on the insect or the background.

As in the still photography, the *background* can be either a setting to show the habits of the insect, or a blurred and unobtrusive one. If you want to show aphids feeding on a stem, or a butterfly probing a blossom, then you must have the stem or the flower in sharp focus, and see that this is properly lighted, as well as the insect. In particular you must see that there are no ugly shadows cutting across the stem or flower, and breaking up its shape so that it may be hard to see just what it is, especially if the picture is in black-and-white. Take care, too, that there are no stray leaves or twigs sticking out towards the camera, so that they appear on the screen as distractingly blurred objects.

Some of the beautiful films of the Shell Film Unit show the behaviour of insects by means of close-ups taken in the studio against a simple background of plain sand, sometimes with a small plant in it. The camera is on a tripod, level with the insect, and at close range, and the sky is suggested by a simple white back-cloth, lighted by blue and white floods. Once the insect has accepted the lighting, and has settled down to behave normally, long sequences can be filmed, showing the behaviour in astonishing detail, quite free from any other distracting or confusing objects. Such films give a realism that could not be achieved in the shifting conditions out of doors.

Activity beneath the soil, or under water, can be filmed in a tank of plate glass, a moveable sheet inside being used to confine the insect so that it is near to the front of the tank. Shell have produced some wonderful shots of egg-laying by locusts, and observation hives and formicaria are obvious subjects of this kind. Here, more than ever, patience is the great requirement, and you have to live with the insects for some time before you can expect to be able to persuade them to perform so publicly for you.

N

STUDYING INSECTS

VIII

THE PRINCIPLES OF ZOOLOGICAL CLASSIFICATION AND NOMENCLATURE

Before we can study insects, or any other things that we may have collected, we have to find some way of arranging the different kinds—that is, a *classification*—and some way of inventing a name for each different thing—that is, a *nomenclature*. You do not have to be a museum man to feel the need for these two things. People in remote villages in the jungle know all the common animals round them, and give them all names in the local dialect. As long as these people never go anywhere else, and do not want to talk to strangers, their local names are sufficient. When men begin to meet together to discuss animals, to write to each other about them, and to pool their varied observations, they feel the need for some agreement about a classification of animals and about the names by which they are to be known.

Let us begin with classification. We have to have some starting-point, some basic unit, which will serve as the brick from which our classification is to be built up. This unit is the *species*. Most of us agree that a species is a natural unit, something that really exists in nature, and not just an abstraction, like a 'school' of painting.

The modern idea is that a species is a population of individuals, all of which are capable of interbreeding with any of the rest. Interbreeding may be restricted, or prevented, in practice, because parts of this population may be cut off from each other by barriers of distance, topography—mountains, or oceans; or climate—deserts, or rain-forests. Such isolated groups may develop peculiarities of their own, as human groups do in the same circumstances, and may form geographical races, or sub-species, but so long as the ability to interbreed remains, they continue to form one big species. This ability to interbreed is the main distinguishing mark of a species, because by this means the hereditary material of all members of the species is pooled, making the species a kind of living organism in itself.

Obviously we cannot easily apply this interbreeding test in practice, and we have to have some other way of deciding which insects belong to the same species. For ordinary purposes we still use the old method of morphological uniformity, which means that we think a group of insects belong to one species if we cannot see any constant differences between them; by 'constant' we mean that we cannot divide them into smaller groups and then say: 'These always have the legs red and these always have them black.'

Clearly this simplified method needs to be used with caution. A queen-bee, a worker and a drone can always be told apart, but experience shows us that they are all members of one species, though they belong to different *castes*. In many insects the males and females are very different, sometimes so different that they would seem to be quite different insects if observation had not shown that they belong together.

Again, isolated groups within one species begin to grow apart, as we have seen, and the entomologist who has to work with dead material cannot use the test of interbreeding to see if they are really one species. He has to rely on his own judgment and experience, taking into account the differences that he knows exist between good species in the same group, the difference he finds between his isolated groups, and how these latter are linked with geographical distribution. This is one of the reasons why accurate labelling of locality is so very important.

In some groups of insects, notably aphids, in which one species may exist in many different forms, and in sexual and asexual generations, the classification has become so complex that it may not be possible to decide what is a species from the dried material alone. It is becoming necessary to rear these insects in a vivarium, and so to study the species as a living population. Those who work with these insects are apt to jump to the conclusion that therefore all work with dead insects is hopelessly out-of-date, but they are wrong to do so. In the great majority of groups of insects our knowledge is still so very incomplete that we shall go on comparing the external appearance of dead insects for many years to come.

CLASSIFICATION

Below the level of species we have already mentioned the *sub-species*, or *geographical race*. This category is fairly clearly understood, but there are others that are less satisfactorily called *varieties*, *forms* or *aberrations*. These three names are used rather loosely, and in different ways, by different authors. Some of the differences between specimens seem to have a genetic basis, so that within one species there may be a certain percentage of, say, a dark-legged form, and the rest be pale-legged; much the same as red-haired and dark-haired humans. Other differences may be linked with the seasons, so that a species may have a spring form and an autumn form, a dry season form and a wet season form. Lepidopterists make great play with 'aberrations', which means simply something that wanders away from the usual, and the interest in aberrations is, indeed, that more proper to collectors of curios than to those interested in a logical classification.

The groups below the species (*infra-specific categories*) are of great importance in groups of animals that have been intensively studied, such as the mammals, the birds and, among insects, the butterflies, the mosquitoes and the aphids. In the great majority of insects, the broad classification into species and categories above this level is as far as we can venture at the present time.

The *supra-specific categories* are as follows: Species are grouped together into *genera*; genera into *families*; families into *Orders*; Orders into *Classes*; and Classes into *Phyla*, the last being the great major divisions of the Animal Kingdom. We shall deal with these units more fully in the next chapter, but before that we must turn to the difficult subject of *nomenclature*: how we give names to these various categories of animals, and what principles regulate the choice and application of such names.

NOMENCLATURE

Many people think that, because ordinary, everyday, or vernacular names for insects are good enough for ordinary conversation, they ought to be used always. Such people imagine (and sometimes say) that the specialists invent a learned jargon with Latin and Greek words, just to make the subject seem difficult, and themselves more learned. This jibe is not entirely without truth: if, instead of talking of a group of species that all occur in the same place, we call them 'sympatric species', we are all apt to have a comforting feeling that we now know more about them.

Having made this admission, we must also admit that you cannot write about an insect under its local English name, and expect to be understood by a Finnish or Peruvian entomologist. Would you understand, if he did the same thing? It is quite certain that a real understanding of the animal world is possible only through a world-wide study by zoologists of all nationalities, using a common vocabulary, even if it is partly clothed in their own language.

Because the organised study of animals began in Western Europe, it was natural to make use of Greek and Latin, as the common languages of educated men at that time. Greek is used mainly to supply roots, or fragments of words, which can then be combined to make names: for example, Lepidoptera, the insects with scaly wings. Latin has never really become a dead language, and survives in some legal and ecclesiastical matters even to the present day. Consequently it seemed natural to the early zoologists to write their papers in Latin, and particularly their descriptions of animals, so that these could be understood by any educated European.

It is from these Latin descriptions that we get our two-worded, or bi-nomial system of names for animals. Thus, a description might have begun: '*Musca flava, pedibus nigris, alis hyalinis. . . .*' 'A yellow fly, with black legs, with clear wings. . . .' This insect can be known for short as *Musca flava*, on the same principle as that familiar in the Psalms, where Psalm CXXI: 'I will lift up mine eyes unto the hills . . .' has the title '*Levavi oculos*'.

The Swedish naturalist Carl Linné, or Linnaeus, perfected this method in a great work called *Systema Naturae*, which in its massive orderliness was such an advance on anything that had gone before that it set the standard for zoological method. The Tenth Edition of this work, appearing in the year 1758, is accepted as the starting-point of zoological nomenclature, and as it appeared early in that year, we begin our names at January 1, 1758. Names that existed before that date are not taken into account in establishing priority (see below).

On the Linnaean, or binomial system, every species of animal receives a double name, which is completed by adding the name of the author and the date, thus: *Musca flava* Linnaeus, 1758. The word *flava* in this (imaginary) example is the *specific name*, while *Musca* is the *generic name*. Thus *Musca flava* would be a species of the genus *Musca*, which contains a number of other species, such as *Musca domestica* and *Musca autumnalis*.

The name of the author is added only in formal lists of references, or when it is necessary to avoid confusion. The latter is an illogical step, because, as we shall see below, we are not allowed to have two different species called *Musca flava*, even though one should be

Musca flava Linnaeus and one should be *Musca flava* Jones. Furthermore, if we should, in the process of reclassifying the group, decide to move Linnaeus's species *flava* to another genus, say *Delia*, it would now become *Delia flava* (Linnaeus), the brackets indicating that the generic placing is no longer that of the original author. The use of brackets in this way puzzles the Printer's Reader, and gets everyone thoroughly confused, and some authors, myself included, think that brackets serve no useful purpose and should be omitted.

The names of categories above the genus follow a set pattern as follows:

> Species: *Musca domestica*
>   Genus: *Musca*
>   Tribe: Muscini
>   Subfamily: Muscinae
>   Family: MUSCIDAE
>   Superfamily: MUSCOIDEA

Above this level the names cease to be based on the name of the genus, and run thus:

> Order: **Diptera**
>   Class: INSECTA
>   Phylum: ARTHROPODA

These groups receive more detailed consideration in Chapter X.

Pronunciation of scientific names. Although the spelling of these names is the same in all languages, and even in papers where everything else is in Russian or Japanese, the names are usually given in the Western form, yet their pronunciation varies between countries and even between individual entomologists. It is thus often difficult to understand a stranger until he writes down the names he is using.

In English we generally use the Old Style Latin pronunciation. Thus Muscini is 'Muss-eye-nye', and Muscinae is 'Muss-eye-nee'. However, someone brought up to the New Pronunciation Latin would give these just the opposite quantities. There are no rules of pronunciation, but it is common sense not to be too pedantic, and to try to meet other people half-way.

The International Rules of Zoological Nomenclature

It is now exactly two hundred years since the Tenth Edition of Linnaeus's *Systema Naturae* appeared, and in the meantime the number of species of insects known has multiplied many times. Although the Linnaean system of naming the genera and species still survives, our ideas of the classification of these, and of their arrangement into higher categories, has changed over the years. Moreover, in the last sixty years or so the number of people who write about insects has also multiplied many times. Whereas in Linnaeus's day entomology was a gentlemanly hobby, it is now also a profession, upon which great sums of money are spent annually.

Such a great number of people clearly must come to some agreement if they are to use names in a sense that all can understand. As long ago as 1842 the 12th Meeting of the British Association for the Advancement of Science, meeting in Manchester, prepared a set of rules known as the Strickland Code. As usual, Manchester's lead was followed, and other, more elaborate codes appeared, and in 1901 the First International Congress of Zoology prepared a code of rules to apply internationally to all groups of animals. The nomenclature of plants was, and is today, organised quite independently from that of animals.

Since then, the International Congresses meet every few years, as far as the political situation allows, and at each Congress a special section discusses the problems arising in the nomenclature of insects. In between times the work is carried on by a committee known as the International Commission on Zoological Nomenclature, which has a permanent office and secretary. For many years past this post has been held by Francis Hemming, C.M.G., C.B.E., 28 Park Village East, Regents Park, London, England.

Let us be quite clear what this body is. Although it has the approval of a majority of the zoologists who attended the last Congress, and ought to have the good will and co-operation of everyone, it is essentially a voluntary body. In its publications the Commission often says that a thing is 'mandatory' (i.e. compulsory) and others are merely 'recommended', but the Commission itself has no power to compel anyone to follow its Rules if they do not want to do so.

As we shall see in a minute, names come into general use only when they have been published, and there is a growing tendency for editors of the zoological journals to state that they will not accept papers that 'do not conform to the International Rules of Zoological Nomenclature'. This would seem to give the Commission a means of coersion, but in fact the Rules have become so complicated and so often contradictory that there are very few

editors in the world who can say whether a particular paper con-
forms to the Rules or not. Some make a fad of one point, some of
another, and it is quite wrong that they should make these a
pretext for rejecting work that is otherwise of a good standard.

It is important to start off with the right attitude to the International Rules. Obviously it makes our work on insects much
easier if we can give them names according to an orderly system,
and if we have such a body as the Commission to consult about the
problems that are certain to arise. The trouble is that many people
like codes of rules for their own sake, and get pleasure out of
manipulating the Rules, and changing the name of an insect, as
if they were making a move in a game of chess. They forget that
the real purpose of entomology is to study insects, and that it is
quite unimportant what name we use for an insect, provided that
other people understand what we mean. The personal satisfaction
of being 'correct' under the Rules is a poor compensation for
confusing everyone else.

So please, when you begin to study insects, do not get side-
tracked into playing with names instead. It wastes a lot of time
and paper, and in the long run it is surprising how little it all
matters.

The present state of the International Rules of Zoological
Nomenclature is more or less as follows: The version that was
published in the *Proceedings of the Biological Society of Washington*,
volume 39, pp. 75–104 (1926) is the last complete Code to
be published, though it has been repeated in later publications,
such as Ferris (1928) and Schenk and McMasters (1956). Since
the Rules were first drafted a great many problems of interpretation have arisen, and zoologists have applied to the Commission
for a ruling to clarify these. So in addition to the Rules we have a
set of *Opinions* rather on the lines of the legal judgments and
precedents which form a body of Case Law. There is now a special
periodical devoted to these matters, called the *Bulletin of the International Commission on Zoological Nomenclature*, published at irregular,
but frequent intervals. Here are published applications that are
made by entomologists (and other zoologists) to the Commission
to use what are called its 'plenary powers' to set aside the Rules,
where their application would cause 'more confusion than uniformity'. Opinions are canvassed among other zoologists working
on the same group, and are published for general information and
debate.

This periodical is useful to professional zoologists, and to those who are forced by the nature of their work to come to a decision about some particularly difficult problem in nomenclature. It is written in an imitation legal style, which involves a good deal of unnecessary repetition.

Finally, in 1953, the 14th International Zoological Congress met at Copenhagen, and issued a series of rulings called the *Copenhagen Decisions on Zoological Nomenclature* and published by the Commission. Here, under a variety of headings, you will find the most recent rulings on what should be done about selecting the 'correct' name for various categories of insects, but the issue of a clear and up-to-date Code of Rules was postponed until the Zoological Congress of 1958.

The International Rules of Zoological Nomenclature would therefore be a useful guide to all zoologists, including entomologists, if they could be obtained and studied, and if everyone used them as a set of guiding principles, and used them to simplify entomology, not to make it more difficult.

In the meantime, there is no point in quoting the 1926 Rules, since they are out-of-date, and all I can do here is to try to summarise the main principles, which are more or less followed by all entomologists of any nationality. It should be understood that this is only my personal version.

1. Names come into being only when they are *published*. Generally this means that they must be printed in a book, or a periodical or scientific journal, or otherwise released in such a way that any interested person has a reasonable chance to hear about them and to get a copy. Private circulation of a limited number of copies is not normally enough.

2. Besides a name (of the kind we have discussed earlier in this chapter) the author must give a description or a figure, or an 'indication'; this last means that he may say 'this is the dark form referred to in Mr. Jones's paper . . .', or something like that. He should explain just how it differs from its nearest relatives, or why he thinks it must be new to science. When naming a new genus he must state what is its 'type species' (see point 3).

3. Each category has a type, or typical member. Thus if the new species is described from a number of specimens, one of these is chosen as the type, or *holotype*, and this specimen is the pattern for all later argument about the species. If you are able to examine the holotype of a species you can generally see many points of detail that are too numerous to be included in the description, and consequently 'seeing the types' is an important step in revising

the classification of a group of insects. Holotypes are valuable specimens, and are kept with great care by museums, or in private collections. If you describe a new species, it is your duty to make sure that the holotype is fully labelled and securely preserved and will be accessible to anyone who needs to see it. If you cannot be sure of this in your home or place of work, you should deposit your holotypes in a museum.

The other specimens seen at the same time are *paratypes**. Sometimes the author decides that none of his specimens is good enough to show all the necessary details for identification, and then he may make all the specimens of equal status, and call them *syntypes*. If he does so, a later worker may come along and choose one of these as the *lectotype*, and once this action has been published, this specimen has all the authority of a *holotype*. If all the original type material of species has been lost or destroyed any author may announce a new specimen as the *neotype* of the species.

The name 'allotype' is very often used for a specimen that either the original author, or a later one, wishes to set up as a pattern for the opposite sex to the holotype: thus, if only males were known at first, someone who later finds a female that he thinks is the same species may declare it to be the allotype. This term is better avoided, because it is subject to doubt and personal opinion. Thus, the holotype of *Musca flava*, provided we are sure it is the right specimen, is not open to doubt of identity: it *is Musca flava*, and always will be. But any second specimen is subject to the doubt whether it really belongs to the same species or not.

The same objection applies to a great many other terms—topotype, plesiotype, and so on—which you will find in entomological papers. These terms are merely shorthand, the first, for example, meaning 'this specimen was found in the same area as the holotype'.

In the same way, a genus has a *type species*, which we used to call the genotype until the geneticists took over this term. Since 1930 this must be fixed at the time of the original description, if the name of the genus is to be validly published, but many earlier genera did not have a type species named. In these cases the type is selected by a later author, from among the species originally included in the genus.

---

* The International Commission, meeting in Paris in 1948, declared that *paratypes* do not directly affect the nomenclature of species, and recommend that they should not be formally recognised, nor defined, in the new Rules, See *Bulletin of Zoological Nomenclature* vol. **4,** p. 185, 1950.

The great value of the type system appears when a group is divided up during reclassification. Thus, if you decide that our *Musca flava* is really a mixture of two species, then you examine the type, if possible, and find out which of the two it belongs to. This species continues to be called *Musca flava*, and you give a new name to the other one. When you divide up a group of insects you always keep the old name for one of the parts.

4. The names of species are binomial, that is they are made up of two words as we have seen above.

5. Sub-species and lower categories are trinomial or quadrinomial, with three or four names. Apart from butterflies, few groups of insects are known well enough to be given these names.

6. The simplest kind of name for a species consists of a generic name that is a Latin or Greek noun, and a specific name that agrees with the first like an adjective. The example we have already used, *Musca flava*, is one of these. There are many other kinds of words that may be used in names. Thus, *Felis leo* consists of two 'nouns in apposition', which need not agree in gender: *Felis* is feminine and *leo* masculine. Other common forms are specific names in the genitive case, formed from proper nouns— like *Cyclopodia sykesi*—or geographical place-names, like *Vespa germanica*. The generic name is given a capital letter and the specific name a small one, and modern practice does not make any exceptions to this.

As the number of species continues to increase it gets more and more difficult to think of new ones. Fortunately, although we have given examples of names that have a meaning, this is not essential, and quite meaningless combinations of letters may be used, though preferably they should be pronounceable.

Sometimes people ask why we do not give numbers instead of names to our species, perhaps reserving certain combinations for certain groups, like the Dewey Decimal System of numbering books in libraries. I think all genuine entomologists would revolt at this because genera and species have a personality to those who study them, and because such a step would reduce taxonomy to the level of ordering a meal in a Chinese restaurant. Besides, think of the confusion that would arise through printer's errors, and the impossibility of checking proofs.

7. It is accepted as a basic principle that if the same name is used for more than one genus or species (*homonyms*), or if more than one name has been given to the same genus or species (*synonyms*), then confusion may arise. In either event, the name

that was published the earliest is accepted (*Rule of Priority*), and the other is renamed or suppressed, whichever is appropriate. This is the reason for the frequent changing of the scientific names of insects, which is so baffling to outsiders.

It is true to say that far more confusion has been caused by altering names in this way than ever existed before it was done. People make the Rules their master instead of their servant, and speak darkly of 'chaos' and 'anarchy' if they find an old and obscure name for a well-known insect, and we do not rush off to use it at once. At last the Commission is beginning to admit the futility of this endless name-changing, and has introduced, in the Copenhagen Decisions, a 'Principle of Conservation', which urges zoologists not to change well-established names unless it is unavoidable. This is what reasonable people have always done.

8. Generally speaking, once a name has been published it becomes common property, and cannot be withdrawn even by the author himself. If a name is not valid, because it has been used before for some other animal, or because it has not been properly published with the right formalities, then the author can publish an amendment, a correction, or a substitute name: but so can anyone else. The original author, in short, has no property rights in his name once it has been published.

As a matter of courtesy, if you find that an error of this kind has occurred in the work of a living author, it is customary to write and tell him, and give him a reasonable time (say ten years!) to put it right before you intervene. Do not make a practice of spotting invalid names in other people's papers and rushing out with substitute names, so that you become technically the author of them. You will look foolish if you appear to be the author of a lot of genera or species in a group of which you have no knowledge.

Names are not rejected, however, simply because they are inappropriate, or even misleading. If an author names a species '*indianus*', and it turns out to be from Turkey, this is not a sound reason for changing the name. A certain amount of alteration is permitted when the original name was obviously mis-spelled, or copied wrongly, or wrongly transliterated (i.e. adapted from one language into another), but the Rules are tricky on this point, and it is best wherever possible to stick to the original spelling.

9. As an extension of the preceding principle, it was once ruled by the Commission long ago (Opinion 4) that if a name had been published in the correct way it had to be used, even though the author of the paper had only mentioned it in passing, and did

not mean to propose it as a name to be used. I think this extreme
Rule may be modified in the new Code, but in the meantime it
is better not to say chattily 'My friend Mr. Jones had this remarkable bug in his collection under the name *Magnicimex absurdus*',
unless you want this name to be brought into use.

10. Subject to the Rules, of which the above is only an elementary summary, new species, genera, or groups of any size may
be proposed by any person, in any language, and they will have
to be taken into account by all future workers on the group,
for ever. So before you add a new one to this burdensome list you
should take care that everything possible has been done to simplify
the task of the people who will come after you. In Chapter XII
we return to the problem of how to record new facts and describe
new species or other categories. In the meantime we must consider the existing classification of insects as it stands today.

May we leave this chapter with a quotation from the late
Mr. C. J. Wainwright, who wrote in the *Entomologists' Monthly
Magazine* (1945, Vol. 81, pp. 232–233): 'The Rules should be
regarded as being for the purpose of providing guidance in cases
where circumstances compel a decision to be taken, and a choice
made between two or more names'; and with a remark attributed
to Sir Winston Churchill: 'We must beware of needless innova-
tions, *especially when guided by logic*'.

IX

WHAT ARE THE INSECTS AND THEIR ALLIES?

Let us begin this chapter by being clear that an insect is an *animal*. Many people, and journalists in particular, speak of 'animals and birds', or 'animals and insects', even of 'animals and fish', as a result of confusing the word *animal* with the word *mammal*. The biological division is a clear one: every living thing that is not a plant is an animal.

It is true that a few groups of organisms fall so close to the borderline between the two Kingdoms, as they are called, that it is a matter of opinion where they should be placed: but there is no doubt about insects. They are animals.

The Animal Kingdom is divided into groups of smaller and smaller size, as we have already seen in the previous chapter. There are six principal categories, as follows:

Phylum
Class
Order
Family
Genus
species.

A *Phylum* (plural *Phyla*) is a group that collects together all the animals that are built to the same general structural plan. Insects belong to the Phylum ARTHROPODA, named from the Greek words for 'jointed legs'. All the animals in this Phylum share a number of characteristic features, of which the most important are:

(*a*) There is no internal skeleton of bones as there is in a frog, or a bird. Instead, the skin is hardened into an *exoskeleton* (or *cuticle*, or *integument*) to which the muscles are attached. This hardening is brought about by the formation of substances called

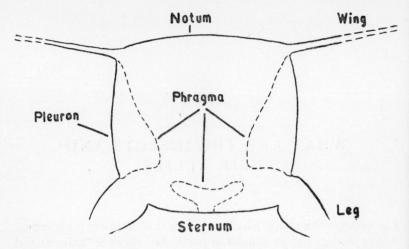

Figure 109. Cross-section of the thorax of an insect (diagrammatic).

chitin and *sclerotin*, which give these animals their horny appearance. The cuticle protects as well as supports the soft parts of the animal, but also prevents it from growing any bigger. Consequently there have to be a number of *moults*, in which the hard cuticle is split and cast off, then the arthropod grows rapidly until the new skin has hardened.

(*b*) In order to make it possible for the arthropod to move, the cuticle has to be divided into a large number of separate plates, like pieces of a suit of armour. In between these the cuticle remains soft, and acts as a hinged joint. The plates—or *sclerites*—are not haphazard in their arrangement. The body is divided up into a number of slices, or *segments*, and the plates are grouped according to the segmentation. This *metameric segmentation* is a notable feature of the arthropods, though it also occurs in some other animals, for example the annelid worms.

To understand how the various kinds of arthropods compare with each other, it is necessary to imagine a basic plan or pattern, which can be modified in different ways to produce animals of different shapes. Such a pattern would consist of a large number of segments, all alike, and each having the parts shown in fig. 109. There is a top (dorsal plate, or *notum*), a bottom (ventral plate, or *sternum*) and two sides (each called a lateral plate, or *pleuron*). At the joint between the sides and the bottom are attached a pair of jointed limbs, or *appendages*, which can be used as legs, but which can also be adapted for a number of other purposes. A *wing* arises from the joint between the side and the top, and can be thought of as if it were a balloon that had been blown out and then squeezed flat, with its two sides stuck together.

A centipede differs little from this general plan. Keep a large number of segments, each with a pair of legs and no wings. At the front end, modify the appendages of three segments into feeding-organs, or *mouth-parts*. At the rear end modify a similar number of segments to form the mating organs, or *genitalia*. And there we are.

On the other hand, to make a spider from this plan would obviously call for a great deal of alteration, merging some segments together, and remodelling others (fig. 111).

In addition to the two characters mentioned, there are a number of others that occur in some or all of the Phylum Arthropoda, but only one of these need be referred to here. This is a method of breathing, by means of branching tubes called *tracheae*, which open to the air by a series of openings called *spiracles*. These last can usually be seen in the side (the pleural membrane) of at least some of the segments of an insect. They are often particularly noticeable in larvæ.

The Phylum Arthropoda is divided into about eleven *Classes*, of which five are of major importance:

CLASS Crustacea: crabs, lobsters, shrimps, woodlice.
Diplopoda: millipedes.
Chilopoda: centipedes (fig. 110).
Arachnida: spiders, mites, ticks, scorpions.
Insecta: insects (fig. 112).

The Class *Insecta* is distinguished from all the others by possessing the following characters:

1. The segments of the body are arranged in three groups (fig. 112):

(a) The *head*, consisting of six segments, very much fused together. The corresponding appendages are modified into one pair of *antennæ*, or feelers, and three pairs of *mouth-parts* (*mandibles*, *maxillæ* and *labium:* see fig. 134).

(b) The *thorax*, consisting of three segments, nearly always with the corresponding three pairs of legs well developed, at any rate in adult insects. Often, but not always, with wings on one or both of the second and third thoracic segments (the *mesothorax* and the *metathorax*).

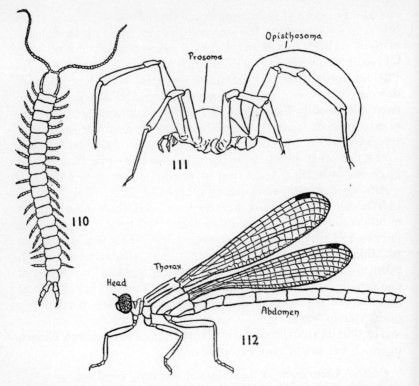

Figures 110–112. Examples of Arthropoda. 110, Chilopoda, a centipede, with many segments alike; 111, Arachnida, a spider (after Whittick, in Smart, 1943); 112, Insecta, a dragonfly of the sub-order Zygoptera.

(c) The *abdomen*, generally without legs, but with the appendages of the last two or three segments modified into genitalia (fig. 135). In adult insects it is generally considered that up to ten segments can be recognised in the abdomen, but there are seldom more than seven segments that can be easily seen.

2. Never more than six (three pairs) of true, jointed walking legs, though sometimes false legs, or *pseudopods* are present (as, for example, in caterpillars): these are soft organs, like swellings of the skin, and may have small hooks, or *crochets*, but never have the joints of the true leg (see fig. 120).

3. Wings, and the power of flight, are found only in the Insecta, though not all insects have them.

The Latin word *insectum* means something that is cut up into pieces, and gives us the name of the Class *Insecta*, as well as the common name 'an insect'. From the equivalent Greek word *'entomon'* we get the name of *Entomology*, the science of insects. Obviously these words would fit equally well any members of the Phylum Arthropoda, but by general agreement their use is restricted to mean animals that have the three characters we have defined above. Thus a spider, or a centipede is not an insect to us, though it might have been to a Roman or a Greek.

THE ORDERS OF INSECTS

An *Order* of Insects is still a big enough group to be recognised as a 'natural' group by ordinary people, and to have a common name. Everyone knows *beetles* (Coleoptera), *butterflies* and *moths* (Lepidoptera), and *dragonflies* (Odonata). Everyone talks about *flies*, but not many people can tell you which are 'true flies' (Diptera), and which belong to other Orders; just as everyone knows a *bee*, a *wasp* or an *ant*, but probably does not know what other insects come into the Order Hymenoptera. Finally, there are a number of Orders, such as the Embioptera and the Strepsiptera that are so obscure that they have no common names at all.

Among specialists, too, there is uncertainty, and dispute, not so much about how the insects should be arranged in natural groups, as about which of the groups should be dignified with the rank of an Order. You will therefore find that different authors give you slightly different lists of the Orders of insects. Do not be dismayed, or confused, by this. The fashion at present is to increase the number of Orders, by separating off any group that is peculiar in its structure or its habits, and making it into another Order. So if you find that one author has more Orders of insects than another it does not (as a rule) mean that the latter has forgotten one or two: merely that one of his names corresponds to two or more of the other author.

The following list is not the most progressive, but some suggested modifications are mentioned later on. The figures given for the numbers of species in the world, and in Great Britain are, of course, only approximate: those for the British species are taken from Kloet and Hincks (1945), and the world figures from Borror and Delong (1954). A key by which to recognise these Orders of Insects is given in the next chapter.

The Orders of Insects

SUB-CLASS APTERYGOTA

ORDER	COMMON NAME	BRITISH	WORLD TOTAL
Thysanura	*Silver-fish; Fire-brats*	23	700
Protura	*None. (Microscopic)*	17	90
Collembola	*Spring-tails*	261	2,000

SUB-CLASS PTERYGOTA

(*a*) EXOPTERYGOTA (HEMIMETABOLA)

ORDER	COMMON NAME	BRITISH	WORLD TOTAL
Orthoptera	*Cockroaches; Grasshoppers; Locusts; Crickets*	38	22,500
Dermaptera	*Earwigs*	9	1,100
Embioptera	*None. (Rare)*	0	149
Isoptera	*Termites*	0	1,717
Plecoptera	*Stoneflies*	32	1,490
Psocoptera	*Book-lice*	68	1,100
Zoraptera	*None. (Rare)*	0	19
Mallophaga	*Biting lice*	251	2,675
Anoplura	*Sucking lice*	35	250
Ephemeroptera	*Mayflies*	46	1,500
Odonata	*Dragonflies*	42	4,870
Thysanoptera	*Thrips*	183	3,170
Hemiptera	*Bugs*	499	23,000
Homoptera	*Greenfly; Scale-insects*	912	32,000

(*b*) ENDOPTERYGOTA (HOLOMETABOLA)

ORDER	COMMON NAME	BRITISH	WORLD TOTAL
Megaloptera	*Alderflies; Snakeflies*	6 }	4,670
Neuroptera	*Lacewings; Ant-lions*	54 }	
Coleoptera	*Beetles*	3,690	276,700
Strepsiptera	*None. (Rare parasites)*	17	300
Mecoptera	*Scorpionflies*	4	350
Trichoptera	*Caddisflies*	188	4,450
Lepidoptera	*Butterflies; Moths*	2,187	112,000
Diptera	*True Flies*	5,199	85,000
Siphonaptera	*Fleas*	47	1,100
Hymenoptera	*Bees; Wasps; Ants; Ichneumon flies*	6,191	103,000
	TOTALS	19,999	685,900

From these estimates it appears that about one in every thirty-five of the world's species of insects occurs in the British Isles, though, of course, very few indeed of these are confined to these islands. Most of them are shared with the continent of Europe, and many with the whole of the Northern Hemisphere (see Chapter XI). A few migrant insects range more widely over the world, but those which are truly world-wide are mostly spread by human agency, like the house-fly, the human louse, the bed-bug, and various fleas.

Notice that, out of the twenty thousand British insects, more than seventeen thousand belong to the four big *Orders:* Coleoptera, Lepidoptera, Diptera and Hymenoptera.

The Sub-Class APTERYGOTA

These insects are what are known as the primitively wingless forms: that is to say that, as far as we know and can deduce from their structure, they are descended from a line of completely wingless ancestors.

They are sometimes called the AMETABOLA, meaning 'without a change', because they hatch from the egg in a form very like the adult, and do not change much at each successive moult.

Order: **Thysanura**

Silver-fish; bristle-tails; fire-brats (fig. 113). Slender, grey or silvery insects, with the head and thorax broader than the tapering abdomen, and with prominent antennæ projecting forwards and two or three long bristles behind. They are mostly less than 12 mm. ($\frac{1}{2}$ in.) long, though an exceptionally big species goes up to 2 in.

The domestic species are found in warm places, in kitchens, bakeries and so on, and come out at night. They scurry away quickly when a light is brought near. The majority of the species of this group, however, are not domestic, but are found in soil, rotting wood, under stones, in leaf-mould, or on the seashore. Many occur in the nests of ants and of termites. The food of Thysanura is debris, mainly of a starchy nature.

Collecting

Extract from soil, leaf-mould, and so on with a Berlese funnel (fig. 38). Pick up from debris, ants' nests, etc., with an aspirator (fig. 20), or with a small brush dipped in 80% alcohol.

Preservation

Keep in 80% alcohol. Special care is needed to avoid their moving about in the fluid, as these fragile insects are easily damaged: a piece of tissue-paper, first soaked in the spirit, may be pushed into the tube gently until the specimens are just kept in place without crushing. Sometimes the insect is difficult to wet with 80% alcohol: then immerse first in absolute alcohol, transferring afterwards to the weaker spirit for permanent storage. Make slide-mounts as described in Chapter V.

Order: **Protura**

Minute insects, all less than 2 mm. ($\frac{1}{12}$ in.) long, which will not be seen until they are collected from soil, turf debris, and so on by means of the Berlese funnel (fig. 38).

Preservation

May be stored in 80% alcohol, but since they are so small and transparent some of them should be mounted on slides (see Chapter V). Polyvinyl lactophenol is recommended because it has a high refractive index, and so increases the contrast between tissues that are almost equally transparent. Failing this, use the various gum-chloral mixtures.

Order: **Collembola**

Spring-tails (fig. 114). Tiny insects, generally less than 5 mm. ($\frac{1}{5}$ in.) long, many of them able to jump actively by means of a special spring-like organ under the abdomen. Always found in moist places, sometimes on the surface of very small pools, on the seashore between tides, or on mountains, above the permanent snow-line, also on leaves and bark. They occur in soil in very great numbers.

Collecting

If on a surface on which they can be seen, they can be picked off with an aspirator (fig. 20), or with a brush dipped in 80% alcohol. If a white-enamelled dish is moved through vegetation like a sweep-net, the spring-tails that jump into the dish can be seen easily. Aquatic forms can be collected with a dipper (fig. 13), or with a sieve of fine net, from which they can be picked with an aspirator. Most Collembola are collected, however, from debris by means of the Berlese funnel (fig. 38).

Preservation

In 80% alcohol or as slide-mounts (Chapter V). Do not use strong reagents when mounting Collembola. Preferably take them direct from 80% alcohol, via absolute into clove oil, and leave for as long as is necessary to clear to transparency. Add a few drops of xylol and then mount in Balsam, or euparal. If the spring-tail is dense and opaque, bleach in 5% NaOH (taking anything up to several hours), neutralise in 10% acetic acid, stain in basic fuchsin in alcohol, and then dehydrate and clear as above (Usinger, 1956).

The Sub-Class PTERYGOTA

All the remaining insects are descended from ancestors with wings. Where the insects of the present day are without wings (e.g. fleas), the structure of the body, and in particular of the thorax, shows traces of the modifications that were needed to accommodate the big muscles of flight, which must have been present in direct ancestors of these insects.

Division: EXOPTERYGOTA (HEMIMETABOLA)

Insects that hatch from the egg in a form not greatly different from that of the adult, except for the absence of wings. As the insect grows there are successive moults, the number of which varies from one to more than twenty, though the average number is about five. Except in the Order Ephemeroptera (Mayflies, p. 226), wings that can be used for flight are not grown until after the last moult, though wing-pads may be visible earlier. The May-flies are exceptional in casting yet another, thin, transparent skin after they have become fully winged.

The young form of the exopterygote insect is generally called a *nymph*; in contrast to this, the young form of the next division, the *Endopterygota*, is totally different from its adult, and is called a *larva*.

Some entomologists, with the mathematician's genius for seeing everything as a special case of something else, consider that this difference is one of degree only, and call the young of both Divisions 'larvæ'.

Order: **Orthoptera**

Grasshoppers; locusts; crickets; stick-insects; leaf-insects; cockroaches. Some authorities divide up this group into three separate Orders: **Dictyoptera** for the cockroaches; **Phasmida** for the stick-insects and leaf-insects; and **Saltatoria** for the grasshoppers, crickets

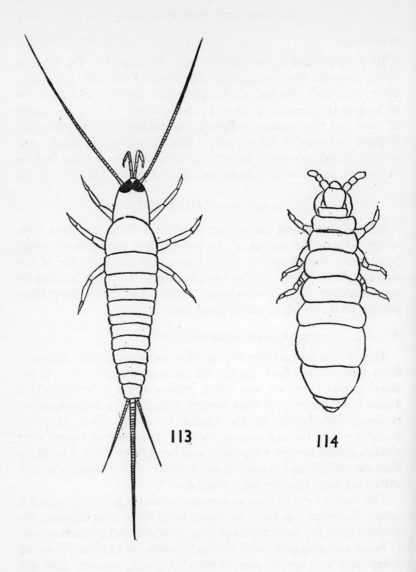

Figures 113, 114. Apterygota—insects whose ancestors have all been wingless. 113, Thysanura, a bristle-tail; 114, Collembola, a spring-tail.

and allied insects. In view of the very different habits of these groups there is much to be said for this view.

Dictyoptera. Cockroaches are of tropical origin, where they grow large, and may be brightly coloured. In temperate countries, they are known mainly from a few domesticated species of 'black-beetles', oval insects, black or dark brown in colour. The large prothorax is like a shield, and covers most of the rest of the thorax, and sometimes the head as well.

Most of the British cockroaches are domestic, though a few wild ones occur in the southern counties of England. They are furtive insects, hiding in the daytime and coming out at night.

Collecting

Trap at night in *pit-falls* (fig. 31), with a bait of syrup or molasses. Beirne (1955) recommends diluting the molasses with an equal quantity of water and adding one teaspoonful of *fusel oil* to each pint. (Fusel oil is a mixture of higher alcohols, obtained during the distillation of grain spirits.)

Preservation

Kill in cyanide, or ethyl acetate and pin. Large specimens may have the abdomen emptied by slitting it underneath at the base along the middle line, and drawing out the contents with forceps. There is no need to stuff the abdomen. Smaller cockroaches, or nymphs, or those wanted for dissection, may be preserved in 80% alcohol.

A small family, the GRYLLOBLATTIDAE, is intermediate between the cockroaches and related Orders.

Phasmida. None of these is British. The stick-insects and leaf-insects are easily recognised from their names, and are found on tropical or subtropical vegetation. Their shape and colour give them very effective camouflage, and they are difficult to find. They are herbivorous and slow-moving, and spend long periods sitting motionless. Stick-insects are often wingless. Leaf-insects may have well-developed wings, especially in the male, but the leaf-like parts of the body are generally not the wings: or at least, not the hind-wings, which are used for flight. The leaf-like appearance comes from extensions of the fore-wings, the abdomen, and parts of the legs.

Mantids are fiercely carnivorous insects, with the fore-legs modified into powerful, spiny grasping organs. The attitude of these legs when the animal is at rest is the reason for the name 'praying mantis'. Mantids fly readily, but clumsily, and with a rustling and clicking sound like the bigger grasshoppers. Their method of feeding is to sit motionless in a likely place until an unwary insect comes within reach, and then to seize and devour it.

Collecting

Stick-insects and leaf-insects by hand-picking or beating; mantids by stalking with a net. Stick-insects can easily be bred in temperate countries if they are kept at a suitable temperature.

Preservation

Pin on long pins: extra pins are advisable to protect the out-stretched legs from accidental breaking.

Saltatoria. These are the grasshoppers and locusts and the groups related to them, and are divided into two *superfamilies*: ACRIDOIDEA (CAELIFERA), with short antennæ, and TETTIGONOIDEA (ENSIFERA) with long antennæ. As a further difference, those forms which have auditory (hearing) organs have them at the base of the abdomen in the ACRIDOIDEA and on the fore tibiæ in TETTIGONOIDEA.

The principal families of the ACRIDOIDEA are the ACRIDIDAE (the locusts and the short-horned, or meadow grasshoppers) and the TETRIGIDAE (grouse-locusts): the latter are distinguished by the very long pronotum of the thorax which extends back to the tip of the abdomen. One or two other small families are known in different parts of the world, distinguished by small details of the head and legs. The ACRIDIDAE are mostly solitary, that is they may be numerous in a field, but they do not herd together in a band or a swarm; they are then known as *grasshoppers* (fig. 59). A few members of this group are solitary for a number of generations, and then change their habits, as well as their appearance, and enter what is known as the 'Swarming Phase'. After this they migrate in enormous swarms, alighting periodically to feed, with great destruction of crops. These are the *locusts* that are such a great plague in some parts of the tropics and sub-tropics.

Grasshoppers are common in grassland in temperate as well as in tropical countries, but are difficult to see as long as they remain both still and silent. When they jump they cover a great distance in relation to their own size, but they are also adept at moving deliberately behind a grass-stem when they are approached. In flight, many species show their brilliantly coloured hind-wings, but when the grasshopper comes to rest these are folded away, and completely hidden underneath the drab fore-wings. It is startling to see how suddenly such a conspicuous flying object can disappear into the background.

Grasshoppers are noted for their song, which is produced by the males only, and only in the daytime. One sub-family (*Acridinae*) produce a buzzing or sizzling sound by rubbing the fore-femora (fig. 120) against the rear edge of the fore-wing; another sub-family (*Oedipodinae*) produce a drier, more crackling sound by rubbing the rear margin of the fore-wing with the fore-margin of the hind-wing instead of with part of the leg. This latter group can produce the sound (which is known as *stridulation*) while in flight, and the approach of a large tropical grasshopper of this group, three or four inches long, can be very impressive. With a noise that has been compared to the sound of a fire in stubble, and a wild waving of wings, it arrives like a miniature helicopter.

The TETTIGONOIDEA include the families TETTIGONIIDAE (long-horned grasshoppers); GRYLLACRIDIDAE (Camel-crickets, a wing-less family); GRYLLIDAE (crickets); and the GRYLLOTALPIDAE (mole-crickets).

TETTIGONIIDAE are softer, less horny than short-horned grass-hoppers, and are more often found in trees and shrubs than on the ground. The males of this group also stridulate, by rubbing together specially modified areas of the fore-wings. Theirs is more properly called 'song', since it is higher in pitch and more musical, some-times rather like the 'singing' of a tea-kettle about to boil. Some of them—e.g. the great green grasshopper, *Tettigonia viridissima*—actually begin to sing about tea-time, but continue to do so far into the night. As they are nocturnal they sometimes come to light (see *sheeting*, fig. 24). In America these big long-horned grass-hoppers are called katydids (pronounced 'katie-did').

GRYLLACRIDIDAE live in caves and hollows, or in dry, stony areas. They are not native to Britain, but occur here in greenhouses.

GRYLLIDAE, the true Crickets, are generally like the long-horned grasshoppers, but have a distinctive shape, short and blunt. They 'sing' with their wings in the same way, and the song of the Cricket on the Hearth was immortalised by Dickens. Besides the domestic cricket there are many ground- or field-crickets, which live in the open, but are mainly nocturnal, several sub-families of tree-crickets, and one group that live in ants' nests. When numerous they may damage vegetation.

GRYLLOTALPIDAE, or mole-crickets are well-named, and have the fore-legs and head highly modified for digging in the ground.

This gives them a very distinctive appearance. They are rare and nocturnal. In spite of their clumsy appearance, they can, and do, fly, and come to light at night. There is one British species, *Gryllotalpa gryllotalpa.*

Collecting

The bigger grasshoppers may be caught individually, sometimes in flight, but more often by watching them carefully until they settle, and then dropping a net over the insect. Keeping the frame of the net pressed down, the bag is raised with the other hand and shaken, so as to disturb the grasshopper and make it jump up into the bag; if this is not done the insect may remain motionless on the ground, ready to jump away as soon as the frame is lifted.

Sweeping grass will get a number of grasshoppers into the net, but they are apt to cling to the netting near the mouth, and to jump out again quickly. Following their song is sometimes a guide, but they are good ventriloquists. This method can be used at night, carrying a torch to flash suddenly when the song seems to be coming from nearby.

Kill with cyanide or ethyl acetate, or use the sulphur dioxide method recommended for dragon-flies (p. 84).

Preservation

Temporarily the grasshoppers may be carried between layers of cellulose wadding or in papers (fig. 45), but they should be pinned as soon as possible, preferably before they have dried, so that they do not need to be relaxed. Pin grasshoppers to the right of the *pronotum* of the thorax. The legs are brittle when dry, and the abdomen is heavy and liable to droop. These parts should be supported by extra pins while the insect is drying.

The bigger specimens are fleshy and liable to decay. The abdomen should be slit lengthwise underneath for about three segments, and the contents drawn out with fine forceps. Wipe out the abdomen with a small wad of cotton wool dipped in borax and glycerine. Only if the species is very big and soft is there need to pack the abdomen lightly with cotton wool dipped in borax and glycerine. This should be done while the insect is still fresh, even if it is not to be pinned immediately: if there is a risk of decay spoiling the specimen it should not be given a chance to start. The embalming fluid described in the section on *Formulæ* may be used.

See that Saltatoria are well-dried before shutting them up in the permanent collection, and examine them frequently for pests. Nymphs and small, soft-bodied adults may be stored permanently in spirit (see p. 132), since they shrivel if preserved dry.

Order: **Dermaptera**

The *earwigs* are well-known insects, distinguished by the large pair of forceps that are visible at the tip of the body. These are more strongly curved and elaborate in the males than in the females. They are grouped into four families: FORFICULIDAE, LABIIDAE, LABIDURIDAE and CHELISOCHIDAE, and include a number of species that are wingless in the adult stage. In size, they vary from 4 to 20 mm. ($\frac{1}{6}$ to $\frac{5}{8}$ in.). Like the Orthoptera, the Dermaptera have been spread about the world by commerce, and a number of species are now cosmopolitan. They are mostly scavengers, feeding upon rubbish and debris, but sometimes they attack flowers and cultivated plants.

Collecting

Found hiding under bark, stones, leaves, etc. Occasionally by sweeping, especially of flowers. The old-fashioned earwig trap for the garden consists of an inverted flower-pot standing on a short post about a foot high, and stuffed with straw, shavings, or egg-packing material.

Preservation

May be pinned, but they are rather soft-bodied, and are better either put in spirit (fig. 77) or carded (fig. 68).

Order: **Plecoptera**

The *stoneflies* (fig. 115) are so-called because the adults though they can fly, are more in the habit of running about among stones at the edges of streams, and hiding under them. They are closely associated with water, and the nymphs are entirely aquatic. They may live in any fresh water, but especially like running streams.

The males of some stoneflies have reduced wings, or none at all, while the females are fully winged. Some do not feed at all as adults, while others visit flowers and feed on pollen. The smaller nymphs are vegetable-feeders, but the bigger ones may be carnivorous.

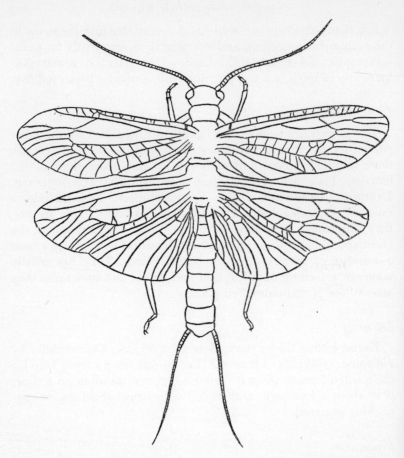

Figure 115. A stonefly, *Order* Plecoptera (partly after Kimmins, 1950).

Collecting

The adult insects may be caught among stones or on posts, etc., near water, by putting over them a pill-box or tube. They may be taken by sweeping among waterside vegetation, or beaten from shrubs. They do fly at times either in warm sunshine or at dusk, and they come to light, especially in the warm nights of the tropics.

Nymphs may be caught by the water-net or the under-water light trap (fig. 30).

Preservation

Stoneflies are soft-bodied, and both adults and nymphs should be preserved in spirit. If they have been pinned, and have shrivelled, before identification is possible, it may be necessary to remove the abdomen and soften it in caustic potash, or in a strong detergent, such as 'Tide'.

Order: **Isoptera**

The *termites* are often called 'white ants', and are much confused with true ants (Hymenoptera), especially by newspaper reporters. They live in colonies, like ants, and have 'castes': within the same species there are individuals of several different kinds, called 'soldiers', 'workers', 'reproductives' (kings and queens), 'nasutes' and so on. Each caste has its duties, either of defending, or feeding, or of the reproduction and feeding of new colonies.

The queen termite is a remarkable creature. The abdomen is swollen into a huge white bag, upon which the small sclerites or plates of the abdomen are visible. The queen, when grown to this size, is immobile, and is a mere egg-laying machine.

The termites are distinguished from the true ants (Hymenoptera) by not having the narrow waist or *petiole*, nor the antennæ bent into an elbow; by having the fore- and hind-wings alike, and held flat over the body (the ants have them different from each other, and held up in the air); and by being pale and soft-bodied, whereas most ants are black or red, and hard-shelled.

The biology of termites is remarkable in two ways, their power to digest wood, and the conspicuous nests that many of them build. The digestion of wood is carried out with the aid of a colony of protozoa in the gut, and the ability to do this makes them very destructive to buildings, and wooden structures of all kinds. These may be eaten away inside without showing any sign of it until they collapse.

The dry-wood termites live entirely above ground-level in living and dead wood. The subterranean termites live in the ground, but extend their nests above ground, sometimes to a great height, in the so-called 'ant-hills' of the tropics. These vary enormously in size and shape, and may set to a cement-like hardness outside; inside there is a network of galleries, with thousands of termites of the various castes.

The termites are grouped into six families: MASTOTERMITIDAE, KALOTERMITIDAE, TERMOPSIDAE, HODOTERMITIDAE, RHINOTERMI-TIDAE, TERMITIDAE. Since the castes are so very different in form, and show different sets of distinguishing characters, it is often not

P

possible to identify single specimens, and whenever possible some
of each caste should be collected

Collecting

By breaking open wood, or hacking a hole in a nest with a pick-
axe or geological hammer; some of the mushroom-shaped nests of
the rain-forest termites can be toppled over by hand, and will
usually break open in the process. When land is being cleared for
cultivation (e.g. groundnuts) it may be necessary to use explosives.
Collect by means of an aspirator (fig. 20), and take all castes, as
well as other insects that are *inquilines*, or lodgers in the nest.
These include beetles of many species; Diptera of the families
TERMITOXENIDAE, and PSYCHODIDAE, and some larvæ of MUSCIDAE;
Thysanura and Collembola; some Lepidoptera larvæ; and the
genus *Termitaphis* of the Homoptera.

Preservation

In 80% alcohol.

Order: **Ephemeroptera**

Mayflies are recognised by the shape of the wings, the fore-
wing being much bigger than the hind-wing, which may be very
small, or even absent; by the network of small veins on both
wings; and by the two or three long, thread-like tails at the tip of
the abdomen (fig. 58). The nymphs are aquatic and have a series
of leaf-like gills along each side of the abdomen, as well as three
tails like those of the adult, or sometimes more feathered.

The name Ephemeroptera refers to the short life of the adults,
which are unable to feed, and which live for a day or two only.
Thus nearly the whole life of these insects is spent as a nymph, the
aquatic stage lasting perhaps a year or more.

Mayflies are the only insects that moult again after they have
developed wings. When the nymph is fully grown it rises to the
surface of the water, the skin splits, and a winged insect escapes
and settles on surrounding vegetation. This is called the *subimago*,
and is dull and drab in colour. Next day, or soon after, it moults
again, splitting off a transparent skin, and becoming a brightly-
coloured insect with sparkling wings. Fishermen call the subimago
a 'dun' and the fully adult insect a 'spinner'.

According to a recent paper by Edmunds (1956) there are mayflies in which both sexes mate and die as subimagoes, some in
which the adults begin to fly as soon as their wings are free of the

last skin, which they carry up into the air and finish shedding there; and yet others in which the last moult takes place in the air during the nuptial flight, the wings, of necessity, not taking part in this moult.

Collecting

Adults are caught by net while in flight. In the evenings, males dance in mating swarms near water. Some mayflies fly after dark and will come to a light-trap near water. Duns are taken by beating among waterside vegetation.

Nymphs live in either running or stagnant water, either among the under-water weeds, or in mud at the bottom. Some are caught by dragging a net through water-weeds, or by fixing a vertical screen in the water and dislodging the stones and plants upstream of it (fig. 16); the mud-liking forms by dredging mud from the bottom and straining it (fig. 17) or pouring it into a white dish. The subimagoes should be handled carefully, and may be confined in a paper bag with branches and leaves to rest on, until they moult to the imago. This should be allowed several hours to harden before being killed.

Preservation

Adults and subimagoes can be pinned but are fragile It is better to keep them in spirit. Nymphs and empty pupal skins should also be kept in spirit. See that the tubes are full of spirit and that the specimens do not move about.

Order: Odonata

The *dragonflies* are divided fairly sharply into two groups: Anisoptera ('unequal wings') are bigger, more robust insects, the hind-wings broader than the fore-wings, and held out sideways when the insect is resting; Zygoptera ('equal wings') are generally smaller, more slender, with very thin abdomen, and the paddle-shaped wings nearly alike in shape, held at rest upright and pressed together above the body (fig. 112). The former are the dragonflies proper, and the latter are often called 'damselflies'.

Most dragonflies are fairly big, an inch or more long and some are giants of up to eight or nine inches. They fly strongly and are carnivorous, catching and eating other insects. They are usually seen near water, where they breed, but the big ones in particular may make long flights away from water, and may be seen high in the tree-tops, or far out to sea.

The dragonfly nymph, like the adult, is carnivorous and is a very rapacious creature. Some of the mouth-parts, the *labium* and the *labial palpi* are modified into an organ called the *mask*, which can be shot out in front of the head to seize small worms and other prey with a pair of hooks. Some nymphs live on the bottom of streams where they are concealed either by their pattern, or by hiding in the mud or sand; others cling to rocks and weeds.

The dragonfly nymph has no leaf-like gills corresponding to those of the mayfly nymph, but breathes by organs at the tip of the abdomen. In the Anisoptera the gills are concealed in the rectum, or last section of the intestine. Water is drawn in there and forced out again, and the nymph can use this as a form of jet-propulsion for rapid movement. In the Zygoptera the gills are external, and take the form of three long appendages, which may be thread-like or leaf-like.

Collecting

The damselflies and the smaller dragonflies are fairly easily caught with a net, either in flight or at rest. The bigger Anisoptera are very powerful fliers, and swerve violently when they see the net coming. It is best to swing the net at them from behind, giving the insect less chance of seeing it, and the collector more time to follow any evasive action of the dragonfly.

The net should have a big, light frame, and a bag of open material, so that air-resistance is as low as possible. The length of the handle is a matter for personal experiment: a long handle will certainly give a longer reach, but makes the swing difficult to control, and you are more liable to overreach and fall into the water.

For extensive collecting of dragonflies, waders are needed. Apart from the certainty that you will step off the bank into muddy water, there is the fact that some of the best specimens will be seen flying up and down out of reach from the bank. Gum-boots are an alternative, but are obviously limited to shallow water, and hesitation about the depth of the water will cause you to miss good material.

Some of the biggest tropical dragonflies are almost impossible to catch in a net, and have to be treated like small birds, and shot with cartridges filled with dust-shot.

Killing and Preservation

The colours of dragonflies are particularly liable to fade after death, so altering the appearance completely. Special methods have been suggested to minimise this fading, and as they have to be applied immediately the insect is dead, it is advisable to take the dragonflies home alive, and to kill them by a suitable method. This technique is explained in Chapter IV, p. 73.

Nymphs

These can be picked out of the water by hand, or collected in a pond-net if they are on vegetation, or a dredge if they are on the bottom. Some may be brought back alive, wrapped in wet leaves, or a wet cloth, and reared in the laboratory (see Chapter III).

Order: **Psocoptera** (**Corrodentia**)

These are usually called '*book-lice*', but this name applies only to a few wingless members that are found indoors. The great majority of the species of this Order live out of doors, and they are better called just 'psocids'.

They are small, soft-bodied insects, often less than 6 mm. ($\frac{1}{4}$ in.) long. Winged psocids can be recognised by the wing-venation (see fig. 116), with its peculiarly twisted veins. Both winged and wingless psocids have chewing, not sucking mouth-parts, and this distinguishes them not only from the aphids (greenfly; Homoptera) which they greatly resemble, but also from most other insects with which they could be confused. An exception is the biting lice (Mallophaga, see key, p. 270).

The outdoor psocids mostly have wings, and are found on vegetation, on tree-trunks, or under bark or stones. The indoor species feed only on moulds, and are found in any fairly warm, moist place, among neglected books or papers, in cupboards, in crevices of various kinds, and beneath loose wall-paper.

Collecting

During sweeping or beating some psocids may be found. Others may be picked up with an aspirator (fig. 20), or with a brush dipped in spirit.

Preservation

In alcohol, or as slide-mounts. Dry preservation by carding (fig. 66) is usually spoiled by shrinking of the specimen, but is sometimes necessary if there are scales, which will be lost in spirit.

Order: **Zoraptera**

These, which used to be included in the Order Psocoptera, have

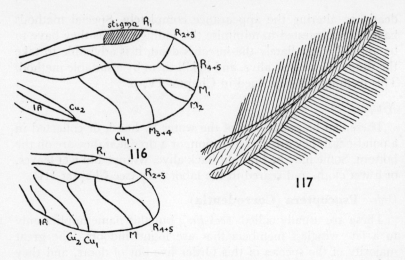

Figures 116, 117. Extremes of wing-shape in two tiny insects. 116, a Psocid (Psocoptera); 117, a Thrips (Thysanoptera).

no common name. They are minute insects (3 mm., or ⅛ in. in length, or less), distinguished from the psocids by the much reduced venation of the wing, and by the 'moniliform' antennæ (segments like strings of beads).

They are found in or under bark, decaying wood, and vegetable humus, and live in colonies rather like termites. They have chewing mouth-parts, and appear to be scavengers. A little-known group, they occur only in the tropics and sub-tropics, such as Florida and Texas.

Collecting

By aspirator (fig. 20), or Berlese Funnel (fig. 38).

Preservation

In spirit or on slide-mounts.

Order: **Mallophaga**—*Chewing lice*; *bird lice.* ⎫ together
Order: **Anoplura** (Siphunculata—*Sucking lice*; ⎬ called
    'lice'. ⎭ **Phthiraptera.**

These wingless, parasitic insects are the true lice, and spend their whole lives on their hosts: Mallophaga generally on birds; Anoplura always on mammals. The Mallophaga chew organic debris among the feathers or hair of their host, and are scavengers.

The Anoplura attach themselves to the skin of their host, and feed by sucking blood.

Collecting

From hosts that are both tame and accessible, the lice can be collected by searching the living animal, otherwise the host must be killed by chloroforming it while it is surrounded by a bag of white paper or linen. Preserved skins may be beaten over a sheet. The lice are picked up with a small brush dipped in spirit.

Hopkins' technique consists of roughly skinning the specimen, and keeping the skin dry, for some time if necessary. At a convenient time the skin is soaked in cold 5% NaOH for about 15 minutes, and then the hair is scraped off with a blunt knife. The hair is boiled up in the same strength NaOH on a water-bath for about 30 minutes. The hair dissolves completely, and the solution is filtered. The lice are retained on the filter-paper, and are rinsed with a fine jet of water, picked off with a brush under a low-power microscope, and out into spirit.

Preservation

In spirit, or as slide-mounts. The specimens cleared in NaOH or KOH, as in Hopkins' technique, above, may be stained before mounting (see p. 140).

Order: **Thysanoptera**

Thrips are small, or minute insects, ranging from about 0.5 to 9.0 mm. ($\frac{1}{50}-\frac{1}{2}$ in.), rather narrow-bodied, usually dark in colour, and often without wings. If wings are present they are fringed with long hair (fig. 117). Thrips are widely distributed in all kinds of plants, but are easily overlooked. They are most easily found in the heads of such flowers as dandelions.

The five families are grouped into two sub-orders: **Terebrantia,** in which the females have a saw-like ovipositor; and **Tubulifera,** in which the abdomen of the female is tubular. Most of the thrips that damage crops are among the Terebrantia.

Collecting

Flowers, foliage, branches may be beaten with a stick over a beating-tray (fig. 8), or shaken over a sheet of paper or white cloth on the ground. Many thrips are caught by sweeping. Pick them up with an aspirator (fig. 20) or a brush dipped in spirit. From soil, leaf-mould and debris, thrips are extracted by the Berlese funnel (fig. 38).

Preservation

Dried specimens on points are apt to shrink, and thrips are usually mounted on slides or in spirit. Plain 80% alcohol is best for permanent preservation, but for killing and subsequent mounting on slides the AGA mixture (alcohol-glycerine-acetic acid; see section on Formulæ) is used. The thrips can be dropped into it alive.

For slide-mounts, specimens already in pure spirit may be mounted direct, but those killed in AGA must be rinsed in pure spirit overnight. Very brittle specimens, or very dark ones, are soaked in cold 5% KOH, washed in water, and then put in spirit. Some authors recommend the gum-chloral medium (but see p. 143): polyvinyl alcohol is satisfactory, but so is Canada balsam.

Order: **Hemiptera (Heteroptera)**

Bugs (fig. 118). This is a big Order of insects, equipped with sucking mouth-parts, which form a proboscis or beak extending back underneath the head and thorax. Hemiptera—or 'half-winged insects'—get their name from the way in which the fore-wing is usually divided into a leathery basal (inner) half and a transparent, membranous apical (outer) half (fig. 131): the hind-wing is entirely membranous. The closely-related Homoptera, in which the fore-wing is not so divided, was formerly generally combined with the Hemiptera into one Order, when the two halves were called Hemiptera-Heteroptera, and Hemiptera-Homoptera respectively. It is now more usual to treat them as separate Orders.

In ordinary conversation, the word 'bug' is used either for the Bed-bug (*Cimex lectularius*) or loosely for any kind of insect, or even for a germ or microbe. In its strictly entomological sense, a 'bug' is any member of the Order Hemiptera.

The two characters of the divided fore-wing and the piercing beak will enable Hemiptera to be recognised whenever they are caught. The terrestrial bugs mostly suck the juices of plants, but some have taken to sucking the blood of man, or of other vertebrate animals. Many bugs live in water, and form a conspicuous and fascinating part of the fauna of ponds and streams. They are all carnivorous, though some CORIXIDAE feed on algæ as well.

There are more than forty families of Hemiptera, of which the following are only a selection:

Terrestrial bugs. There are about forty families of these, of which seventeen are recognised as British by Kloet and Hincks (1945). These families can be identified by using Moreton's book for the British fauna, and Imms, or Borror and Delong for the world fauna. The following are the ones most likely to be seen when collecting.

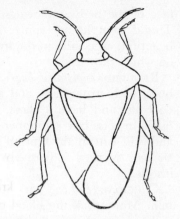

Figure 118. A shield-bug (Hemiptera; Heteroptera).

PENTATOMIDAE (*Shield-bugs*) are the most easily recognised of bugs, because of the great development of the thorax into a shield-like triangular plate, extending back between the bases of the wings (fig. 118). They are sometimes called 'stink-bugs' for obvious reasons. Some are plant-feeders, others eat insects, and some do both.

LYGAEIDAE (which include the *American Chinch-bug*) and PYRRHO-CORIDAE (which include the *Cotton-stainers*) are two rather similar families of often highly-coloured bugs, mostly feeding on plant-juices. Some Lygaeids are carnivorous, and have the fore-legs equipped with spines for seizing prey. Some of these bugs are serious pests of crop-plants, which they damage by removing sap, and by spreading disease-producing organisms from one plant to another. The Lygaeids have *ocelli* between the eyes (fig. 119): the Pyrrhocorids have none.

MIRIDAE (= CAPSIDAE) are another big family of plant-bugs, containing a large number of species, and abundant everywhere. They are more soft-bodied than the families so far mentioned, and are recognised by being almost the only bugs to have a *cuneus*, one of the divisions of the fore-wing (see fig. 131). MIRIDAE nearly all suck plant-juices, though a few prey on aphids and other insects.

ANTHOCORIDAE (*Flower-bugs*) are predaceous, and feed on other small insects. They have the division of the wing called an *embolium* (fig. 131).

ARADIDAE (*Bark-bugs*) are small, flattened insects, and live mostly under bark, feeding on fungi.

TINGIDAE (*Lace-bugs*) get their common name from the lace-like pattern which may be developed in the adults on the upper surface of the body and wings, by a series of ridges and hollows. Tingid nymphs are spiny. Although some TINGIDAE are very beautiful, especially in the tropics, they are harmful to the plants on which they feed.

REDUVIIDAE (*Assassin-bugs*), and the NABIDAE, are rather elongate bugs, with strong legs, and are efficient runners. They are predaceous, and have a short, powerful proboscis: many feed on other insects, but a number suck the blood of small mammals, and will bite man. One of the blood-sucking species, *Rhodnius prolixus*, is used extensively for studies on the physiology of insects.

CIMICIDAE (*Bed-bugs*) are known to everyone, at least by reputation. Many suck the blood of birds and mammals, and feed at night. The common Bed-bug, *Cimex lectularius*, is just one species that happens to flourish in association with man. CIMICIDAE have the wings reduced almost to vanishing point.

POLYCTENIDAE are other wingless bugs that live as parasites in the fur of bats: they do not occur in Britain.

Water-bugs. The bugs, like the beetles, have colonised ponds and streams very successfully, and there are a number of families of water-bugs. It seems as if adaptation to life in the water has taken place more than once in the evolution of the Hemiptera, and in consequence the different families of water-bugs are not as closely related as would seem from their similar appearance. Authorities differ in the way in which they arrange these families, and the text-books should be consulted. The following is just a list of the principal families of bugs that live in or near the water.

(*a*) *Surface-living, or 'skating' forms.* These are air-breathing bugs, which are able to walk or run over the surface of the water without sinking into it, and include the well-known *Pond-skaters*. The families concerned are HYDROMETRIDAE—*Water-measurers*; small, but elongate, stick-like in shape, usually without wings; MESOVELIDAE —*Water-treaders*; and HEBRIDAE—*Velvet Water-bugs*, so-called because of the velvety coating of fine *hydrofuge* (water-repellent) hairs. The SALDIDAE, or *Shore-bugs* come into this group too. The family AEOPOPHILIDAE includes one species only, living in the intertidal zone of the European seashore, including Britain. GERRIDAE, the *Water-striders* are somewhat like the HYDROMETRIDAE. They are long-legged forms that run about on the surface: they are all fresh-water forms, except the genus *Halobates*, which is a pelagic form, living on the surface of the sea, far from land.

All the surface-living forms are predaceous, and feed on insects that fall into the water, and which, not being protected against wetting as the bugs themselves are, become trapped by surface tension.

(b) *The true water-bugs.* These live completely submerged in the water, though they still breathe air, and so they have to carry a supply of it with them, trapped as a bubble against the body.

They include CORIXIDAE, or *Water-boatmen*, so-called because their flattened legs work like oars to propel the bug along; NOTONECTIDAE, the *Back-swimmers*, conspicuous because they swim upside down; NEPIDAE, the *Water-scorpions*, which get their name because the grasping fore-legs and the breathing-tube projecting from the tail give them something of the shape of a scorpion; NAUCORIDAE, or *Creeping Water-bugs* that creep about among submerged vegetation; and GELASTOCORIDAE or *Toad-bugs*, which resemble small toads in appearance, and haunt the waters-edge. The most spectacular family of this group is the BELOSTOMIDAE, the *Giant Water-bug* of the tropics, which may reach a length of four inches, and are bulky and heavy in proportion.

Except for the CORIXIDAE, which also eat algæ, all the water-bugs are carnivorous, and most of them can, and will bite humans, quite painfully sometimes. Most of them have wings when adult, and may leave the water and fly. Some fly at night, and will come to light; the giant BELOSTOMIDAE do this, with great effect.

Collecting

Hemiptera are found in such a variety of situations that all the collecting methods apply, though perhaps collecting in the air, with a net, is least useful. Flight in this Order is generally purposeful, from here to there, and most of the time is spent crawling, swimming or stationary and feeding.

Aquatic bugs are caught with a pond-net or a dredge (fig. 14); terrestrial bugs by sweeping, beating, or by careful examination of foliage, bark, fungi, leaf-mould and so on. An aspirator (fig. 20) is useful. The margins of water, including the seashore, should be given special attention, looking under stones, on the surface of sand and under seaweed. Some are caught in light-traps, including the underwater ones (fig. 30).

Kill by cyanide, ethyl acetate, or sulphur dioxide. The aquatic forms may also be killed in hot water, or in alcohol with a little ethyl acetate added, as for larvæ.

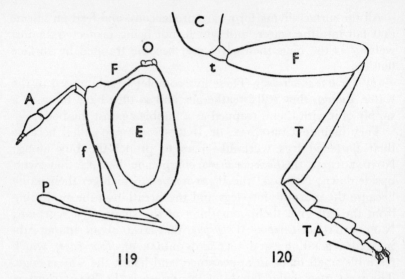

Figure 119. Head of a fly, showing principal parts. A, antenna; O, ocelli, situated on the vertex; F, frons; f, face; E, eye; P. proboscis (mouth-parts).

Figure 120. The leg of an insect (diagrammatic). C, coxa; t, trochanter; F, femur; T, tibia; TA, tarsus, ending in claws.

Preservation

Mostly dry, by pinning or pointing. Care is needed in either method, because the beak and other structures used in identification are on the under (ventral) side, and these should not be destroyed by the pin, nor buried in a mass of adhesive. Very small species, soft-bodied ones, or the aquatic bugs can be preserved in 80% alcohol. The giant Belostomidae should be slit open and the viscera removed; they need not be stuffed.

Order: **Homoptera**

Aphids (Greenfly); Whiteflies; Scale-Insects; Cicadas. These were formerly united with the Hemiptera (Heteroptera) but are now generally considered to be a separate Order. All Homoptera are plant-feeders, and many of them are sedentary, remaining for long periods in one place, with the proboscis inserted into a plant. There are two Sub-orders: the Auchenorhyncha, which have three segments in the tarsi, and very short, bristle-like antennæ, are active insects, and include several families of jumping bugs;

the Sternorhyncha, with only one or two segments in the tarsi, and generally with longer antennæ, are mostly sedentary.

The number of families recognised in the Homoptera is much a matter of personal opinion, but there are about ten generally accepted groups, which are called families by some authors, and superfamilies by others.

In the Auchenorhyncha, the CICADIDAE are, of course, the cicadas, well known for the loud song of the males. The sound-producing mechanism is different from that in grasshoppers (see p. 221), and consists of a vibratory structure (*tymbal*), and organs of resonance, all situated on the ventral surface of the first abdominal segment. The nymphs of the cicadas live in the ground, often for a long period, before becoming adult: the record is held by the '17-year cicada' of North America. Some of the tropical species are very large, up to two inches in length, and come to light at night.

MEMBRACIDAE (*Tree-hoppers*) are mostly tropical, with absurd deformations of the thorax into spines, and shield-like structures.

CERCOPIDAE (*Froghoppers*) are small jumping insects, with a few big spines on the hind tibiæ, and their nymphs live in the frothy masses called 'cuckoo-spit', that are found on grasses and other vegetation.

JASSIDAE (CICADELLIDAE) (*Leaf-hoppers*) are more elongate than cercopids, with a row of small spines on the hind tibiæ, and without the froth-forming habit. They are a very large family.

FULGORIDAE (*Lanternflies*) are a related family, distinguished from the two preceding ones by having the antennæ below the level of the compound eyes. Some tropical fulgorids are very big, and are famous for their brightly-coloured snout, or bulbous swelling of the head. The nymphs of many fulgorids are covered with a waxy substance.

PSYLLIDAE (*Jumping Plant-lice*) are rather like aphids, except for the longer legs and longer antennæ. Since their nymphs often cover themselves with wax, they can easily be mistaken for woolly aphis. Some of them produce galls (see p. 18).

The Sternorhyncha include the well-known APHIDIDAE (*Aphids; Greenfly; Blackfly*), which are found in vary large numbers, and in a variety of different forms. The body is often pear-shaped, with two small tubes (*cornicles*) at its rear end, through which a wax is secreted. *Honeydew*, a syrupy liquid particularly associated with aphids, is not produced by the cornicles, but is passed through the anus: it is greatly attractive to other insects, especially to ants.

The life-history of aphids may be very complicated, with winged and wingless forms, and sexual and parthenogenetic generations succeeding one another at different seasons of the year. Aphids do great damage to plants, by the great quantity of sap that they withdraw, and by the many diseases they pass from one plant to another—notably the 'mosaic' diseases caused by viruses. Some aphids live on the roots, as well as on the exposed parts of the plants.

COCCIDAE (*Scale-insects; Mealy-bugs*) have wingless females, which often lack legs as well, and remain stationary on the plant. During the later nymphal stages a shell, or 'scale' of a waxy or resinous substance may be produced for the protection of the insect, and may either remain soft, or may become detached and hard. Many scales are severe pests of plants: some, like the lac insect, from which shellac is obtained, are of commercial value. The male coccids are winged insects, with only one pair of wings, and may be mistaken for true flies of the Order Diptera (see p. 252).

ALEYRODIDAE (or ALEURODIDAE) (*Whiteflies*) are covered with powdery white wax, and live on the underside of leaves. They are tiny (2–3 mm.) and active. Some of them are serious pests of glasshouse crops.

Collecting

The active ones by net, or by sweeping. Cicadas are often difficult to stalk, because they are good ventriloquists. The biggest tropical ones are sometimes shot with dust-shot.

The sedentary forms may be picked off the plant with an aspirator (fig. 20), or with a brush dipped in spirit. In all cases, but most particularly with the sedentary forms, it is important to note the name of the food-plant, or to take a sample of it. This last is a convenient way of taking home scale-insects and whiteflies. It is advisable to make a note of the colour of the living insects, since these soft-bodied forms easily change colour when they are preserved.

Preservation

The bigger Homoptera, as well as the Cercopids, Jassids, Psyllids and Aleyrodids are usually either pinned or pointed. Aphids shrivel if they are preserved dry, and they should either be kept in 80% alcohol, to which some authors recommend adding one-third volume of 70% lactic acid, or should be mounted on slides (figs. 84–90). As many different stages and forms as possible should be preserved when dealing with aphids. Male scale-insects are treated like Aphids; female scales can be collected with a portion of the plant on which they occur, which is then dried and pressed between papers, like a plant-specimen.

Making slides of Homoptera is a delicate process, because the specimen can so easily be caused to shrivel. It should first be cleared in 5% caustic potash or caustic soda for one to two days; this process can be hastened by warming gently, but boiling will damage the specimen. The specimen is then washed in water, stained in acid fuchsin, and dehydrated. Since the specimens are very soft-bodied, they must be dehydrated carefully with first 80%, then 95% alcohol, then absolute, and not by the shorter method described on p. 140 for heavily chitinised material. Clear in xylol containing a little phenol. Some workers use polyvinyl lactophenol, or gum-chloral as a mounting medium, instead of Canada balsam.

Division: ENDOPTERYGOTA (HOLOMETABOLA)

Order: **Neuroptera.** Lacewings

Order: **Megaloptera.** Alderflies

These two Orders together contain a variety of insects with four transparent wings, each subdivided by a network of cross-veins. They have a pupal stage in their development, and so belong to the Holometabola (p. 309). The larvæ are carnivorous, and many of them are aquatic. There are about thirteen Families of the two Orders:

SIALIDAE (*Alderflies*), CORYDALIDAE (*Dobson flies*) and SISYRIDAE have aquatic larvæ, which have well-developed thoracic legs, and more or less fringed lateral processes on the abdomen. The adults range in size from about 12 mm. (½ in.) to the big Dobson fly, *Corydalis cornutus* L., which has a wing-span of 4–5 in. The adult insects are found resting on waterside vegetation. RHAPHIDIDAE (*Snakeflies*) are remarkable for the long 'neck', formed by the elongation of the prothorax, giving them the appearance rather of a tortoise than a snake. The rare Family MANTISPIDAE also have the prothorax long, but have grasping fore-legs, placed at the forward (anterior) end of the prothorax, like a mantis. The larvæ of Rhaphidids live under bark, and those of Mantispids are parasitic upon spiders' eggs.

HEMEROBIIDAE (*Brown Lacewings*), and CHRYSOPIDAE (*Green Lace-*

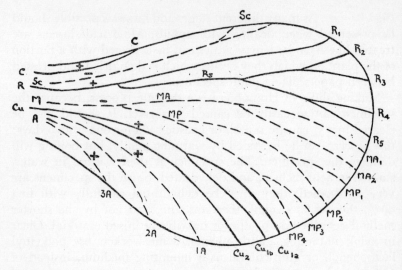

Figure 121. A diagram of the basic pattern of wing-veins, according to the Comstock-Needham system. The longitudinal veins are: C, costa; Sc, subcosta; R, radius; M, media; Cu, cubitus; A, anal. Numbers indicate branches of a main vein; MA, MP are major branches of the media; + and − indicate convex (positive) and concave (negative) veins respectively, when seen from the upper surface. (See p. 278).

wings) are predaceous, and have carnivorous larvæ that are found on vegetation, preying upon aphids. The adult insects are nocturnal, and the green lacewing, *Chrysopa*, with its beautiful golden eyes, is a familiar visitor to light-traps, as well as to lighted rooms. The eggs of the Chrysopids have stalks, by which they are attached to vegetation.

NEMOPTERIDAE are tropical insects, with extremely narrow and elongate hind-wings. The larvæ are predaceous and live in dust, as do those of the more familiar *Antlions*, MYRMELEONIDAE. The larvæ of the latter have huge mandibles, and live in conical pits in the sand or dust. There is one larva to each pit, and it feeds upon the small insects that fall in, especially ants.

CONIOPTERYGIDAE are tiny insects, covered with whitish powder and looking like aphids. The larvæ prey upon aphids, scale-insects and mites. A few species of this Family occur in Britain.

Collecting

The adults of these two Orders are caught by stalking and

catching with a net, or at a sheet or light-trap at night. Many of them can bite. The larvæ of the aquatic forms by water-net; the terrestrial larvæ, under bark, by hand-picking. Ant-lion larvæ are most easily collected by kneeling down and blowing sharply into the pit, taking care to close one's eyes first. The sudden blowing away of the dust exposes the larva before it has time to burrow out of sight; it is then picked up with forceps.

Preservation

Kill adults with cyanide or ethyl acetate. If colours are greenish and delicate, bring home alive in tubes and kill with sulphur dioxide, as described for dragonflies (see p. 84). Pin and set (figs. 52–55). Larvæ can be brought home alive in wet moss, killed in hot water, and kept in alcohol.

Order: **Coleoptera**

Beetles are one of the most distinctive groups of insects as well as being by far the biggest Order. According to the estimates given in the Table earlier in this Chapter, about 40% of all known insects are beetles.

Despite these large numbers, there is a uniformity of appearance that makes beetles easy to recognise. The fore-wings are nearly always hardened into *elytra*, which are not used for flight, but serve as covers beneath which the hind-wings are elaborately folded when they are not in use. In most beetles the elytra cover the abdomen too, but in a few groups, such as the STAPHYLINIDAE (*Rove-beetles*) the elytra are short, and the tip of the abdomen sticks out beyond them. When the wings are folded, most beetles have rounded outlines, and are hard-bodied, the various plates or sclerites, especially those of the legs, giving even more than usual the appearance of a miniature suit of armour.

Beetles have mouth-parts of the chewing type, with mandibles, and nearly all of them feed by chewing their food. A few are parasitic, and in these the mandibles are sharpened and grooved, so that they can be used for sucking blood. One beetle or another will eat almost every possible kind of food: fungi and moulds; organic debris, both vegetable and animal; all parts of living plants; stored vegetable or animal products; or other insects. Some will even bore into metal, and wood-boring beetles are among the most destructive of all insects.

The beetles have true larvæ, which are totally different from the corresponding adults, and which undergo complete meta-

Q

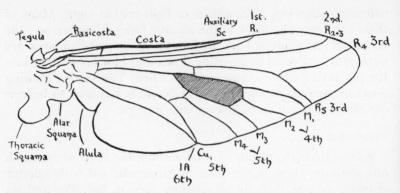

Figure 122. Wing of a horse-fly (Diptera), with a venation that is fairly easily derived from the basic pattern. Veins labelled in Comstock-Needham symbols, and also in a system of numbering that starts from the fore-margin, the opposite of that in Lepidoptera shown in fig. 123. Note that the numbering starts with vein R_1. Other structures at the base of the wing are named; the shaded area is the *discal cell*. (See p. 280).

morphosis by means of a dormant pupal stage. All the larvæ have a well-developed head, and most of them have three pairs of jointed true legs on the thorax. There is great variation in both the habitat and the structure of beetle-larvæ, and many that live in sheltered places, such as wood, or underground, have no legs at all. Beetle-larvæ never have prolegs (*pseudopods*) on the abdomen, except possibly one at the very tip.

Despite the uniformity of general plan, already mentioned, beetles vary enormously in size, from 1 to 100 mm., or $\frac{1}{25}$ to 4 in. They also vary in colour and pattern; in the sculpturing of the crests, hollows and pits on the surface of the body, including the elytra; and in other details of structure, especially of the head and legs. This great variety, together with the ease with which beetles can be collected, and the great beauty of the collection when it is made, give Coleoptera a popularity second only to that of the butterflies and moths.

In a work like the present it is impossible even to list all the families, much less to give any adequate key to them, and merely to mention one or two is no help to the collector. It is better to buy or borrow a book on the beetles of the region in which the collector is interested. Such books exist at all levels of precision, from those which give coloured pictures of a limited selection, to those which offer detailed keys to all the known species.

Recommended examples are: Fowler, W., 1887–1891, *Coleoptera of the British Islands*. Joy, N., 1932, *A Practical Handbook of British Beetles*. Walsh, G. B. and Dibb, J. R., *The Coleopterists' Handbook*, published by The Amateur Entomologists' Society. Crowson, R. A., 1956, *Coleoptera: Introduction and Keys to Families*, in Handbooks for the Identification of British Insects of The Royal Entomological Society of London.

Collecting

Beetles may be caught on the wing, but the greater number of specimens are taken by sweeping or beating. Whereas such groups as flies or bugs can be swept from the upper parts of long grass, the beetle collector needs to be able to reach the lower stems of plants, and to sweep among tougher herbage, such as heather or bracken. The net-frame should therefore be very strong, with one or more flat sides, so that it can move close to the ground. Fig. 11 resembles the shape recommended by Bechyne (1956).

A *sieve* is needed for sifting small beetles from soil, leaf-mould, rotting wood and moss. The bigger beetles are picked off the sieve, while the sifted debris is caught in a bag, and can be taken home for more detailed examination.

Water-beetles are collected as described on p. 33. They are numerous, and make a fascinating study in themselves.

A collecting-bottle with a small tube in the cork (Plate X, B) is standard equipment for collecting beetles, and is sold as a 'Coleoptera collecting-bottle'. It may be obtained with a plastic cork that can be removed with two fingers of the same hand that is holding the bottle, thus making it easier to reach up into awkward places on tree-trunks, walls and so on. The small tube is placed over the insect, and by gentle movements the latter is persuaded to move off the original surface and to stand on the wall of the small tube. As soon as this happens, a smart tap with the hand on the bottom of the bottle will bring the specimen down into the interior.

Beetles too big for this collecting-bottle can be enticed into bigger tubes, or pill-boxes, and afterwards transferred to a wide-mouthed killing-bottle. They may also be carefully picked up with forceps.

Preservation

Kill with ethyl acetate, to which a little creosote (1:50) is added. Beetles more than ½ in. long may be pinned direct, passing the pin through the right elytron. Smaller beetles are carded (fig. 66); triangular cards make it easier to see the underside of the specimen, and a card point may be turned up slightly at the tip and stuck to the *side* of the specimen, which is then visible almost from any angle (fig. 65).

Larvæ are killed and preserved by van Emden's method (p. 82). Duffy (1950) points out that Longicorn larvæ are very fatty and must be placed in 30% alcohol with one or two drops of acetic acid and heated to just below boiling for 20–30 minutes on a water-bath (see p. 138); they are then stored in 80% alcohol. Other larvæ he places for 2–6 days in Pampel's fluid before transferring to alcohol.

Order: **Strepsiptera**

This Order of minute insects has no common name; some authors (e.g. Crowson, 1956) include it in Coleoptera. Only the males have wings, and these are the hind-wings: the fore-wings are reduced to halteres, thus reversing the condition found in Diptera (see below). The females are wingless.

A few Strepsiptera of the family MENGENILLIDAE (merged with MENGEIDAE by some authors) are free-living, and both sexes of these are found under stones. The rest of the Order, divided into four or five families, are all parasitic: STYLOPIDAE (XENIIDAE) on bees and wasps; ELENCHIDAE on bugs of the family FULGORIDAE; and HALICTOPHAGIDAE on crickets and bugs.

The female is found between the abdominal segments of the host, with the anterior part of the body protruding. After being fertilised by the winged male, the female produces several thousands of tiny larvæ, of a type called *triangulin*, which are very active. These leave the original host, and find another, feeding inside the body, and there pupating. Any males which thus emerge leave the host, but the females remain in position.

The life-history is remarkable for the fact that the female is viviparous—not an uncommon state in insects—and that the young larvæ escape from the thorax of the mother by special apertures.

The metabolism of the host insect is often seriously affected by the presence of the parasite. Besides distorting the shape of the abdomen, which allows a 'stylopised' bee or wasp to be easily recognised, there is often damage to the gonads or internal genital organs. By upsetting the balance between male and female hormones, this may result in intersexes being produced.

In Britain there are five families of Strepsiptera, and seventeen species.

Collecting

The few Strepsiptera that live under stones are only rarely found: some of them occur in southern Europe, but none in England. The parasitic forms are obtained by finding 'stylopised' Hymenoptera, or other insects, and keeping them alive until th adult Strepsiptera are matured.

Preservation

In 80% alcohol or as slide-mounts.

Order: **Mecoptera**

The *Scorpionflies* are so-called because the male genitalia of the Panorpidae are curved upwards like the sting of a scorpion. In the family BOREIDAE the wings are reduced in the males and absent in the females, but the other Mecoptera have four membranous wings, the two pairs being similar, and having many cross-veins. The most obvious recognition feature of this Order is the long face, the chewing mouth-parts being mounted at the tip of a snout, a long way from the eyes.

The BOREIDAE are found in moss, and sometimes on snow, and are believed to feed on moss. The PANORPIDAE look like a rather stout crane-fly, or 'daddy-longlegs', with spotted wings, and fly about rather lazily among vegetation. They feed on living insects, dead ones, or on nectar. The BITTACIDAE, of which there are no British examples, are even more like crane-flies, and hang from twigs by their fore-legs, catching and devouring other insects.

The larvæ of Mecoptera are rather like caterpillars, and live on, or in the soil, feeding on living or dead insects.

Collecting

BOREIDAE are picked up with forceps, and brought home alive in damp moss. PANORPIDAE and BITTACIDAE are netted, taken by sweeping: some of them come to light at night. Beirne (1953) recommends that PANORPIDAE, after capture, should be held alive in the fingers until they have voided the intestine, because otherwise they will do this in the killing-bottle and foul other specimens.

Preservation

Boreidae may be pointed (fig. 64), or put in spirit. The other adults may be pinned and set like Lepidoptera (figs. 52–55). The larvæ are kept in spirit.

Order: **Trichoptera**

Caddisflies are best known for their aquatic larvæ, most of which live in cases that they make from sand grains, pebbles, bits of wood, leaves, and sometimes silk, using either silk or cement for binding the materials together. The base is carried about while the larva is growing and feeding, but is attached to a fixed anchorage, and sealed, while the larva is pupating. The mature pupa breaks out of the case, swims to the surface, and climbs out on to an exposed object before the adult insect emerges. The larvæ feed mostly on vegetable food, though some are predaceous. There is one terrestrial British species found in damp moss at the roots of trees.

The adult caddisfly is somewhat like a moth, but has the wings hairy rather than scaly, and holds them like a roof over the body. Trichoptera are not seen much in general collecting, but can often be found in great numbers on vegetation near water. They do not fly very actively, but are sometimes seen in swarms in sunlight. Many Trichoptera fly at night, and are often caught in light-traps, or at a sheet.

Identification is not easy, and depends a good deal on the state of preservation of the specimen.

Collecting

At night, by sheeting (fig. 24), or in a light-trap. In the daytime by sweeping or netting in flight, but usually they have first to be disturbed from their hiding-places by beating waterside branches with a stick. From nooks and crevices they can be collected by an aspirator or a pill-box.

Larvæ are collected by hand-picking from stones in the water, and by dredging from the bottom, or by net from among aquatic vegetation. Larvæ can be kept in an aquarium and the adults bred, and this is the best way of getting perfect specimens or of getting adults of some of the rarer species.

Preservation

Kill adult Trichoptera by cyanide or ethyl acetate, and preserve them in 80 % alcohol. If it is more convenient to do so at the time, take them home between layers of cellulose wadding and immerse afterwards. A little absolute alcohol may be needed at first to wet

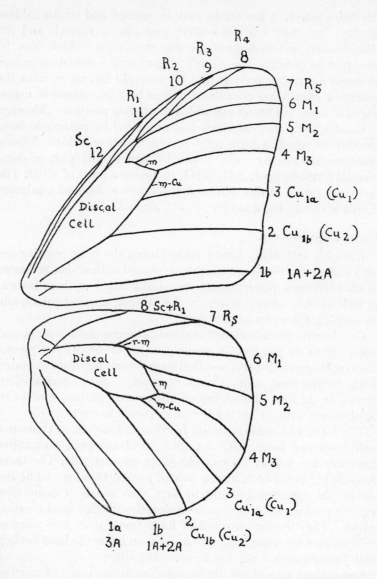

Figure 123. Wing of a butterfly, *Danaus*, with the Comstock-Needham symbols, and the English nomenclature, starting near the hind-margin (cf. fig. 122). (After Corbet and Pendlebury.)

the hairy insect. A few adults may be pinned and set for cabinet display, but they are soft-bodied, and apt to shrivel, and the classification is based upon thoracic structures, which may be obscured by pinning. Use a setting board with a very deep groove to avoid damaging the legs and try to avoid having to relax the specimen after it has once dried. It can be kept relaxed in tissue-paper if a few cut leaves are added to provide moisture (Mosely).

Caddis larvæ may be killed and preserved by putting in 80% alcohol, to which a little ethyl acetate has been added. Mosely recommends 2% formalin, made by adding one part of commercial formalin (40% CH_3CHO) to nineteen parts of water. The larvæ are stored in this, but on first immersion he used a mixture of this with half the quantity of 90% alcohol.

Order: **Lepidoptera**

Butterflies and *Moths* form a large Order, the most popular one with collectors. The large wings are covered with scales, arranged in characteristic patterns, and the classification of these insects, as well as their attractiveness in the cabinet, depend principally on keeping the scales undamaged.

One family, MICROPTERYGIDAE, have chewing mouth-parts, and a few others do not feed as adults. The great majority of species have sucking mouth-parts, and feed from flowers, sap from wounded trees, rotting fruit, animal remains, sewage, dung, perspiration, or any liquid food of a sugary or nitrogenous nature, which can be obtained without having to bite or pierce to get it.

The larvæ of Lepidoptera are familiar as *caterpillars*. There is a well-developed head, with mandibles and antennæ, and above the latter are usually six spot-like ocelli on each side. The three thoracic segments each have a pair of jointed true legs, while the abdominal segments 3–6 and 10 have each a pair of fleshy false legs, or prolegs, sac-like organs equipped with tiny hooks, called *crochets*. The 'looper' caterpillars have fewer than five pairs of prolegs, and bend the body into an arch to bring the hind prolegs well forward each time, and so move rapidly.

Caterpillars should not be confused with the larvæ of sawflies (Hymenoptera, below): the latter have only one ocellus on each side of the head, and generally have more than five pairs of prolegs, in particular having a pair on the second abdominal segment; the prolegs have no crochets.

Most lepidopterous larvæ feed on plant material, chewing the leaves, or mining in the leaves or stems. Some make the plant produce galls, and a few are predaceous. Caterpillars produce silk from modified salivary glands, opening at the base of the labium, and use it for folding or rolling leaves to make a shelter, for spinning a cocoon to shelter the larva during pupation, or for attaching a pupa to a twig. The silkworm, *Bombyx mori*, is bred for the sake of the silk cocoons that it makes, and now exists only as a domesticated species.

The popular division of the Lepidoptera is into *Butterflies* (Rhopalocera), which have clubbed antennæ, are generally brightly coloured, and fly by day, and *Moths* (Heterocera), which have unclubbed antennæ, are generally drab, grey or brown, and mostly fly by night. Microlepidoptera are the smaller moths, which attract their own enthusiasts; they are numerous, and difficult, and comprise about half the species of Lepidoptera. Though this division is not a strictly scientific one, it is very nearly so, and is a long-established and convenient grouping for collecting purposes.

A great many books have appeared, and continue to appear, on butterflies and moths, and one of these should be consulted for the identification of families, genera and species. The more conspicuous members can be spotted from coloured plates of the pattern of the wings, but for serious study of the great majority of Lepidoptera it is necessary to study wing-venation and genitalia. Venation is discussed in Chapter X (see figs. 123–125).

Collecting

Butterflies, and day-flying moths by netting in flight. Since many of them have a fluttering, erratic flight, the net should be light, and of open mesh, so that it can be manipulated easily. A black, or dark-green material is less easily avoided by the insect, and shows up white moths very well.

Since the pattern of the wings is so important, it is essential not to rub off the scales, or damage the membrane. A fresh, strong killing-bottle should be used, so that the insect does not flutter about inside before collapsing: cyanide is best, but ethyl acetate is safer to use. Bigger specimens may be held carefully in a fold of the net, and pinched sharply either killing them outright, or at least immobilising them before putting them into the killing-bottle. Apart from this, handling of the specimen should be avoided as much as possible. If the cork is taken out of the killing-bottle, and the bottom part of the bottle is held in the hand, it can be inserted into the net until it is below the specimen, when a

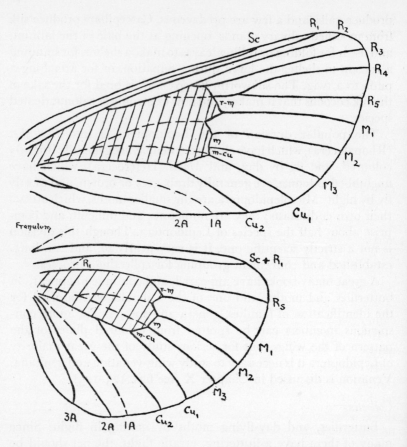

Figure 124. Wings of a member of the Lepidoptera frenatæ: shaded
area = discal cell (after Borror and Delong).

sharp tap will knock the insect into the bottle without having to
handle it (as in Plate V).

Day-flying Lepidoptera can often be captured on tree-trunks,
posts, or walls, by putting either a pill-box or a wide-mouthed
killing-bottle over them. The same method is used at night for
collecting at a sheet (fig. 24), or at sugar, and the great majority
of moths that are collected are taken at one or other of these
sources. Butterflies also come to small pools, boggy patches or
wounded trees which exude sap.

It is important that Lepidoptera, whether living or dead, should
not be stored in bottles or other containers with insects of other

Orders, and the containers should not afterwards be used for other insects until they have been cleared of all loose scales. To pick off a score of butterfly scales from a bristly fly, without breaking off any of the bristles, is a heartbreaking task.

Lepidopterous larvæ (caterpillars) are collected by hand-picking from leaves and twigs, and should be taken home alive, in a pill-box, with some of the leaves on which they were found. Both adults and larvæ are often closely associated with a particular food-plant, and this should be noted at the time. If it cannot be identified with certainty, then a sample should be taken.

Preservation

Adult Lepidoptera are nearly always displayed as pinned and set specimens (see figs. 52–55). Ideally they should be pinned and set as soon as they are killed, and this can normally be done for occasional captures in or near home. During a day's collecting, or on a longer trip, it is not usually possible, or desirable to do this because the setting apparatus, and the set specimens themselves, take up a lot of room, and because the delicate manipulation cannot be done so easily out of doors in a wind.

In the field, Lepidoptera should not be crowded in the killing-bottle, and should not be left there to be shaken about while the collector is chasing other insects. As soon as they are dead they should be papered (fig. 45), the details of capture being written on the envelope before putting in the specimen. Layering between sheets of cellulose wadding is less laborious, but the layers should be carefully packed so that the specimens do not shake into a heap.

If specimens are being taken in large numbers, the quickest method is to lay them flat, with the wings extended upwards, while they are still moist after killing, and then impale a number of them on the same pin. The pins are then stuck into the bottom of a relaxing-tin (Plate X, D), and carried home in it. After arrival at home, the specimens are relaxed (p. 96), pinned neatly through the thorax, and set (p. 100). Since Lepidoptera are rarely staged, the pin chosen should be thick enough to stand up to a fair amount of moving from box to box: sizes 1 to 3 are generally the most useful for butterflies and the bigger moths.

Microlepidoptera are best pinned in the field, using the smaller sizes of pin, down to 000, and brought home in a pocket collecting-tin (Plate IX). The wings can be roughly spread by blowing on the specimen, or miniature setting boards can be carried in a special box.

Larvæ of Lepidoptera (caterpillars) are most easily stored in 80% alcohol, with a careful record of the plant on which they were found. For cabinet display the dried skin should be blown as in fig. 60. The method of freeze-drying (p. 108) is excellent for caterpillars, either for display or for permanent storage, provided that the expensive apparatus is available.

Order: **Diptera**

The true *flies* are distinguished from all other insects except the male Coccids (Homoptera) by having only the fore-wings functional, the hind-wings being modified into knobbed organs called *halteres*. The halteres vibrate during flight, and recent theories of their function indicate that they may act as gyroscopes controlling the stability of the flying insect. Many flies have the wings reduced, or have lost them altogether, and these can only be recognised as Diptera by their general structure, in particular that of the thorax, according to the key in Chapter X.

Flies occur everywhere, indoors and out of doors, and in all climates, in the Arctic, in the tropics, on mountains and in caves. The mouth-parts are adapted for the sucking of fluids, either through a tube formed from the elongate labium, mandibles and maxillæ, or through the spongy lobes of the labium, which are then called *labella*; or, in some groups, making use of both. Principal sources of food are the nectar of flowers and the liquid products of fermentation and putrefaction, but in several families of flies the mouth-parts may be hardened into a piercing organ by which either the body fluids of other insects, or the blood of vertebrates may be obtained as food. Some of the last group have become parasitic, and spend their whole adult lives clinging to and feeding upon their vertebrate host.

Flies have as big a range of size as any Order of insects. They vary from about 1 to 2 mm. in the smallest midges, to a wing-span of 2–3 in. (50–75 mm.).

The larvæ of flies are totally different from the adult, and often live in a totally different situation. The larvæ have no true (thoracic) legs, though they sometimes have false legs, or pseudopods. Some are cylindrical, with a distinct head, but most are either maggot-like or grub-like: that is, either they have one end pointed and the other blunt, or they are fleshy and barrel-shaped, the same at both ends. Many are aquatic, but the majority of dipterous larvæ live in decaying vegetable or animal matter. A few larvæ, such as that of the *Warble-fly* of cattle, are parasitic on mammals, and a great many TACHINIDAE parasitise other insects. Some others (e.g. the *Tsetse-flies*, and certain *Blow-flies*) are viviparous, dropping not eggs, but mature larvæ. Some aquatic groups, notably the *Mosquitoes*, have active pupæ, but most dipterous pupæ remain quiescent in the soil, or in wood. Generally speaking, pupæ of the more primitive families of the Nematocera and Brachycera (see below) show the shape of the adult; those of the higher Diptera, the Cyclorrhapha, are hidden within a seed-like case made from the hardened last larval skin.

Diptera vary in appearance from fragile, long-legged and long-winged *Crane-flies*, *Mosquitoes* and *Midges*, to short, bristly *House-flies* and *bluebottles*. The first group, which generally have slender antennæ of many segments, are the sub-order Nematocera. The house-flies and bluebottles and their allies form the series *Calypterae*, and are joined with the *Hover-flies* (*Aschiza*) and a large group of small flies such as *Drosophila*, the small *Fruit-fly* (*Acalypterae*) to make up the sub-order Cyclorrhapha. In between is a third sub-order, the Brachycera, which comprises a number of rather diverse families of mostly middle-sized or big flies, such as ASILIDAE (*Robber-flies*), BOMBYLIIDAE (*Bee-flies*), and TABANIDAE (*Horse-flies* and *Clegs*).

The major groups of Diptera are difficult to define by clear characters, but fortunately most of the families are distinctive in appearance, and with a little practice many of them can be spotted at sight. Colyer and Hammond's book in Warne's *Wayside and Woodland* series is an excellent introductory volume to the Diptera.

Collecting

The Diptera are so diverse that all methods of collecting can be applied to them, except possibly beating. Swarms of midges, etc., can be collected with a large net. Catch SYRPHIDAE (*Hover-flies*) and BOMBYLIIDAE (*Bee-flies*) when they are hovering over blossoms, ASILIDAE (*Robber-flies*) when they are in flight after a victim, and both ASILIDAE and BOMBYLIIDAE by dropping a net over them when they are resting on twigs or stones. A great many small Diptera are taken by sweeping: sometimes, as when catching DOLICHO-PODIDAE on wet vegetation, most of the specimens in the net may belong to one or two common species, and this is the time to put one's head into the net (Plate IV) and pick out a selection of specimens with the aspirator, afterwards releasing those that are not wanted.

Collect small flies from tree-trunks, fence posts and walls with an aspirator (Plate VI). Stirring up leaf-mould and heaps of vegetable material will bring out numbers of small flies that can either be picked up from the surface with the aspirator, or netted as they rise in flight: this kind of habitat will yield flies even in winter. Taking home such material and keeping it in an emergence box (fig. 36) will often reveal the existence of interesting species that are seldom caught on the wing.

For bloodsucking species it is helpful to have a bait animal, which may be one's self, a companion (Plate VII), or a horse or cow. The best specimens are obtained by waiting until the fly is biting, and then quietly placing a tube over it, gently dislodging the fly, and quickly putting in the cork. If your bait animal is not co-operative enough for this, a rapid sweep of the net, following the sound rather than the sight, will often catch the fly before it settles. The way *not* to catch biting flies for a collection is to slap them with the palm of the hand.

The various bot-flies and warble-flies are not often seen in flight, but can be bred from the larvæ, provided that these are not removed from the host animal until they are fully fed, and quite ready to pupate. They are then kept in moist soil or sand.

Fly *traps* can be used to collect flies, as well as merely to destroy them. The baited traps discussed in Chapter II are specially suitable for catching flies, and some selective collecting is possible by varying the bait. Basden (1954) gives an excellent account of bait-traps for small Diptera. Certain Diptera—notably midges and crane-flies—are numerous in catches at light-traps, but when taken in this way they are seldom of much value as specimens for a collection. The light-trap is useful rather for studying behaviour than for obtaining specimens.

Dipterous larvæ are found in dung, in leaf-mould and compost, in fruit, in carrion (decaying meat and fish) and in water, either fresh or brackish. A few species are intertidal, or even pelagic.

Preservation

Kill in cyanide or ethyl acetate; the latter is very suitable, and is convenient to use with an aspirator. Pin the larger and middle-sized flies, preferably in the field, and bring them home, unstaged, in small pocket-boxes as in Plate IX. Those that are more than 8 mm. long may be given a pin long enough for permanent storage. Smaller ones should be staged on polyporus (fig. 63) and the smallest ones pointed (fig. 64). If the collection is too numerous

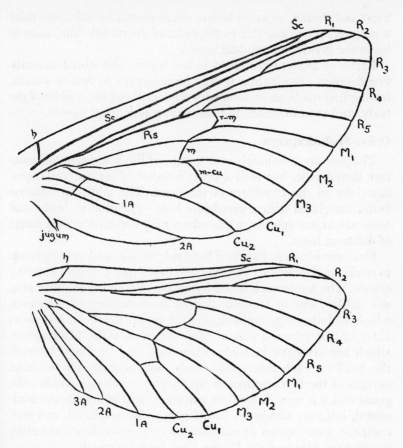

Figure 125. Wings of Lepidoptera jugatæ (after Borror and Delong).

to be pinned on the spot, bring them home between layers of cellulose wadding. *Do not put adult Diptera into spirit*—it only ruins them. The idea that spirit is more 'scientific' than pins is a rationalisation of laziness. An exception may be made of parasitic Diptera, HIPPOBOSCIDAE, NYCTERIBIIDAE and STREBLIDAE, which are more easily studied in spirit.

Diptera can be set, and a few set specimens make a good display, but it is often difficult to see the sides of the thorax, and even the legs, properly in set specimens. It is better just to make sure that the wings and legs are separated as much as is necessary for every part of the body to be accessible. Classification of Diptera is based a great deal on *chaetotaxy*, the position of bristles on the

head and thorax, so avoid breaking the thorax by using too thick
a pin, and try to put this to the right of the middle line, so as to
leave the bristles on one half intact.

Larvæ of Diptera are killed in hot water, and stored in spirit.
For detailed examination it may be necessary to boil in potash,
having first made an incision with scissors about the middle of the
body, and then to mount in balsam on a slide (figs. 84–90).

Order: **Siphonaptera**

The *fleas* are a homogeneous group, of the same general structure throughout, but with a great number of bizarre variations,
especially in the structures of the head. The adults are always
found associated with a vertebrate host—mammal or bird—and
some are highly specific, while others may occur on a wide range
of different hosts.

Fleas are wingless, flattened from side to side, and very resistant
to crushing. The legs are strongly developed into powerful jumping
organs. The adults suck blood by means of piercing mouth-parts,
not unlike those of Diptera. Besides these striking mouth-parts,
which include long, multi-segmented palpi, the head has short
antennæ, sometimes a pair of eyes, and often stout, black spines,
which are arranged in *combs*. These last may be found beneath
the head on each side (*genal* comb), or vertically on the hind
margin of the first segment of the thorax (*prothoracic* comb); the
genal comb is seen in greatest variation, and is not always horizontal, but may sometimes be oblique, or near-vertical, and may
comprise many spines or only one or two. Some fleas, including
the Human Flea and the Plague Flea, have no combs.

Adult fleas live on the host continuously, generally leaving it
only when it begins to cool after death. The eggs are laid in the
coat of the host animal, and fall off into crevices round its haunts:
e.g. the sleeping-box of a dog or cat, or the nest of a bird. The
larvæ are worm-like and have distinctive long bristles. They feed
on organic debris, not by sucking blood, and so they remain
independent of the vertebrate host until they are fully fed and
have pupated. The pupal stage is of rather indefinite duration,
and may be prolonged until the dormant adult is stimulated by
vibration. Thus in disused buildings, especially in winter, a reoccu-
pation, with the lighting of fires and movement of furniture, may
bring out a hidden infestation of newly-hatched fleas, all looking
for a meal of blood.

Only a limited number of fleas are associated with man or

domestic animals, and the great majority are parasitic on birds, bats or small mammals. To be suitable as a regular host for fleas —as distinct from being occasionally bitten—an animal must have a nest, den or sleeping-place.

Collecting

As for lice, by killing the host animal after enclosing it in a linen bag to entrap the fleas. In an infested room, by putting down flake naphthalene and leaving it for a day or two, then sweeping it up and looking for fleas among it. They may also be trapped by putting out sheets of greased paper. Sometimes they can be seen moving about on the living host—particularly on hedgehogs, where the fleas can be seen moving about among the spines—and then they may be picked off with a brush dipped in spirit.

Preservation

Preserve in spirit or as slide-mounts: preferably mounted. Although specialists have their pet methods, perfectly satisfactory slide-mounts can be made by boiling in 10% KOH, rinsing in water, dehydrating in glacial acetic acid, and clearing in clove oil, or cedar-wood oil, and finally mounting in Canada balsam, as illustrated in figs. 84–90.

Order: **Hymenoptera**

Although this is one of the biggest Orders of insects, it has no collective common name, such as 'beetles' or 'flies'. The name means 'having membranous wings' and applies equally well to several other Orders. The best we can do is to call them *'Bees, Wasps, Ants* and allied insects'. Richards (1956) gives a general account of the Order, and a Key to the families occurring in Britain.

The Order is divided sharply into two sub-orders: **Symphyta** and **Apocrita.** Symphyta have the abdomen sessile, that is to say that it is not separated from the thorax by a *petiole*, or wasp-waist. Their larvæ are like caterpillars, with three pairs of thoracic legs, and usually with abdominal prolegs as well. The family URO-CERIDAE (SIRICIDAE) are large, or very large yellow-and-black insects, known as 'wood-wasps'. The female has a very long ovipositor which is used to penetrate the bark of trees, and lay a single egg in the wood. The larva burrows in the wood, and can do great damage. The British fauna includes the yellow and black *Uroceros gigas*, and a metallic blue species, *Sirex noctilio*.

R

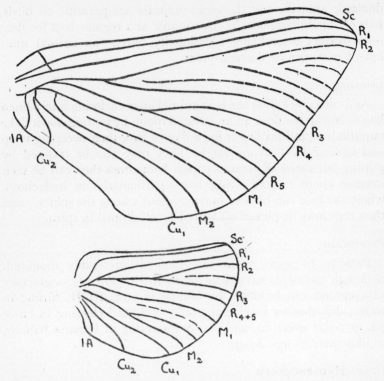

Figure 126. Wings of Ephemeroptera, showing *intercalary veins* (dotted) inserted between those of the basic pattern. The network of cross-veins that is so characteristic of these insects is omitted for clarity. (After Kimmins, 1950.) (See p. 279.)

The other families of Symphyta are known as *Sawflies* because with one exception, the female ovipositor is saw-like, and is used for cutting a way into young shoots or leaves of plants in order to lay eggs there. The larvæ of these families are distinguished from the true caterpillars of Lepidoptera by the fact that the sawfly larvæ have prolegs on the second abdominal segment, and that these prolegs have no hooks (*crochets*). These larvæ live on vegetation, and may do great damage to plants; the Gooseberry Sawfly is a familiar example to gardeners.

The exception mentioned above is the family CEPHIDAE, the stem sawflies. These have a short ovipositor, and their larvæ live in the stems of cereals. The Wheatstem Sawfly damages wheat by making a weak point in the stem, at which it breaks.

The family ORYSSIDAE (called ORUSSIDAE by those who fancy their Greek) is somewhat intermediate between the two sub-orders, and has a legless larva that is parasitic in Buprestid beetles.

The Sub-order Apocrita is further subdivided into the Aculeata —the stinging Hymenoptera—and the Parasitica. These divisions are not entirely logical, since some Aculeata are parasitic in habit, and some Parasitica are not. The classification of the Hymenoptera is very difficult, because the families are numerous, and their definition is often a matter for debate. There is general agreement about a number of Superfamilies, and these are sufficient to give a general picture of the Order.

The families of the Aculeata are grouped into the Superfamilies FORMICOIDEA (*Ants*), VESPOIDEA (*Wasps*) and APOIDEA (*Bees*). Those of the Parasitica are ICHNEUMONOIDEA (*Ichneumon flies*), CHALCIDOIDEA (*Parasitic Wasps*) and CYNIPOIDEA (*Gall-Wasps*). The Superfamily PROCTOTRUPOIDEA are small wasps which look like CHALCIDOIDEA, and are also parasitic, but which are placed by some authorities into the Aculeata, near the VESPOIDEA.

The striking feature of the biology of the Aculeata is the development of social life, with great colonies of individuals belonging to a number of different castes, and an elaborate organisation for rearing and protecting the larvæ. The bees, wasps and ants all have members which have evolved such a communal life. Not only is the community highly organised, but sometimes, as in the honey-bee, the behaviour of the individual is as complex as that of many vertebrate animals.

At the same time, these Superfamilies include solitary members, such as the ground-living bees and wasps, which rear their individual families in separate burrows. Although a colony of such burrows may be found close together, there is none of the communal organisation of the social insects.

The larvæ of the Aculeata are legless and helpless, and are looked after by the adults, who provide them with food. The larvæ of the Parasitica are also legless, but they are provided for by the parents, who deposit their eggs in another living insect, upon which the larvæ can feed. ICHNEUMONOIDEA choose larvæ of other insects, in particular caterpillars, beetle-larvæ and fly-maggots; CHALCIDOIDEA are mainly egg-parasites, but some attack larvæ, including larvæ of other parasitic insects, thereby becoming *hyperparasites*. PROCTOTRUPOIDEA have similar habits. CYNIPOIDEA, the gall-wasps, are best known as making such familiar structures as the 'pin-cushion' and the 'marble' galls.

Collecting

The larger winged forms by netting or stalking, taking care in handling the larger bees and wasps in the net, so as not to be stung by them. Sweeping produces large numbers of sawflies, parasitic forms and the smaller bees and wasps, but getting the smallest ones out of the net is difficult because they are lost among vegetable material. If the material is put into a dark box, in the side of which a glass tube is fixed, most of these small insects will crawl out towards the light (fig. 36). It is a matter for personal choice whether it is easier to take the box into the field, or to bring back the flower-heads, grass, twigs and so on for examination later at home. They must be put in a box, or a botanist's vasculum, and not into a sack coarse enough for the tiny insects to escape through the mesh.

Large numbers of small Hymenoptera can be brought home in Malaise's tube (fig. 46), or between layers of cellulose wadding.

To collect bees and wasps from a nest is difficult because they are numerous and aggressive. A small nest hanging from a branch can be cut down and let fall into a box, or tin, or a bag of closely woven material. If it is bigger, or is in a tree, or in the ground, the insects will come out and attack if it is cut open. First make a small hole and pour in a little carbon disulphide, blocking the hole again at once. After an interval, preferably overnight, the nest can then be opened and inspected.

The nests themselves are difficult to preserve if they are too big to be kept in spirit. The larvæ and the stores of food inside the cells decay and smell, and it is best to cut a shallow section to show the construction of the nest, but allowing all the cells in it to be opened and cleaned out. In any case a big, dry nest is a troublesome and dusty object to have about.

Casual sampling of ants' nests can be made by digging them open with a trowel or hedging spade, if the collector is alert and agile enough to avoid being swarmed over and bitten: heavy clothing is advisable. Use of the suction-tube is not recommended, because of the formic acid released by the captive ants.

CYNIPOIDEA are best obtained by collecting the galls and keeping them until the adults emerge: see warning on leaf-miners, p. 18. Parasitic Hymenoptera are best obtained by collecting other insects that seem to be attacked, especially if they seem unhealthy, or are dead and black, but not rotting. In the winter numerous pupæ of

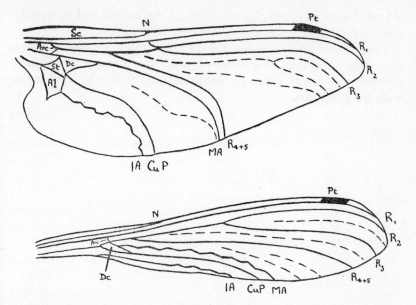

Figure 127. Wings of dragonflies (Odonata). Above, Zygoptera, hind-wing; below, Anisoptera. Showing veins additional to those of the basic plan (dotted); network of cross-veins omitted for clarity. N, nodus; Arc. arculus; Dc, discal cell; St, subtriangle; Al, anal loop (after Fraser, 1949). (See p. 279).

Lepidoptera can be found under bark, and in the hollow stems of dead plants, and if these are kept they will produce hymenopterous parasites.

Sawfly larvæ should be brought home on their food-plant, and reared like caterpillars (see fig. 39).

Preserving

The larger adults should be pinned, those which are too small or too weak to take a long pin being put on a short pin and staged. Very small ichneumons and other Parasitica should be pointed to avoid breaking the thorax, or if minuten pins are used, these should be inclined slightly backwards so that the head and pro-thorax are not detached from the rest of the insect. They should not be put in spirit if this can be avoided; if this must be done, some workers advise first dehydrating in 95% alcohol, followed by absolute, and then returning to 80% for permanent storage.

Sawfly larvæ may be blown like caterpillars (fig. 60). Sometimes it is desirable to insert the blowpipe at the mouth end to avoid damaging characters at the extreme tip of the abdomen.

Care should be taken that the names of the foodplant of saw-flies, the host-plant of gall-wasps, and the host-insects of the parasitic forms are correctly recorded on the labels, and kept with the specimen.

X

HOW AN INSECT IS IDENTIFIED

In the preceding chapter we have seen where insects belong in the Animal Kingdom, and how they are divided into the major groups, Orders and Families. Let us now approach from the opposite direction: we have an insect before us—how do we begin to identify it.

In practice three methods are used: *general appearance; spot characters;* and *keys*.

Identification by *general appearance* means getting to know one's insects by sight. It is a mistake to underrate this kind of knowledge, because this is the way that most identification is done in practice. An entomologist will look at an insect and give you a name for it. Ask him how he recognises it, and he will recite a number of small details that you know he could not have seen with the naked eye. If he were frank he would say: 'I know it is an *Andrena*, because I know *Andrena* by sight, just as I know my uncle by sight. If you press me to do so, I can mention details that will prove its identity, just as I could prove my uncle's identity by looking at the label inside his coat. In both cases I feel sufficiently confident to rely on my general impression.'

The fact is that the eye, and the brain, can register a complex image of an insect far more detailed than any description or illustration. Getting to know the insects means filing away in one's brain a multitude of such images. The other aids to identification, spot characters and keys, are simply indexing devices to make us think of the right mental picture more quickly, or to help if we have never seen this particular insect before.

Spot characters are the rough-and-ready checks we all use: 'scaly wings?—Lepidoptera; clubbed antennæ?—butterfly'. There is no certainty in this method, because other insects may have scaly wings or clubbed antennæ, but it gives a clue, and provides a check on a perhaps uncertain memory.

The most important aid to the memory in making an identification is the *key*, and since keys are among the most important tools of the entomologist we must give some consideration to them.

KEYS

Keys work by a process of elimination, gradually narrowing down the number of possibilities. It is important to understand that a key is much more trustworthy in proving that your insect is *not* A than that it *is* B. It might be C, a species not mentioned in the key. A key does not prove anything positive, it only suggests possibilities.

People are just as faddy about the sort of key they like as they are about their nets and killing-bottles, but the arrangement that has the greatest merit for simplicity and directness is the *dichotomous* key, so-called because at each step it asks you to choose between two alternatives. Thus:

1. Two pairs of membranous wings 2
   Only one pair of membranous wings, the second pair being either hardened into wing-cases, or absent ... 29
2. Fore-wings and hind-wings alike 3
   Fore-wings and hind-wings different 18
3. ... (and so on).

If the insect agrees with the first alternative, then read on at couplet 2; if the second alternative is correct, then jump over all the intervening couplets, and read on at couplet 29. Go on like this until you come to a final choice:

35. With jointed legs on thorax ... ... Larvæ of beetles
    Without any jointed legs ... ... Larvæ of flies

If you are lucky this will give a correct identification, but do not be surprised if it does not. Using keys is only slightly less difficult than making them in the first place. Remember what we have said above, that the details mentioned in the key are not the real reasons why we believe an insect is such-and-such: they are only pointers towards something we can recognise. The real identification is made by comparing the specimen with another specimen that is already named, or with a drawing, or with a good, detailed description.

People commonly make one of two mistakes in using keys. The first is to be over-cautious, taking every word literally, and refusing

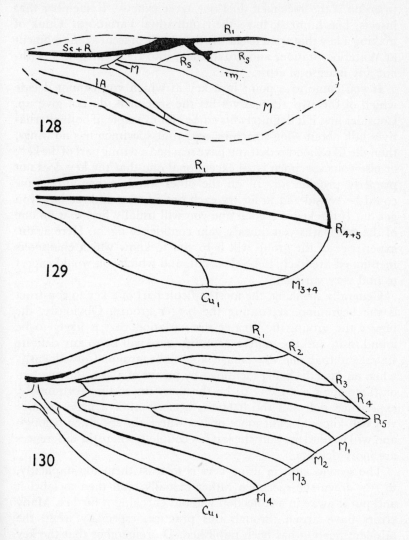

Figures 128, 129. Two wings with greatly reduced venation. 128, a
Chalcid (Hymenoptera), after Richards, 1956; 129, a Cecidomyiid
(Diptera), after Freeman, 1949.

Figure 130. A venation resembling the basic pattern. A Psychodid
(Diptera), after Freeman, 1949.

to go on if the specimen does not agree exactly. Remember that insects, like humans, have their individual variations. Think of making a key that tried to classify the people present at one moment at Waterloo Station, and group them into rigid categories, without any margin of error.

If you come to a point in a key at which you cannot decide which of the two alternatives fits the specimen, do not give up. Consider first if it definitely fits *neither*: for example, if both alternatives talk about wing-structure, and your specimen has no wings, then the likelihood is that you have reached a wrong part of the key; or else your specimen is an exceptional one that the key does not properly provide for. If, on the other hand, either alternative could be considered to fit, try each one in turn and see how you get on. If the key is a good one you will usually find that on one of the two paths you quickly gain confidence again. Here again, experience of the group will help you to know which characters mentioned are likely to be clear-cut, and which you would expect to find very variable.

Generally speaking, the most difficult part of a key to construct is the beginning, separating the bigger groups. Obviously, the bigger the group, the greater the variation that is likely to be found in it, and the more exceptions there will be to any definite statement that one may make about the group. Consequently, when an insect is being identified by means of a key, the first two or three steps are likely to be the most uncertain. Fortunately, experience redresses the balance, because after a little practice you will know at sight more or less where the specimen belongs, and will need to use only the last few couplets, where the differences are more definite.

The second fault in using keys is to trust them too implicitly, to run down the specimen rather casually, and then to label it and put it away in a collection without checking it further. Many errors have arisen through this practice, especially when the misidentification has been published. Do remember that the key does not identify the specimen: it only gives a hint of what it might be.

The correct attitude to keys—at least to keys made by other people—is to be sceptical without being defeatist. One's own keys come into a different category, because when we read a couplet in a key we ourselves wrote, we have the advantage of a great many mental impressions that are not mentioned in the couplet, and which are denied, of course, to anyone else. That is why so often the only person who can use a particular key successfully is the author.

The arrangement of couplets illustrated above is the commonest, and to my mind incomparably the best one. The advantage of having the two alternatives side by side, so that you can weigh up your specimen against each of them, far outweighs the benefits claimed for other arrangements. Many entomologists, particularly those of an older generation, prefer the following style:

1.	(16)	Two pairs of membranous wings	...	...	2
2.	(9)	Fore- and hind-wings alike	...	...	...	3
3.	(7)	. . .			
9.	(2)	Fore-wings different from hind-wings		...	10
16.	(1)	Only one pair of membranous wings...		...	17
		. . . (and so on)			

This kind of key is often significantly called a 'Table', and is said to show the grouping of the insects better, while the numbers in brackets, referring to the other half of each couplet, make it easier to trace a way through the key, both forwards and backwards. Bracketed numbers can, of course, be used in the other type of key to help in retracing one's way. The need to turn over, sometimes, many pages to find the alternative character in a 'Table' of this kind, makes the operation into too much of a hurdle race.

Other arrangements of keys exist, in which the contrasting alternatives are shown by setting-in the beginnings of the lines to varying distances; by using letters, A—AA, or A—A; or by using pairs of symbols or hieroglyphs out of the printer's fount. All these are wasteful of space and time, confusing to the user, and without any practical advantage over the simple kind we first described above.

Beware of keys in which more than two alternatives are presented at one time, especially if the author does not bother to indicate this very clearly. This is bad practice, because it defeats the first object of the dichotomous key, which is to proceed by a series of clear choices between simple and mutually exclusive alternatives. Occasionally, it is true, the insects fall naturally into three or more co-equal groups: e.g. if the legs can be red, or black, or yellow. But such a choice can nearly always be set out in couplets with a little more trouble, and the slightly greater printing space is more than compensated for by the assistance it gives the reader. Often the key with multiple alternatives simply means that the author got tired of trying: I know one splendid example with *eleven* alternatives. Such an absurdity, of course, no longer serves the purpose of a key, since it does not act as an index to the various groups, but presents its information in an undigested state.

Another thing to look out for in keys—and to avoid in your own—is 'leapfrogging', like this:

40.	Femora greatly swollen	...	...	...	...	41
	Femora slender	...	...	...	...	42
41.	Femora with spines beneath ...	...	...	...	71
	No ventral spines on femora ...	...	...	...	85
42.	Eyes hairy	...	...	...	...	...	48
	Eyes bare	...	...	...	...	...	43

Of course, if you read this carefully, you will have no trouble, but keys are meant to give help in quick identification, and you should always try to keep to the logical order.

The construction of keys is a very searching test, not only of how much you really know about a group of insects, but also of whether your knowledge has been assimilated by a tidy and logical mind. When an author publishes a complicated and disorderly key, you will find that the rest of his work shows evidence of a chaotic and turbulent state of mind.

Constructing and adapting keys

For all that we have just said, do not think that making keys is only for the professional entomologist. If you have studied a group of insects, it is well worth while to make a key to them, for your own use, even if you have no idea of publishing it. It is even more useful to be able to modify an existing key and adapt it to your needs: for example, to take a key to the European genera and species of a family and to abstract from it those which occur in Britain; or to combine two or more short keys into one that is more comprehensive. You may need to do this if you do not own the books concerned, but have to borrow them from a library, and return them after a limited time. Then you can pick out just the parts you need, without having to copy out a great deal that is of no value to you.

For all key-making, I use a system based upon a card-index, using standard cards 5 × 3 in. Suppose we begin by copying a short key from a volume borrowed from a library. Write each couplet on a separate card, and stack the cards in a filing cabinet,

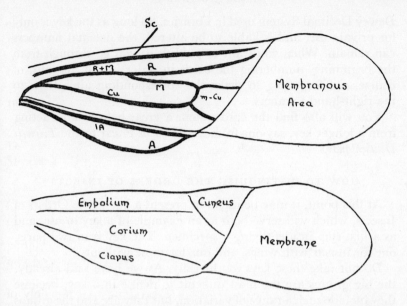

Figure 131. Reduced venation of Hemiptera (Heteroptera). Above, names of veins; below, major divisions of the wing, not always all present in one species.

or in one of the small portable index-boxes (called, for some mysterious reason, a 'trial outfit'); or at worst, hold the cards together with a rubber band. Then if you want to add more names to the key, run each one down as far as it will go, and add another card at that point, using a decimal system of numbering, thus:

21.	Face flat	...	...	...	21.5	
	Face swollen		...	...	genus *Rostera*	
21.5.	Eyes bare	...	...	...	genus *Phara*	*(new card)*
	Eyes hairy	...	...	...	genus *Nera*	
22.	... (etc., etc.)					

The use of cards avoids all the crossing out, cutting-up and pasting together that is needed if you copy the original key on to sheets of paper. Such a card-key can be expanded indefinitely, each time just for the labour of adding a new card, and making a small alteration on the previous one. To put a card between 21.5 and 22 you may give it the number 21.6; if you need one between 21.5 and 21.6, then it becomes 21.55, and so on, like the

Dewey Decimal System used in libraries. So long as the key is only
for private use, and is liable to be altered, the decimal numbers
can remain. When you want to publish it, you go through from
the beginning, numbering the cards in order in red ink and, of
course, not forgetting to make the corresponding alterations to
the right-hand numbers.

You will also find the card system a great help in abstracting
from a longer key, say one from the *Faune de France* or the *Tierwelt
Deutschlands*.

HOW TO DISTINGUISH THE ORDERS OF INSECTS

At this point, it may be useful to present a key to the Orders of
Insects, which will serve both as an example of a key in use, and
as a first step in identifying a specimen. The key is in two parts,
one for insects with wings, and one for those without.

Do not take these keys too literally. As we have said already,
the big groups are the most difficult to define in a key, because
they include such a range of variation, but they are also the groups
that one can most easily learn to know by sight. The present keys
are introductory, not exhaustive, and will not track down obscure
and difficult species; for these a text-book of entomology will be
needed.

A. WINGED INSECTS

1. Insects with four wings (two pairs) 2
   Insects with only two wings (one pair) 18
2. Wings covered with scales. *Butterflies* and *Moths*
   Lepidoptera
   Wings not covered with scales, though they may be
   hairy 3
3. Only the hind-wings are used for flight; fore-wings
   partly or entirely horny or leathery, used as covers
   for hind-wings 4
   Both pairs of wings membranous (flexible) and used for
   flight 7
4. Mouth-parts tube-like, adapted for piercing and sucking.
   Bugs (figs. 63, 118; Plate XIII, K)
   Hemiptera and some **Homoptera**
   Mouth-parts adapted for biting and chewing 5
5. Fore-wings with veins like hind-wings, though rather
   stiffer, and serving as covers for hind-wings ... *Grasshoppers*, etc. (fig. 59; Plate XIII, J) ... **Orthoptera**

Fore-wings without veins, and modified into hard, horny
cases for hind-wings 6

6. Fore-wings short. Tip of abdomen with characteristic
pair of forceps (*cerci*). *Earwigs* ...**Dermaptera**
Fore-wings nearly always long, covering abdomen and
enclosing hind-wings: if they are short (e.g. Staphylinidae), then there are no *cerci*. *Beetles* (Plate XIII,
F, M) ... ... **Coleoptera**

7. Wings as in fig. 117, narrow without veins, but fringed
with long hairs. Very small insects, about 5 mm. long.
Thrips ... ... **Thysanoptera**
Wings more fully developed, and with veins present ... 8

8. Hind-wings much smaller than fore-wings 9
Hind-wings similar in size to fore-wings 13

9. Fore-wings with a large number of cross-veins, making
a net-like pattern. Abdomen with two or three long
'tails'. *Mayflies* (fig. 58) ... **Ephemeroptera**
Fore-wings with fewer veins, nor forming a net-like
pattern. Usually without 'tails' 10

10. Wings obviously hairy. Mouth-parts very small, except
for *palpi* (cf. fig. 134). *Caddisflies* **Trichoptera**
Wings not obviously hairy, though tiny hairs can be seen
under the microscope. Mouth-parts well developed... 11

11. Mouth-parts tube-like, adapted for sucking. *Aphids;
Cicadas* (Plate XIII, K) ... ... **Homoptera**
Mouth-parts not tube-like, but adapted for chewing ... 12

12. Very small insects, soft-bodied, mostly less than 6 mm.
in length. *Tarsi* (fig. 120) with only two or three segments. (Wings as in fig. 116.) *Book-lice* **Psocoptera**
Often much bigger, wasp-like or bee-like insects; or if
very small, then hard-bodied, with abdomen narrowed
at its base into a *petiole*, or 'waist'. *Tarsi* of four or
five segments. *Bees, Wasps, Ants, Sawflies* (fig. 62;
Plate XIII, I, L) ... ... **Hymenoptera**

13. *Tarsi* with three or four segments (fig. 134) 14
Tarsi with five segments 16

14. Wings as in fig. 115, with few cross-veins, and with the
hind-wings greatly expanded posteriorly. *Stoneflies*
Plecoptera
The fore- and hind-wings very similar in shape; or if
hind-wings are enlarged posteriorly, then cross-veins
are much more numerous 15

15. Small insects, generally less than 1 in. (25 mm.) with long *antennæ*, and with wings folded flat over body. *Termites* ...   .   **Isoptera**

Generally longer than 1 in., with very short antennæ. Wings held away from body when at rest. *Dragonflies* (fig. 112) ...   .   **Odonata**

16. Along fore-margin of wings there are very few cross-veins. Mouth-parts prolonged into a beak. *Scorpionflies* (Plate XIII, H) ...   .   **Mecoptera**

Along fore margin of wings are a number of cross-veins. Mouth-parts short   17

17. Hind-wings broader than fore-wings, at any rate at base, and at rest this area is folded like a fan. *Alderflies; Snakeflies* (Plate XIII, G)   ...   **Megaloptera**

Hind-wings similar to fore-wings, without this fan-like area. *Lacewings* ...   .   **Neuroptera**

18. Hind-wings reduced to knob-like organs called *halteres*. Mouth-parts either tube-like, for piercing, or sponge-like for sucking. *True Flies* (fig. 64; Plate XIII, N)

Diptera

(Also males of Homoptera, family Coccidae, but these are rarely seen.)

Hind-wings entirely absent; no *halteres*. Some *Mayflies* ...   .   **Ephemeroptera**

B. WINGLESS INSECTS

1. Some segments with jointed legs, which can be used for movement   2

No jointed legs; or if these are present and can be seen, then they are enclosed in membrane, and cannot move   ...   Larvæ and pupæ of **Endopterygota**

2. Parasites, living on warm-blooded animals, or found closely associated with them   3

Not parasitic on warm-blooded animals: either free-living, or parasitic on other insects, snails and so on ...   8

3. Body flattened from side to side, hard and bristly, with strong legs. Jumping insects, found on birds and mammals. *Fleas*   ...   ...   **Siphonaptera**

Body either rounded or flattened from above ('dorso-ventrally'); not jumping insects   4

4. Mouth-parts adapted for chewing   5

Mouth-parts adapted for sucking   6

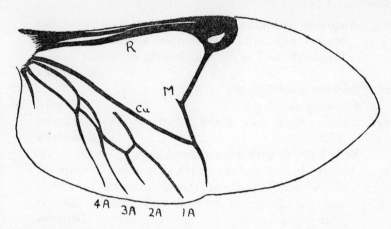

Figure 132. Reduced venation in the hind-wing of a beetle (Cantharoid type), after Crowson, 1956.

5. Posterior end of the body with *cerci*. On bats and small rodents. Tropical. *Parasitic earwigs*   **Dermaptera**
    Posterior end of body without *cerci*. On birds or mammals. World-wide. *Chewing lice*   **Mallophaga**
6. Flattened, rather spider-like insects, with head fitting into a notch on thorax, and with *antennæ* hidden. Claws hooked. *Louse-flies* and *Bat-flies*   **Diptera**
    Not spider-like. *Antennæ* clearly visible   7
7. Snout (proboscis) short, unjointed. Body long and narrow. *Tarsi* of legs with one large, hooked claw. Permanent parasites of birds and mammals. *Sucking lice*   ...   .   **Anoplura**
    Snout (*proboscis*) longer, jointed. Body more oval. *Tarsi* with two small claws, not hook-like. Only temporary parasites. *Wingless bugs*   ...   ... **Hemiptera**
8. Terrestrial: living on dry land, or on animals other than mammals and birds   9
    Aquatic: mostly nymphal forms of terrestrial insects ...   29
9. Mouth-parts not visible. Abdomen with appendages on some of the abdominal segments, or with a forked 'spring' near tip   10
    Mouth-parts clearly visible   11
10. Abdomen with six segments or fewer, usually with a forked appendage ('spring') near tip. No long bristles at tip. *Springtails*   ...   ...   **Collembola**

S

Abdomen with nine or more segments. No spring, but several segments have simple appendages. Long, bristle-like *cerci* at tip of abdomen. *Bristletails*
Thysanura

11. Sucking mouth-parts 12
Chewing mouth-parts 16

12. Body covered with scales, or dense hairs. *Wingless Moths* ... ... **Lepidoptera**
Body bare, or with few scattered hairs 13

13. Almost whole of thorax that is visible above is composed of the middle segment, the mesothorax: prothorax and metathorax both small and hidden. *Wingless Flies* ... ... **Diptera**
Mesothorax and metathorax about equally developed. Prothorax also is usually visible from above 14

14. Snout (*proboscis*) small, cone-shaped. Body long and narrow. Claws usually absent. *Thrips*
Thysanoptera
Snout (*proboscis*) longer, jointed. Body more or less oval. Claws present 15

15. *Proboscis* arising from front part of head. Abdomen without *cornicles* at tip. *Wingless Bugs* **Hemiptera**
Proboscis arising from hind part of head. Abdomen often with two *cornicles* at or near its tip. *Aphids*
Homoptera

16. Abdomen with false legs (*pseudopods*), which are fleshy, and different from the jointed legs of the thorax. Caterpillar-like forms 17
Abdomen without any kind of legs 19

17. Five pairs of false legs, or fewer, with none on the first or second abdominal segments; these false legs have minute hooks (*crochets*) on their margins
Caterpillars of **Lepidoptera**
Six to ten pairs of false legs, and always one pair on *second* abdominal segment. No *crochets* present ... 18

18. Head with a single *ocellus* (small eye) on each side. *Larvæ of Sawflies* ... ... **Hymenoptera**
Head with several *ocelli* on each side. *Larvæ of Scorpion-flies* ... ... **Mecoptera**

19. *Antennæ* short and indistinct. Larvæ 20
Antennæ long and distinct. Adult insects 22

20. Body Caterpillar-like 21
Body not caterpillar-like. *Larvæ* of some **Neuroptera** and many **Coleoptera**

21. Head with six *ocelli* (small eyes) on each side
Caterpillars of some **Lepidoptera**
Head with more than six *ocelli*.
Larvæ of some **Mecoptera**

22. Abdomen with a pair of movable forceps at tip. *Earwigs* ... ... **Dermaptera**
Abdomen without such forceps 23

23. Abdomen strongly constricted at base into a 'waist'. Sometimes antennæ are bent into an elbow. *Ants and wingless Wasps* ... ... **Hymenoptera**
Abdomen not constricted into a waist 24

24. Head prolonged underneath body into a long beak, which bears mandibles at its tip. *Scorpionflies*
Mecoptera
Head not prolonged into a beak 25

25. Tiny soft insects 26
Fairly small, to very big, usually hard-bodied insect ... 27

26. *Cerci* absent. *Booklice* ... ... **Psocoptera**
Cerci present ... ... **Zoraptera**

27. Hind-legs enlarged for jumping. *Grasshoppers* and *Crickets* ... ... **Orthoptera (Saltatoria)**
Hind-legs not enlarged for jumping 28

28. *Tarsi* of legs with four segments. Pale, soft-bodied insects living in wood or soil. *Termites* ... **Isoptera**
Tarsi of legs with five segments. More highly coloured insects, living in the open, or domestically, but not in wood. *Cockroaches, Stick-insects, Leaf-insects*
Orthoptera (Dictyoptera and Phasmida)

29. Mouth-parts adapted for piercing. *Nymphs of Water-bugs* (**Hemiptera**) and *larvæ of some* **Neuroptera**
Mouth-parts adapted for licking and chewing 30

30. Body enclosed in a case made of pebbles, sand and debris. *Caddisflies* ... *larvæ of* **Trichoptera**
Not living in such a case 31

31. Abdomen with external *gills* 32
Abdomen without external gills 33

32. With two or three long processes at tip of abdomen (fig. 58). Trace of wing-cases in later instars. *Nymphs of Mayflies* ... ... **Ephemeroptera**

Only one process at tip of abdomen, and no wing-cases visible. *Alderflies* **Megaloptera (Sialioidea)**

33. Head with a 'mask', bearing the jaws, and capable of being extended forwards. Nymphs of *Dragonflies*
Odonata

Head without such a mask 34

34. With long *antennæ*; and long filaments at tip of abdomen. *Larvæ of Stoneflies* ... ... **Plecoptera**
Without such filaments. *Larvæ of Beetles* **Coleoptera**

IDENTIFICATION OF THE LOWER CATEGORIES OF INSECTS

The preceding 'Key to Orders' makes use of broad distinctions, such as 'mouth-parts adapted for chewing', and 'without any jointed legs'. Ordinary language will express most of these, without the need for a special vocabulary.

When we come to try to distinguish between families, genera and species, we have to go into greater detail, and so have not only to have more knowledge of the structure of the insects, but also to have to have special names for many details for which there are no names in common language.

There is such a great range of structure through the Class Insecta that it is impossible to give a simple account of all the structures that may be used in keys. A selection of some of the most important ones is given in the Glossary at the end of this book. There are, however, two parts of the body, the wings and the mouth-parts, which are so often mentioned in keys and descriptions of insects that it is desirable to try to give some simple account of these. In modern systematics of insects an increasing amount of attention is being paid to the structure of the appendages of the last three or four segments of the abdomen, known as the terminalia, or genitalia, but unfortunately there is as yet no standard terminology in different Orders, and so we cannot treat them in a book of this scope.

WING VENATION

The supporting ribs, or *veins*, of an insect's wing do not occur haphazardly, as they are so often shown in advertisements, or in cartoons. On the contrary they follow a precise plan, which is different in the different groups of insects, and which may often show small, but quite constant differences between closely related genera, or even species.

Obviously, before such differences can be studied some basic

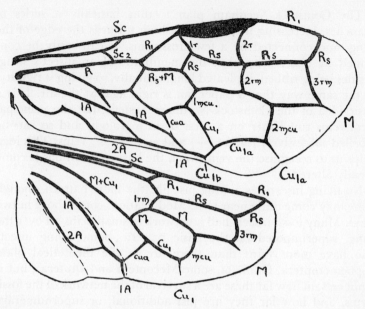

Figure 133. A complicated venational pattern: wings of a sawfly (Hymenoptera) as interpreted by Richards (1956).

plan must be recognised, and all the component parts given names. Unfortunately, it is easier to do this for a restricted group than for insects as a whole, and so a number of different systems are in existence, one for grasshoppers, one for bugs, one for Hymenoptera, one for butterflies, and so on. An attempt to provide a single system for all groups was made as long ago as 1898, and this, the Comstock-Needham System as it is called, can be applied with a varying amount of success in all Orders. It is least successful in Hymenoptera.

It will be remembered that the wings of insects are essentially flattened, sac-like outgrowths from the wall of the thorax (fig. 109), in which the upper and lower membranes have become pressed together. During development, before the wings are fully formed, the wing-bud is supplied with tracheae, and the Comstock-Needham System claims that the wing-veins are based upon the tracheae, which persist as hardened tubes running between the two membranes of the wing. Even in fully-grown insects the veins may contain both body-fluid, which can be seen pulsating, and air, which can be seen as a silvery band, like a thread of mercury, in slide-mounts of the wings.

The Comstock-Needham plan is thus basically a series of branches, increasing in twig-like fashion towards the edge of the wing, and connected by a few cross-veins. It can easily be confirmed by observation that the membrane of an insect's wing, besides being ribbed, is pleated longitudinally, so giving it rigidity, in the same way that a paper fan is rigid against the air. It is a basic idea of the Comstock-Needham System that the principal stem-veins run either on a crest or in a trough, and so can be labelled successively *positive* ($+$) and *negative* ($-$) veins. This idea helps us to recognise the veins when the basic pattern has become greatly altered.

No living insect has a wing just like the basic pattern, though some may come quite near to it. Modifications come about in two ways. Many fossil insects had a network of small veins all over the wing, superimposed on the basic pattern. Some living insects also have more veins than there are in the theoretical plan. (Ephemeroptera, Odonata, some Mecoptera and Diptera), but it is not certain how far these are a survival of the network of the fossil forms, and how far they are just additional, or supernumerary veins.

On the other hand, the very many modifications of wing-venation seen in living insects are mostly brought about by reduction, and can be explained—or described, which is perhaps not the same thing—as the loss of some veins by fading, and a merging of two or more branches into one.

Fig. 121 shows the hypothetical basic plan of the Comstock-Needham System, with the names and code-letters of the veins. There are three principal stem-veins: the *Radius* (R); the *Media* (M); and the *Cubitus* (Cu). The various branches of these occupy most of the area of the wing, and give the most characteristic features of its venation. The *costa*, though shown on the plan as separate vein, is really the stiffened fore-margin of the wing. Sometimes this thickening may extend all round the edge of the wing, but more often only the 'leading edge' is thickened, and the hind-margin, or 'trailing edge' is left without a support. It must make a difference in the operation of the wing in flight, whether the hind-margin is stiff or flexible, but I do not think anyone has compared the flight of the insects concerned to see exactly what is the effect.

Immediately behind the costa is a much weaker vein the *sub-costa*, which lies in a trough, and so is known as a *concave vein*. Veins R_1 and Cu_1 are usually strongly *convex*, standing on top of a definite ridge, and because of this fact they are easily recognised, forming landmarks from which the rest of the pattern can be identified. Vein M is a concave vein. Most authorities consider that a whole branch of this vein, known as MA, has disappeared in living insects, and that the remaining branch (MP) is divided into four; but some recent authorities claim that parts of MA exist, while some parts of the Radius (R) have vanished. The only reason for mentioning this here is that you may be confused in using a paper by these authors; if you do come across what seems to be confusion between M and R, check with a figure of wing-venation, either in the same paper, or in an earlier paper of the same author.

Behind vein Cu is the *anal area* of the wing, with a number of *anal veins*. This region, which is a highly flexible membranous area, concerned with the control of stability rather than with propulsion, is the most variable part of the wing. Look in turn at the hind-wings of Orthoptera (fig. 59), Ephemeroptera (figs. 58 and 126), Odonata (fig. 127) and Coleoptera (fig. 132). In consequence the anal veins are arranged according to practical needs rather than to an ancestral pattern.

The other wings shown in figs. 122–133 are labelled according to the Comstock-Needham System, and show how this system deals with veins that have united, or fused together. This is indicated by combining the code-letters: i.e. if R_4 and R_5 do not fork, but run to the margin as one vein, this vein is called R_{4+5}. If R_5 and M_1 meet before the margin, and continue as one vein, this is called $R_5 + M_1$.

The Comstock-Needham System is useful for purposes of comparison, to enable us to show how one group is related to another. As a code of reference it is useful in groups where the arrangement of the veins is fairly close to the hypothetical pattern. Where great modification has taken place, not only is there disagreement as to the correct letter for the remaining veins, but the letters that are finally agreed may be too cumbersome to use. For example, a recent author wants to call a vein in a fly's wing $R_5 + ir \ R_5 + R_4R_5 + R_4/R_5$. This sort of thing reduces the Comstock-Needham System to an absurdity.

Because of difficulties of this sort, specialists in a number of groups of insects prefer older systems, which are handier to use, but make it difficult to compare one group of insects with another. The figures 122, 123 are chosen to show two of these systems, and to give their equivalents on the Comstock-Needham System. These systems are often quite illogical: in Lepidoptera, for example, the veins that reach to the wing-margin are numbered in sequence from behind forwards; in Diptera they are numbered from the front backwards, but the numbers follow an obscure convention, so that in a mosquito 'the sixth vein' may actually be the tenth on the wing-margin.

It is unfortunate, too, that similar names are used differently in different systems. Thus the 'cubital vein' of some older systems is the Radius of Comstock-Needham, and not their Cubitus.

The veins divide up the membrane of the wing into areas that are called *cells*. The nomenclature of these is even more difficult than that of the veins. Comstock and Needham named each cell after the vein that forms its fore-border; some authors use capital letters for the veins and small letters for the cells, but it is best to avoid confusion by saying 'cell R_4', and so on. A more serious drawback is that in the wings of many insects the veins have been reduced in number by disappearance of some, and merging of others, and then to find the right name for the cells that are left is very difficult. In most groups of insects there is an old-fashioned system of arbitrary names for the cells—which are called 'first basal', 'second posterior' and so on—and it is usually best to use this, while keeping to the Comstock Needham system for the veins.

Preparing the wings for study

When an insect has been set the wings are preserved flat and horizontal, and are easily studied with a hand-lens or under a binocular microscope. The wings of Lepidoptera need to have the scales bleached, as described on p. 144. The wings of unset insects can be examined bit by bit by turning the specimen under the microscope, but for detailed examination, and especially for photography, one wing should be removed and mounted on a slide, as described in Chapter V.

MOUTH-PARTS

The mouth-parts of nearly all insects are modified from a common pattern. The *labrum*, or upper lip, and the *epipharynx*, which is sometimes part of it and sometimes separate, are really hinged parts of the head-capsule (the helmet-like case of the head) of the insect. The other mouth-parts are developed from the paired appendages of three segments of the head, and are called respectively the *mandibles*, the *maxillæ* and the *labium*: the last is a single structure produced by the union of what are in effect a second

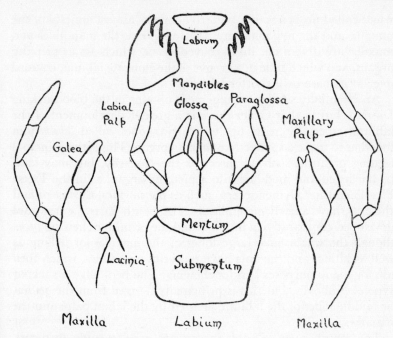

Figure 134. The mouth-parts of an insect of biting and chewing habit, showing the component parts from which all more specialised mouth-parts are developed.

pair of maxillæ. The labium forms the lower lip, and lying just above it is another single structure, the *hypopharynx*, which carries the salivary duct.

Fig. 134 shows the dissected mouth-parts of the cockroach, an omnivorous insect, whose mouth-parts are therefore built for general biting and chewing. The mandibles are strong, and well adapted for crushing food. A maxilla (and one-half of the labium, which is similar) consists essentially of two basal lobes and a multi-segmented appendage, called a *palp* (plural *palpi*). The caption to the figure gives the names of some of the other parts.

These various structures are extensively modified in different groups of insects, in close correlation with their feeding-habits. The extent of modification is least in chewing types such as beetles, and greatest in those which suck liquid-foods, such as bugs, butter-flies and fleas. In Lepidoptera, for instance, although a full set of generalised mouth-parts is present in the primitive MICROPTERY-GIDÆ (which are put in a separate Order by some authorities), the usual coiled proboscis of a butterfly consists almost entirely of the maxillæ and the hypopharynx. In Hemiptera, the mandibles and maxillæ are drawn out into grooved *stylets*, which act as piercing organs, and which slide in a groove of the elongate labium, covered over at its base by a shorter labrum.

An essentially similar arrangement obtains in the bloodsucking Diptera, but in that Order there is a greater development of the labium, especially at its tip, where two lobes called *labella* join together to make a sponge-like sucking organ. This is the principal feeding organ of such an insect as the Housefly, but may itself be hardened and modified into a piercing organ, as in the Tsetse Fly. The biting Hymenoptera, such as the sawflies, the wasps and the ants, have a fairly generalised set of mouth-parts: i.e. they are developed comparatively little beyond the primitive chewing type, though the wasps have large lobes of the maxillæ for licking as well as biting, and the ants have powerful mandibles, which they use for many purposes besides chewing. The bees have a sucking type of proboscis, but this is principally derived from the *glossae*, or middle lobes of the labium, assisted by the labial palpi and the maxillæ.

The mouth-parts of adult insects are easy to study in detail, because they are so easily cut off and made into slide-mounts. Since they reveal so much about the feeding-habits, and hence the way of life, of the living insect, the making of such preparations is well worth while.

The nymphs of the hemimetabolous insects, since they are generally smaller editions of the adults, often have much the same feeding mechanism. In Ephemeroptera, where all the feeding is done in the nymphal stages, it is the nymph that has the complete mouth-parts, while those of the adult are reduced almost to vanishing-point. The voracious nymphs of dragon-flies have the labium modified into an extensible mask, which can be shot out to seize the prey.

On the other hand, the larvæ of the exopterygote insects are very different from the adults, both in habits and in structure, and the mouth-parts show a corresponding range of variation. The larvæ of beetles, like the adults, have mouth-parts of the mandibulate, or chewing type, occasionally modified for sucking as in *Dytiscus*. The rapacious larvæ of the ant-lions (Neuroptera) have sickle-like mandible and maxillæ, for piercing and sucking their prey. In contrast to these well-developed types, the legless larvæ of the Diptera and Hymenoptera have the mandibles reduced

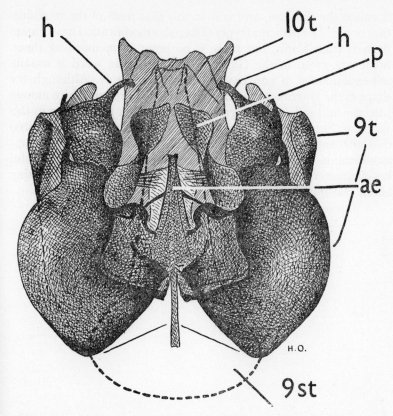

Figure 135. Genitalia of a male robber-fly (Diptera), showing the
component parts derived from the ninth and tenth segments. 9t, 10t,
tergites; 9st., ninth sternite; ae, aedeagus; p, paramere; h, hooked
process of ninth tergite.

to mere hooks, and in the higher Diptera the true mouth-parts are
replaced by a 'cephalopharyngeal skeleton', the origin of which is
a matter of dispute.

THE ANTENNAE

The structure of the antennæ is greatly used in the detailed
classification of insects. The range of possible variation in antennæ
is almost unlimited, and it is impossible to summarise it here. The
important point to remember is that the first two segments have
special names (*scape* and *pedicel*), and in most insects these segments have an individuality of their own. The rest of the antenna

is called the *flagellum*, and it is in this that most of the modification occur. The principal types of flagellar modification have names derived from Latin, but there is no point in memorising them. Some are given in the Glossary, but the Latin word is usually self-explanatory, if you have a dictionary handy. Although the shape of the antenna sometimes gives a clue to relationships among insects—and indeed large groups of beetles get their name in this way, e.g. Superfamily LAMELLICORNIA—it should be remembered that the antenna is a sensory organ, and is subject to abrupt modification between closely related groups. It is a very useful key-character, but needs to be used cautiously when theorising about classification.

XI

FURTHER READING

A schoolfellow of mine once asked the mathematics master: 'Sir, is there any geometry beyond our book?' I do not remember whether the reply filled him with anticipation or despair, but I am certain that the volume of writing about geometry that lay ahead of him could be only a small fraction of the immense literature about insects. I hope that the present volume will have aroused your interest to the point at which you want more information about the insects that you have caught, and about the great number that still await your net. In this chapter I shall mention a number of sources of further information, and the full details of these works are given in the list of References.

Many of the works that you will read concern the insects of some particular part of the world, so before going on to the works themselves it may be helpful to give a rough outline of the standard divisions, or Zoogeographical Regions, into which the world is divided for the purpose of the study of animals. The study of the distribution of insects is a fascinating link with geography, climatology and history. Collecting insects is a necessary first step towards working in this field, and conversely a sound classification of insects can be worked out only if their geographical distribution is known and properly interpreted.

ZOOGEOGRAPHICAL REGIONS

The major Regions are shown in Map I. A striking point about them is that the oceans and seas are not nearly so great a barrier to distribution as the deserts of the world. Thus we have:

1. PALAEARCTIC REGION. Europe, Asia and North Africa, down to the desert belt that includes the Sahara, the Arabian and Persian Deserts, and those of Central China.

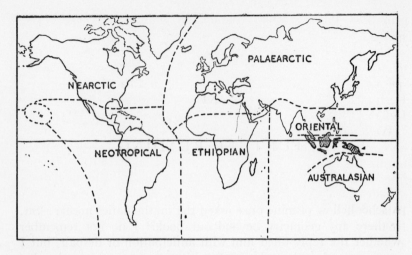

Map I. The six Zoogeographical Regions, the main divisions of the world so far as animals and plants are concerned. The islands of the South Pacific are linked mainly with the Australasian Region, and to some extent with the Oriental. The volcanic islands of the Hawaiian group belong to none of the Regions, but present an interesting problem in insect migration and colonisation. As stated in the text, there is much overlapping on the borders of the Regions, especially in the Austro-Oriental Region, shown shaded.

2. NEARCTIC REGION. The American continent down to the deserts of the United States/Mexico border.

3. NEOTROPICAL REGION. The whole of South America.

4. ETHIOPIAN REGION. All Africa south of the Sahara, plus Madagascar, Southern Arabia, and the islands connecting the two.

5. ORIENTAL REGION. A Region centred on India, the Malayan Peninsula, Indo-China and Indonesia, but with rather ill-defined boundaries in all directions, and overlapping considerably with the next.

6. AUSTRALASIAN REGION. Australia and New Zealand, and the island groups of the South Pacific.

These six major Regions are useful for general purposes, but there is a good deal of overlapping of their borders. Our point about the incomplete barrier that an ocean makes is shown by the fact that many insects are *Holarctic* in distribution, that is, they range right round the world north of the subtropical deserts. The beautiful bee-fly, *Bombylius major*, which hovers over the primroses and wild violets in England in spring is one of these species.

The Middle East, from Libya to Baluchistan, from the Caspian to Aden, is a cross-roads for insects as it is for humans. African species can be seen in the Jordan Valley, and Palaearctic ones in Kashmir. Oriental species often spread round the shores of the Indian Ocean, down through the Seychelles to Madagascar.

We have still to mention the Polar Regions. These can hardly be said to have their own insect fauna in a truly Regional sense, but instead, the severity of the climate puts its own pattern on the insects. In these conditions we find large numbers of individuals of only a few species. The Arctic insects are clearly part of the Palaearctic or Nearctic fauna, with a high proportion that are Holarctic (see above). In the Antarctic the climate is more severe, and the places where insects can live are further apart. Here we see the effects of extreme isolation, and small groups of wind-swept islands have a few insects, which are often wingless or have reduced wings; this development is often found among insects that live in a precarious situation, where active flight might cause them to be blown away.

The BRITISH ISLES are an outlying part of the Palaearctic Region, and nearly all the insects that occur here are also found on the adjoining continent. In general those of southern England are like those of France, Holland and Belgium, while those of Scotland often occur in Denmark and Scandinavia. A few seem to be related to the insects of Spain and Portugal, and a very few species (and rather more sub-species and local forms) are found only in the British Isles.

If we cross to the continent of Europe we shall see most of our native British insects, together with many others that are never seen here, or occur only as scarce migrants. This fauna of which we are a part is that of the North-Western Sub-region of the Palaearctic Region; the western Mediterranean has a sub-regional fauna of its own; another one occurs in the eastern Mediterranean, and the fauna changes again as we go on into Asia.

WORKS ON BRITISH INSECTS

The collector of British insects will want to begin with a popular or semi-popular book on British insects in general, or on one particular Order.

For all the British insects there is an excellent introduction in

Moreton (1950), who gives a list of recommended books about each Order. The list published by the Systematics Association (1953) is also very useful.

The Royal Entomological Society of London, in its series of 'Handbooks for the Identification of British Insects', will one day cover all the British insects, but this will not be complete for a very long time, since it is difficult to find authors who are able to prepare parts on the more difficult groups. The Registrar of the Society, 41 Queen's Gate, London, S.W.7, will supply a list of the parts already published.

Popular works rely on plates, often coloured, and on a simple classification and an easily understood Key. To be able to do this they have to confine themselves to the more distinctive insects, and those which can be recognised from their general appearance. Any work that tries to include all, or even the majority, of the known species has to go into greater detail, and at once becomes harder to use, and more confusing to a beginner. You cannot have it both ways. Amateur collectors of insects often suspect—and sometimes say—that the professionals make their keys difficult just to show how clever they are; the professionals retort that if they knew a simpler classification they would use it.

Where there is no suitable work in English, the British insects can often be identified with the help of Continental works. The *Faune de France* series has grown to an immense size over the years, and covers most groups of insects. So do the *Tierwelt Deutschlands* and the *Tierwelt Mitteleuropas*. Besides these works on a big scale there are many Continental works on a limited group, say the Dragon-flies of the Bernese Oberland, which can be traced through the Zoological Record, as described below.

TEXT-BOOKS OF ENTOMOLOGY

If your interest extends further afield, to one of the bigger and more sparsely populated continents, to matters concerning the insects of the world, or to general problems concerning all groups of insects, then a compact work of this kind may not exist. Then you have to start somewhere to collect the information you need, and a *text-book of entomology* is a good place to start. If you do not own one you will probably be able to see one in a Reference Library, or get your local library to get one for you from the National Central Library.

The standard British text-book is Imms's *General Text-book of*

Entomology, of which an up-to-date revision by Richards and Davies has just appeared. The American text-book by Borror and Delong (1954) is a rival volume, and comparison of the two is interesting. Imms is tremendously learned, and makes you feel that nothing ever published on entomology can have escaped his notice. On the other hand, no one would call Imms an enticing author (at least in the editions that appeared in his lifetime). I once knew a student who claimed to have read Imms from cover to cover, but he was odd in other ways too. Borror and Delong is a much more readable book, but is frankly American in outlook, and gives only a passing glance at the rest of the world. So you have a choice of a stiff dose of facts from Imms, or a sweeter, but less effective pill from Borror and Delong.

MONOGRAPHS AND PERIODICALS

The works we have mentioned so far are always either incomplete or out-of-date. People commonly assume that all, or nearly all the insects of the world have been discovered long ago, and that the discovery of a new one is a rare event. If this were so it would be a comparatively easy task to collect all the facts about, say, the British Insects, and put them into a popular book; and with rather more labour, to write a text-book on insects in general. In fact, very large numbers of new genera and species are described every year, and a great many papers on classification, identification, biology and distribution are published. You will find, therefore, that as soon as you become interested in one small group of insects, first the popular book, and then the general text-book will fail to satisfy you, and you will want more detailed, and more up-to-date, information.

For this you will have to go to original papers, which give new information for the first time. If these are big enough they are published separately as a book, bound or unbound. Some bigger papers, and most smaller ones, are sent to one of the entomological or zoological periodicals. A paper which deals thoroughly with one topic—the world species of one genus, for example—is called a monograph in whatever form it may be published.

We have seen in the last chapter that 'publication' means in effect printing and offering for sale. Anyone is free to do this, in any language, and consequently it might seem to be an impossible task to track down every paper that may appear on the group in which you are interested. Fortunately, because of the high cost of

T

printing, and the small profits to be made out of this sort of publishing, there is a limit to the number of places where papers may be published.

Most original descriptions of new genera and species, records of distribution and occurrence, and keys for the identification of particular groups, appear in the first instance in fairly short 'papers' in a periodical. The problem of finding these is greatly simplified by two key works.

The Zoological Record

This is an annual volume, published under the direction of the Zoological Society of London; the *Insecta* part, the biggest single section, is prepared by the Commonwealth Institute of Entomology, 56 Queen's Gate, London, S.W.7. Recorders comb through all likely periodicals, and receive copies of nearly all the relevant monographs and books. The information extracted is arranged in the Zoological Record in three sections.

The first is a list of all the papers and books, arranged alphabetically under authors' names, and numbered serially. Then the same papers are grouped according to subject, so that if you want to know about anatomy, or parasitism, or the insects of South America, you can see the year's new work at a glance. Finally comes the systematic section, in which all new genera and species described during the year are arranged in a classified list, with exact reference, down to the page-number.

The Record comes out once a year, and nowadays is from one to two years in arrear; at the time of writing, December 1956, the latest published volume is for the year 1954.

If you want to take up the study of a particular group of insects it is a useful beginning to go to a library where the Zoological Record can be seen, and to sit down and make from it a card-index of all the species and genera in your group, with references, right back to the last monograph or catalogue. In many families of Diptera, for example, the *Catalogus Dipterorum* of Kertész (1906–8) listed all the genera and species known at that date, and so your card-index can run from the *Catalogus* to the present day. The Zoological Record began in 1862.

The World List of Scientific Periodicals

The Zoological Record gives abbreviated titles of the periodicals concerned, but does not tell you the full titles, nor where the periodical can be seen. For this you need the *World List of Scientific*

Periodicals, which will almost certainly be available in the same library. This great tome lists not only the entomological and zoological periodicals, but many technical and trade journals, which can only dimly be called scientific.

In addition to the full title, place of publication, and years during which the journal has run, the World List gives two other valuable pieces of information. One is the 'World List Abbreviation', which is accepted as standard by the Zoological Record, and by most editors and authors. The general principles of shortening the names are mostly what one would expect, except for an odd fad that words in the title that are adjectives must begin with a small letter: thus 'Annals and Magazine of Natural History' becomes *Ann. Mag. nat. Hist.* Apart from pleasing those who like rules, this serves no useful purpose: if you observe it you will please the editor and confuse the printer's reader.

The World List also tells you, most helpfully, which libraries in Britain take the periodical in question. This is a great boon, especially to the person who works alone, as he need not waste time in applying to the wrong libraries.

REVIEWS AND ABSTRACTS

Complete lists of what has been published are all very well, but they do not also supply the time to read all the papers they mention. Moreover, the Zoological Record is mainly concerned with 'pure' entomology, and of necessity omits a much larger number of papers on applied entomology, eradication of pests, application of insecticides, and so on. The Commonwealth Institute of Entomology also publishes the *Review of Applied Entomology* in two series, A (Agricultural) and B (Medical). If you work through the index of this *Review* you will find that there is very little in applied entomology that is not mentioned, in title, at least, and generally as an abstract or a review.

The Americans publish *Biological Abstracts*, which is something between the *Record* and the *Review*.

PUBLICATIONS IN FOREIGN LANGUAGES

Entomological papers may be published in any modern language, or in Latin, so that if you do much reading about insects you are bound to come upon problems of translation.

By far the greatest number of entomological papers are written in English, German, French or Latin, and for serious study of insects you need a little knowledge of these four. The standard required is not very high. Descriptive papers, and works of identification, are usually written in an artificial, telegraphic style in all languages (as far as I know: I would not dare to say that this is true of Chinese or Japanese), and many of the technical words have a familiar look about them. In Latin, for instance, there is much use of ablative absolute (*pedibus rufis* and so on), and the style is the blunt style of Caesar, not the elegance of Horace. It can easily be hacked out with a dictionary.

Many Latin or Greek words are transferred bodily into the other three principal languages, as you will see if you look at the Glossary at the end of this book. Very little knowledge of grammar and syntax is needed, so long as you confine yourself to reading keys and descriptions, but discussions, and accounts of biology and habits, give the author scope to spread himself more. Most trouble comes from adverbs, especially in English and German: it makes a lot of difference whether a structure is said to be 'greatly', 'slightly', 'conspicuously', 'seldom', or 'always' developed.

Most English students will have enough French for this purpose, and the necessary German is easily learned at home. *Basic German for Science Students*, by M. L. Barker (Oliver and Boyd, 1957) is excellent. Latin helps in understanding Italian, Spanish and Portuguese, while German helps one to make a guess at the other teutonic languages, Dutch, Flemish, Danish, Norwegian, Swedish, and Afrikaans.

A fifth major entomological language is Russian, and here the alphabet is the great obstacle. Russian authors normally use Roman print for the names of genera and species. Before the Revolution they often wrote in French, and at various times since they have given summaries in German, French or English. Recently, however, many papers, dealing with a fauna of great entomological importance over a big area of Asia, are entirely in Russian, except for the names of the insects. If we are not to have two lots of people studying the insects of the world independently, we shall either have to learn each other's language, or set up a really efficient translation service.

Meanwhile, the Commonwealth Institute of Entomology does provide abstracts of the Russian papers available to it, and the Department of Scientific and Industrial Research from time to time publishes a 'Translated Title-list of Russian Periodicals'.

REPRINTS, OR SEPARATA

Articles and papers in entomological periodicals are not normally paid for in cash. It is generally considered that the Society that publishes the paper is doing a service to the author, as well as to entomology in general, by doing so, and the only material return to him is a number of free copies of his work. This is usually either twenty-five or fifty, and more can usually be bought by the author at a reduced price, provided that he orders them before the paper is printed.

Reprints (or separata) should have the same page-numbers as in the original volume, so that they can be used in every way as an authentic copy for purposes of reference. The author can give his copies away to anyone who is interested, and receive in return reprints of papers by them. In this way each can built up a set of the papers dealing with the insects in which he is interested, and need not keep borrowing the periodical from a library.

If you see an article that interests you you may write to the author, addressing him care of the periodical, if you do not know his personal address, and ask for a separate. But remember that he has only a few, and do not ask for one unless you really need it. Some young students make a collection of reprints on all manner of subjects, like collecting autographs or matchboxes. This is selfish as well as silly, since it may deprive someone who really needs the paper.

XII

RECORDING NEW FACTS, AND
DESCRIBING NEW SPECIES

You will not get far in studying insects before you find out something that no one seems to have noticed before. If you take up almost any group of insects, except perhaps the butterflies and the bigger moths, you will be astonished to find how little is really known about them with certainty and precision. It is natural to think that 'the expert' knows everything, but you can ask quite simple questions and be told, apologetically, that in fact no one actually knows the answer. 'Where do flies go in the winter-time?' is a Music Hall joke, but the most up-to-date monograph on the housefly cannot do better than give you a list of five possibilities.

However modestly you start out with the feeling of being a beginner, anxious only to learn from the experts, sooner or later you will have some information that you feel compelled to pass on to other people. It is like writing letters to the papers: all of us feel sometimes so amazed at the blindness and perversity of other letter-writers that we cannot resist the impulse to join in.

WHEN, AND WHAT, TO PUBLISH

It is true to say that too much is written and published about insects. Printing in the average entomological journal costs upwards of four pounds per page, and is increasing all the time, so that quite a moderately long paper of 20–30 pages means a capital outlay by the publishing Society of about £100. Even though some of this may be recovered by the sales of the periodical, it is obvious that no Society can afford to print all the manuscripts that may be submitted to it.

Many entomologists, especially professional ones, would say that a work like the present one should discourage publication because the journals are overcrowded already. I think that is bad advice. It is not that we have too many papers written, but that we have not enough good ones. Already some very able entomologists are so reluctant to 'rush into print' that they spend a lifetime studying a group without committing their discoveries to print: or, worse still, they put out only an occasional fragment which makes the surrounding darkness more obscure. One entomologist is reputed to have said that he would not publish his findings because it would deprive others of the pleasure of finding out for themselves!

This is a dog-in-the-manger attitude, and an easy way of getting a reputation for knowledge without running the risk of being found out. It is also wasteful of time if other people have to cover the same ground again.

In this, as in most activities, a middle course is needed. Do not rush into print with every trivial observation, but do not hoard your knowledge in a miserly way until it dies with you.

Undoubtedly, the most valuable papers to write are those which take a limited subject and clarify it. Entomology has grown so big that it is now no longer possible to be an expert in many different groups of insects; even within one Order there is work for very many lifetimes. The first essential is to be able to limit your subject, not to be baffled or confused by the immensity of the field of knowledge, but to pick out one family, one genus, one small group of species, and study them thoroughly and precisely.

Be tidy. Do not jump from one thing to another, but collect your facts in an orderly way, and file them away properly. This is a card-index age, so acquire the habit, literally. Almost any kind of information, descriptions, keys, references, drawings, can all be written on standard 5 × 3 in. index cards: this book has been entirely written on such cards. Do not make notes on odd scraps of paper, or in old exercise books. Stick to the cards, file them in an orderly arrangement, and assemble them with a definite purpose in view. In this way a paper such as a review of a small group of insects, or a monograph of a Family, will build itself up almost painlessly. Moreover, if you do fail to get to the point of publication before you die, things will be much easier for your entomological executor.

It is true that sometimes it is desirable, if not essential, to publish very short notes, giving a small fragment of information. If you take a particular insect under very unusual circumstances, at quite the wrong time of year, or behaving in an unfamiliar way, there may be no prospect of keeping the information and working it up into a larger study. In the same way all of us now and then may justifiably describe a single new species, or a new genus founded upon a single specimen, if these are sufficiently rare and outstanding. I recently described a wingless fly from one of the sub-antarctic islands of New Zealand, because wingless flies are rare and interesting, and because people seldom collect in the sub-antarctic islands. I also described a single new species from a well-frequented part of Africa, because it had been discovered in the course of medical research work, and people wanted it to have a name so that they could talk about it.

Do not describe new species just for the pleasure of seeing your name as author. Describing one's first new species is an adventure, but like all adventures it is cheapened by too much repetition. Before starting to describe new species, every entomologist should read the Obituary Notice of Francis Walker, published in the *Entomologists' Monthly Magazine* for 1874, Vol. 11, p. 140.

Above all, do not take up valuable printing space with papers about nomenclature. Writing about names is not entomology. Professional entomologists sometimes cannot avoid doing so, just as they cannot escape other unprofitable chores, but if you are an entomologist for love, and not for money, give your time to the insects.

WHERE AND HOW TO PUBLISH

Consider where a paper is likely to be acceptable before you write it. Study *The Entomologists Monthly Magazine*, *The Entomologist*, *The Entomologists' Record*, *The Annals and Magazine of Natural History*, and the *Proceedings* and *Transactions* of the *Royal Entomological Society of London*, the *South London Entomological and Natural History Society*, and the *Society for British Entomology*. If you live in the north, look at the *Naturalist*, the *North-Western Naturalist* and the *Scottish Naturalist*, and in other countries ask the librarian for the corresponding local entomological periodicals.

Read carefully the Instructions to Authors, which are generally printed on the paper wrappers, and bound up at the front or back of the year's volume. Find out whether papers are accepted only from members or subscribers; from anyone who is introduced, or 'presented' by a member; or without any restrictions.

You will soon realise that every periodical has its own character. One will cater mainly for records of occurrences of butterflies and moths, effects of the weather on early and late appearances, and accounts of collecting excursions. Such a journal will give space to brief notes of a line or two recording a single interesting observation. Another will take only papers of a moderate length, setting out formal descriptions of new genera and species. Yet another may have mainly papers on biology and habits, or those dealing with insects of agricultural or medical and veterinary importance. It is a waste of your time, as well as the Editor's, to send your paper to a journal that does not print communications of that particular kind.

You know what it is you want to write about; you have examined the periodicals, and selected one that seems to be appropriate; the next step is to study the style of your chosen journal and model your paper on it. Notice how such a paper is set out. Sometimes it is enough just to give the new facts, observations of descriptions as concisely as possible, and in that case you will do well to be brief. At other times it is necessary to introduce the paper with some background information before the significance of the new facts can be appreciated. As a general rule authors write too much rather than too little, yet it is a loss if useful facts are lost because the author was not allowed enough space to explain their significance. Those who will quote to you a terrible jingle about 'boil it down' are viewing matters from the editor's standpoint, not the author's, nor the reader's.

At this point let me say again that a paper ought to be freshly written for publication, and not adapted. I have in mind, particularly, the Ph.D. thesis. Examiners for this degree are often required to certify that the thesis deserves to be published, or even to recommend that it should be published. The author, encouraged by his professor, feels that so much hard work ought not to be wasted, so he sends off one of his copies to an editor.

A degree thesis is seldom suitable for publication. It is written to satisfy examiners who are assumed—sometimes correctly—to be out of touch with everything except their own speciality, and to be unwilling to give the candidate credit for any knowledge at all. Consequently the thesis patiently plods all round the subject, trying to forestall all the supplementary questions that the examiners might ask. Tables are given on the smallest excuse, even quoting from the almanacs.

If you send this sort of thesis to an editor he is bound to point out that the proportion of original matter is small. Sometimes, if he is unwise, he will try to help you to prune it, but this is essentially hopeless, and will not give a creditable paper. The proper course is to go through the thesis ruthlessly, picking out only what is really new. Then write this up again in the style of an appropriate journal, giving only such background as is strictly necessary to support the new work, and you will make a compact little paper out of it.

Manuscripts should be typed, with double spacing, on one side of the paper only. Do not make the excuse that you are not a good typist. A perfect typescript looks nice, but if it is accepted, the printer will send it back to you covered with inky thumb-prints and tea-stains. It is sufficient that the editor and the compositor should be able to understand clearly your intentions. On the other hand, if you submit a paper in longhand it will probably be refused, since the printer is likely to charge extra because of the slowing down of the compositor's output; and if it is accepted, you will be driven to fury by the absurd misreadings of your perfectly legible handwriting.

Try to save the editor's time by setting out paragraphs, cross-headings and references in the style used in the particular journal. If the journal puts names of countries in capitals, do the same in your typescript. In particular, do follow the arrangement of references most carefully. Editors are very fussy about keeping these uniform, because it improves the appearance of the periodical. Use the abbreviated titles given in the World List of Scientific Periodicals: if you cannot see the List, get the List of Periodicals in the Library of the Royal Entomological Society of London, and follow that. If the journal puts the years between brackets in its references, do the same. It is useless to be obstinate, and will only lead to argument and errors, because once a set of references has been set out in print it is one of the most difficult of all compositions to alter or correct.

Observe the rules about illustrations. If your journal does not accept half-tone plates (i.e. photographs) without special arrangements, do not send any illustrations except line drawings in ink. Sometimes half-tone work is accepted if you pay extra for it, but do not assume as a matter of course that this is so. Make sure that your drawings are of a size and shape that will reduce to fit on to a page without wasting space, and do not send either small, thumbnail sketches, or enormous drawings full of fine detail that will be lost on reduction (see above, Chapter VI).

When labour was cheap, authors used to be advised to send in the individual drawings on small pieces of paper or board, with the lettering, and even the shading, indicated roughly in pencil.

The blockmaker's artist would then arrange the figures into plates, and do all the lettering with professional neatness. Now the high cost of such services means that you must do your own hand-work, and try to submit figures that are in every way ready to go to the blockmaker.

You may number each separate drawing, or you may number each group that will form one block, and give letters to the separate parts. Thus, if you want to show the heads of four species for comparison, they may be numbered 'Figs. 1–4', or 'Fig. 1A, B, C, D'. In the former case you have to insert the number 1, 2, 3, 4 on the drawing, so that they become parts of the block; in the latter case it is the letters A, B, C, D that are inserted. The letters may be printed in Indian ink, using a stencil as a guide, or you may cut out printed letters and figures and stick them in place.

Note that the legends of the figures—i.e. the captions, or explanatory remarks that appear below them—are not a part of the block, but are set up in ordinary type by the compositor. You should type all the legends, correctly numbered, at the end of your manuscript. It is permissible to write them lightly in pencil on the backs of the drawings for purposes of reference, but make it clear to the blockmaker that you do not expect him to add these as lettering to the figure.

You will usually be sent a set of galley-proofs, long strips of paper in which the text is continuous, without division into pages. Read these very carefully several times. You will find that it is difficult to take in the sense of what you read, and at the same time to notice printer's errors, because in general reading we do not examine each word carefully letter by letter. So try to do first one and then the other; to read first for meaning and then for mistakes. G. K. Chesterton pointed out that the easiest place in which to hide anything is where people would least expect to find it, that is in full view. This applies to printer's errors, so be very careful in checking the big print, the main headings, the title, and of course your own name; a recent massive volume dedicated to the honour of a distinguished entomologist had his name wrongly spelled on the frontispiece.

While it is possible to alter, delete from, or add to papers that are in proof, the printers will charge extra for doing this, and you will be unpopular with the editor. At first it is hard to visualise from the typescript how your paper is going to look in print, and when you see a proof you will wish you had arranged it differently.

Do not get into the bad habit of relying on alterations in galley-proof, but take special care to do all your planning on the typescript.

After the galley-proof has been corrected by the author and the editor, it is sent back to the printer, who makes corresponding alterations in his type, mounts the blocks in their proper places, and divides the whole thing up into pages. You will not necessarily see a page-proof of a short paper in a journal, but you will probably get one for a longer paper, or a book. Corrections in page-proof are much more troublesome than in galley, because there is no room to allow the text to be lengthened or shortened; consequently every letter that you wish to add or to take out has to be compensated for in another place on the same page.

Papers accepted for publication in an entomological journal are not generally paid for, at least in cash. Usually the author is given a number of free reprints: twenty-five is the most usual number, sometimes fifty; a few journals give none at all. If you want more than this they can usually be supplied at a reduced rate, provided that you order them when you send back the proofs, so that the printer can run them off economically when he is printing the journal, or at some other time that is convenient to him. The copyright of a scientific article generally lies with the publishers of the journal, and if you want to use any of it again you should get their permission. This is normally given freely, and there is an arrangement by which certain journals agree to waive some of the formalities among themselves. The law of copyright, however, is a difficult one, and if you feel that you may wish to retain rights in the text or illustrations of a paper you are going to write it is best to consult the publishers of the journal before you submit it.

APPENDICES

SOME USEFUL FORMULAE AND
REAGENTS

A.G.A. mixture

95% alcohol, 8 parts; distilled water, 5 parts; glycerine, 1 part; glacial acetic acid, 1 part.

Bouin's fixative

Saturated solution of picric acid in water, 30 parts; 40% formaldehyde, 10 parts; glacial acetic acid, 2 parts.

Caustic Potash

Potassium hydroxide (KOH) is bought in pellets or in sticks and is dissolved in water to give approximately a 10% solution: 5 gm. solid in 50 c.c. is near enough. The solid is likely to burn the skin, and rot clothing, and is of course very poisonous if taken. If not kept in a tightly corked jar it absorbs carbon dioxide from the atmosphere and becomes coated with potassium carbonate. The 10% solution is less caustic, but if spilled it should be immediately diluted with plenty of water, and mopped up with an old rag. The solution has a slightly soapy feeling on the skin, which should be washed until this feeling is gone. Take great care when boiling potash, and do not splash it either on to the skin or on to paintwork or fabrics.

Cedar-wood Oil

An alternative to clove oil as a clearing agent. Does not stain, nor harden, and will clear from 95% alcohol.

Chloral hydrate

Used in 5% solution. The insect is slit open and warmed in this solution, but not boiled, for one minute. Drain on blotting-paper, put in fresh solution, and change this after one week.

Embalming Fluid

Xylol, 60 c.c.; 3% butyl alcohol, 25 c.c.; ethyl alcohol, 15 c.c.; phenol, 5 grams; paradichlorbenzene, 20 grams; Canada balsam in xylol, 10 drops. Inject this mixture with a hypodermic, pushing it first to the far end of the insect and slowly withdrawing it while injecting fluid. (B M. *Instructions for Collectors*, 1954, p. 143.)

APPENDICES

Euparal

A compound mountant sold by Flatters and Garnett. Having a refractive index of 1.483 (Canada balsam = 1.536) it gives better contrast with very transparent tissues. It also clears, so can be used straight from alcohol, without the need for clove oil or other clearing agent. It should be thinned with the special medium (euparal essence).

Fuchsin

Acid or basic fuchsin are dyes bought in the solid state, and used in solution, generally in 20% alcohol.

Gum Chloral (de Faure's medium)

Distilled water, 50 c.c.; gum arabic, 30 grams; glycerine, 20 c.c.; chloral hydrate, 50 grams.

Isopropyl alcohol

Is sometimes used instead of ethyl alcohol, because there is no excise trouble. Mixes in all proportions with xylol, cedar-wood oil, and water.

Pampel's fluid

Glacial acetic acid, 4 c.c.; distilled water, 30 c.c.; formaldehyde (40%), 6 c.c.; 95% alcohol, 15 c.c. Van Emden halves the quantity of acetic acid.

Picro-chlor-acetic fixative

1% picric acid in 95% alcohol (industrial methylated spirit), 12 parts (volume); chloroform, 2 parts; glacial acetic acid, 1 part. Fix for 12 hours, rinse in several changes of 80% alcohol, and preserve in 80% alcohol.

Polyvinyl lactophenol

Polyvinyl alcohol, 2.5 grams; distilled water, 12–20 c.c.; lactophenol solution, 25–32 c.c. The polyvinyl alcohol is obtainable in varying viscosities, and the quantities of the other two constituents are increased according to the viscosity used; this gives a medium of decreasing refractive index. Also used as a clearing agent.

Wood Naphtha

Useful as a relaxing agent.

GLOSSARY OF TERMS AS USED IN
ENTOMOLOGY

abdomen. The third of the principal divisions of the body in insects.

acephalous. Without a distinct head.

aculeate. (*a*) With a sting (Hymenoptera). (*b*) With minute bristles under the scales of the wing (Microlepidoptera).

acuminate. Tapering to a long point.

adfrontal. Areas or structures adjoining the frons, or forehead.

adventitious vein. One that is not part of the regular plan, but appears in either one species, or a single individual; or the result of two or more true veins happening to be in line with one another.

aestivation. Being dormant during the hot, or dry season.

agamic. Reproducing without mating, e.g. parthenogenetically, or paedogenetically.

alula. The outermost lobe at the base of the wing (fig. 122).

alveolate. Having cells, or alveoli; deeply pitted.

amphipneustic (larvæ). Having functional spiracles only on the first abdominal segment, and the last one, or two.

amplexiform (wing-coupling). Brought about by extensive overlapping of the two wings.

anal. (*a*) Of the abdomen: concerning the last segment, which bears the anus. (*b*) Of the wing: the area behind the cubitus, and the veins belonging to it.

annulate(d). Bearing rings, or arranged in the form of an annulus or ring.

annulus. A ring-like marking, or a ring of hard cuticle.

anus. The posterior opening of the intestine.

antenna. One of a pair of appendages of the head, above or before the mouth-opening; the feelers.

anterior. Nearer to the head of the insect, or facing in that direction.

aphidivorous. Feeding on Aphids (greenfly).

apical. At or towards the apex, or tip of any part of the insect.

apodeme. A ridge or shelf of the body-wall, projecting inwards, acting as a stiffening rib, and as an attachment for muscles (cf. *phragma*, and see fig. 109).

apodus. Without true legs (fig. 120).

appendage. Any attachment to the body that is hinged to the head, thorax or abdomen by a joint; antennæ, legs, wings, and so on.

appendix. Any attachment; particularly used of a short, stump-like vein.

apterous. Without wings.

apterygote. Belonging to the Apterygota, or insects whose ancestors have always been wingless.

aquatic. Living in water, either fresh or salt; in practice salt-water forms are usually described as marine.

arcuate. Bent like a bow.

areole. A cell of the wing in some Lepidoptera, between veins R_3 and R_4.

arista. A bristle-like structure arising from the antenna in some Diptera.

arolium. A pad-like structure at the tip of the foot, between the claws.

articulated. United by a joint, as in a leg.

aspirator. A sucking-tube (see Plate II).

atrophied. Reduced in size; withered away.

attenuate(d). Drawn out and made thin.

auditory organs. Organs by which an insect can hear sounds, or perceive vibrations.

basad. Towards the base, and away from the tip or apex.

basitarsus. The first segment of the tarsus; sometimes, erroneously, called the 'metatarsus'.

bifid. Double; divided into two parts, or lobes.

bifurcate. Forked; divided into two, but usually only partly so (see *bifid*).

biramous (of limbs). Having two branches.

blade. A flat, thin structure; especially used of mouth-parts and antennæ.

bucca. A part of the head below the eyes; the jowl.

buccal cavity. The mouth-opening.

bulla. A blister-like structure; a weak point on a wing-vein.

callus. Any rounded swelling (see *tubercle*).

camera lucida. An apparatus for drawing with the microscope (Plate XIV).

campodeiform. Long, flattish, with well-developed legs and antennæ, like the genus *Campodea* (*Thysanura*); used for a type of larva.

canthariasis. Condition arising when beetle larvæ live in the body of another animal (cf. *myiasis*).

capitate. Having a knob.

carina. A ridge, or raised keel.

carnivorous. Feeding on the flesh of other animals, including other insects. 'Cannibalistic', usually only when an insect feeds on others of its own species.

caterpillar. The larva of Lepidoptera, Mecoptera and sawflies.

caudad. Towards the anus, or posterior tip of the body.

cell. An area of wing enclosed between several veins, or between veins and the wing-margin.

cercus (pl. *cerci*). One of a pair of appendages at the tip of the abdomen.

chaeta. A stiff hair, or thin bristle (see *seta*).

chitin. A principal constituent of the hard skin of an insect; often used rather inaccurately for any piece of hard integument.

chorda. The stem of vein R_{4+5} in some Lepidoptera.

chordotonal organs. Structures believed to enable an insect to hear sounds or to perceive vibration.

clavate. Club-shaped; getting thicker towards the top.

clavus. An area of the wing in Heteroptera (see fig. 131).

clypeus. The lowest division of the face, immediately above the labrum or upper lip.

coalescent. Running together, merging; as of wing-veins.

coarctate pupa. One enclosed in the hardened skin of the last larval stage (e.g. Diptera).

cocoon. A silken pupa-case (Lepidoptera); a case of earth, wood-fragments or other debris, protecting the pupa.

comb. A group of stiff setæ or spines, arranged like a comb.

compound eye. An eye consisting of a number of separate lenses, each contributing its share to a single image (see *ocellus*).

contiguous. Touching each other.

corium. An area of the wing in Heteroptera (see fig. 131).

corneous. Horny.

cornicles. Horns at the tip of the abdomen in Aphids.

costa. The vein nearest the fore-margin (leading edge) of the wing, in most insects forming the margin itself; sometimes continued all round the margin of the wing.

coxa. The first segment of a leg, joining it to the thorax; the hip (fig. 120).

coxite. The base of a reduced appendage, especially one of those on the last two or three segments of the abdomen.

crepuscular. Active during the period of twilight; either at dusk, or (more rarely) at daybreak.

cuneus. An area of the wing in Heteroptera (see fig. 131).

cursorial. Adapted to running habits.

diapause. A resting-period during the development of an insect, especially of larvæ in winter.

desiccation. Excessive drying, either by natural loss of moisture, or by artificial means.

disc. The centre of any sclerite, away from its edges.

discal. On the disc, or main surface of any part of the body as opposed to '*marginal*', near its edges.

discal cell. Any large cell in the centre, or disc of the wing; more particularly cell 1st M_2 in Diptera and cell R in Lepidoptera (figs. 122–125).

distal. Towards the tip of any organ; opposed to *basal*.

diurnal. Active during the hours of daylight.

dorsal. Towards the back, or upper surface; opposed to *ventral.*
dorsum. The dorsal surface or plate.

ecdysis. Moulting, or shedding the skin.
ectoparasite. One that lives on the outside of its victim, or 'host'.
elateriform larva. One shaped like a wireworm (*Elater*).
elytron (pl. *elytra*). The hardened fore-wings, or wing-cases, of beetles
    and some other insects.
embolium. An area of the wing in certain Heteroptera (fig. 131).
empodium. A bristle between the pulvilli of the foot in certain Diptera.
endoparasite. One that lives inside the body of its victim, or 'host'.
endopterygote. With the wings developing internally until the final moult;
    an insect with complete metamorphosis.
eruciform larva. Like a caterpillar.
exarate pupa. One in which the appendages are free, not stuck down to
    the surface.
exopterygote. With the wings developing externally in all stages; insect
    with incomplete metamorphosis.

face. The part of the head below the antennæ and above the mouth-
    opening.
facet. A lens, or hexagonal division of a compound eye.
femur. The first long segment of the leg; the thigh (fig. 120).
flagellum. All the antennal segments after the first two.
fossorial. Adapted for digging.
frenulum. A group of bristles on the fore-margin of the hind-wing of
    adult Lepidoptera, part of the wing-coupling apparatus (fig. 124).
frons. The area of head from the median ocellus to the mouth-opening;
    but sometimes restricted to the part above the antennæ.

gall. A swelling of the tissues of a plant, caused by the presence of an
    insect.
geniculate. Elbowed, or sharply bent; as of some antennæ.
genitalia. The sexual organs, more particularly the chitinised parts, or
    those visible externally.
gills. Extensions of the body-wall, used for breathing by aquatic insects.
gynandromorph. An insect which has some of its structure of the male
    form and some of the female; a sexual mosaic (see *intersex*).

halteres. A pair of knobbed organs, taking the place of the hind-wings
    in Diptera and in male Coccidæ (Homoptera).
head. The first, or most anterior, major division of the body (fig. 112).
hemimetabolous. Developing gradually from a first stage nymph to an
    adult, without any sudden changes; as in exopterygote insects.
herbivorous. Feeding on growing plants.
hibernation. Inactivity during winter (cf. *diapause*).

holometabolous. Having a complete metamorphosis: i.e. changing abruptly from a larva, through a pupa, to a very different adult; as in endopterygote insects.

homonym. One of two or more examples of the same name being applied to different animals.

host. The animal or plant upon which an insect regularly feeds, or takes shelter.

humeral (*-lobe* or *-callus*). (*a*) The swelling on each side of the anterior margin of the mesothorax. (*b*) The region near the base of the anterior margin of the wing, often broadened and supported by a short vein.

hyaline. Clear and transparent, like glass.

hypopharynx. One of the unpaired mouth-parts, often carrying the salivary duct.

imago (pl. *imagoes* or *imagines*). The adult, fully developed stage of an insect.

inquiline. An insect, or other animal, that lives in the nest or the gall of some other species.

instar. A stage of an insect's development, between two moults.

integument. The outer skin, including both the sclerotised plates and the membrane between them.

intercalary vein. An extra longitudinal vein inserted into the basic pattern in some groups, e.g. Ephemeroptera (fig. 126).

intersex. An insect with its general sexual characteristics intermediate between male and female.

intertidal. Occurring on the beach between high-water and low-water levels.

invagination. A folding-in, or projection towards the inside of the body.

joint. The hinge connecting two segments; often wrongly used for the segment itself, especially of the legs or antennæ.

jugum. A process on the hind-margin of the fore-wing in Lepidoptera, part of the wing-coupling apparatus (fig. 125).

labella. Lobes at the tip of the glossæ of the labium, developed as sponge-like sucking organs in some Hymenoptera and Diptera.

labium. One of the unpaired mouth-parts (fig. 134), which often forms a channel for the others in sucking insects.

lamella. A small sheet, or blade-like plate.

larva (pl. *larvæ*). The immature form of a holometabolous insect, greatly different in form from the adult.

lateral. Referring to the sides (left or right).

leaf-miner. An insect, usually a larva, that makes a tunnel between the upper and lower surfaces of a leaf.

littoral. Shore-dwelling, either the seashore or the edge of fresh water.

maggot. A larva without legs, and without a distinct head, usually pointed anteriorly, and blunt posteriorly.

mandible. One of the first pair of mouth-parts (fig. 134); a device for chewing.

mask (of dragonfly nymphs). The elongate labium, which can be thrust forward to seize prey.

maxilla. One of the second pair of mouth-parts (fig. 134).

membranous. Thin, flexible, often transparent.

mesad. Towards the middle line of the body.

mesonotum. The dorsal sclerite of the mesothorax.

mesothorax. The second, or middle segment of the thorax.

metanotum. The dorsal sclerite of the metathorax.

metapneustic. Having functional spiracles only on the posterior segments of the abdomen.

metatarsus. An erroneous term for the first segment of the tarsus (see *basitarsus*).

metathorax. The third or posterior segment of the thorax.

moult. The process of shedding the skin.

myiasis. Infestation of some other animal by larvæ of Diptera.

naiad. An aquatic, gill-breathing nymph.

neoteny. Retaining larval characters when fully adult (see *paedogenesis*).

nocturnal. Active at night, i.e. during the period of complete darkness (see *crepuscular*).

notum. The dorsal surface of a segment, especially of the thorax.

nymph. An immature stage of one of the Exopterygota, resembling the adult, except for the absence of wings.

occiput. The back of the head.

ocellus (pl. *ocelli*). A simple eye; even if several are placed close together they are not combined into one organ (see *compound eye*).

ommatidium. One of the optical units in a compound eye.

oral. Any structure connected with the mouth.

ovipositor. An egg-laying tube of a female insect, whether stiff and fixed in length, or flexible and telescopic.

paedogenesis. Reproduction by an immature form, especially a larva (see *neoteny*).

palpus (pl. *palpi*). One of a pair of segmented appendages of the mouth, those of insects being associated with the maxillæ (fig. 134).

parasite. An animal that lives in or on the body of another during at least part of its life-history.

parthenogenesis. Reproduction from unfertilised eggs, without mating.

pectinate. With branches or outgrowths like the teeth of a comb.

pedicel. The second segment of the antennæ.

pelagic. Living out in the open ocean.

penultimate. Next to the last.

peripneustic. Having spiracles all along the abdomen.

phragma. One of the apodemes (see above, and fig. 109).

physogastric. Having the abdomen grossly swollen, and mainly or entirely membranous, the sclerites being small and widely separated (e.g. a queen termite).

pile. Thick, short hairs, giving the appearance of velvet.

pilose. Covered with hairs.

pleuron (pl. *pleura*). A lateral sclerite of the body, the side of a segment.

porrect. Extending forward horizontally.

posterior. Towards the rear, or anal end of the insect; opposite of *anterior.*

predatory (*predaceous*). Attacking and preying on other animals, usually smaller ones.

proboscis. The mouth-parts, when they are extended like a snout or beak.

produced. Drawn out, extended.

proleg. A fleshy, abdominal leg, not a true segmented appendage.

pronotum. The dorsal sclerite of the prothorax.

prothorax. The first, or anterior division of the thorax.

proximal. Nearer to the base of; opposite of *distal.*

pseudopod (pl. *pseudopodia*). Same as a proleg.

pterostigma (see *stigma*).

pulvillus (pl. *pulvilli*). A pad beneath each tarsal claw.

punctate. Pitted, covered with small punctures.

pupa. The stage between a larval insect and the adult, non-feeding, and usually motionless.

quadrate. Four-sided.

raptorial. Modified for seizing prey, as of fore-legs.

rectum. The posterior section of the intestine, opening to the anus.

reticulate. Covered with a network of veins or ridges.

retinaculum. A locking mechanism beneath the base of the fore-wing in some Lepidoptera, part of the wing-coupling apparatus.

retractile. Capable of being drawn in.

rostrum. Beak; snout; proboscis; the mouth-parts as a composite organ.

rudimentary. Never having developed beyond an elementary or incomplete stage (cf. *vestigial*).

scape. The first segment of the antenna.

scavenger. One that feeds on dead animal or vegetable matter, or on any waste material.

scholechiasis. The vomiting or evacuation of caterpillars.

sclerite. One of the hardened parts of the integument.

scutellum. A subdivision of the notum of one of the thoracic segments, more especially of the mesonotum.

scutum. The bigger division of notum of a segment, immediately before the scutellum.

segment. A division of the body, or of an appendage (see *joint*).

sense organ. Any structure by which an insect can see, smell, feel or hear.

seta (pl. *setæ*). A bristle (see *chaeta*).

spiracle. An opening from the exterior into the tracheal system.

spur. A thorn-like projection of the legs.

sternite. The ventral, or underneath surface of a segment.

stigma (or *pterostigma*). A thickened, opaque spot on the fore-margin of the wing, towards the tip.

stridulate. To make a shrill, squeaking noise by rubbing two hard surfaces together, as do grasshoppers.

style. A short, more or less cylindrical appendage.

subimago. The earlier of the two winged stages of the Ephemeroptera.

suctorial. Of mouth-parts; adapted to sucking liquids or powdery substances.

suture. The flexible boundary between two plates or sclerites.

synonym. One of two or more different names that have been applied to the same insect.

systematics. The practice of naming and classifying anything (see *taxonomy*).

tarsus. The foot, or last region of the leg; usually divided into from 2 to 5 parts, which are called 'segments', though they have no separate muscles (fig. 120).

taxonomy. The study of classification, more particularly of its general and theoretical side (see *systematics*).

tentorium; *tentorial pits.* The internal framework of the head; its attachments as seen from outside.

tergite. The upper surface, or dorsum of a segment.

terminal. Situated at the end furthest from the base.

terrestrial. Strictly, living on the ground; usually, living on 'dry land', i.e. not in association with water.

thigmotactic. Showing a tendency to press the body against a surface, or into crevices and corners.

thorax. The second great division of the body in insects (see fig. 112).

tibia. The second major division of the leg; the shin.

trachea (pl. *tracheae*). One of the branching tubes that convey air to different parts of the body in insects.

transverse suture. A division across the body; more particularly across the dorsum of the thorax.

trochanter. A small segment of the leg, coming between the coxae and the femur (fig. 120); sometimes appears to be double, e.g. in certain Hymenoptera.

tubercle. A small, rounded swelling (see *callus*).

tympanum. A drum-like part of a hearing-organ in certain insects.

type. The specimen that sets the pattern for a species; or the species upon which a genus is based.

typical form. (*a*) A type, see above; (*b*) the usual form of a species, as distinct from a variety or an aberration (for which, see p. 199).

vein. One of the stiff ribs of the wing.

vertex. The extreme top of the head.

vestigial. Having been reduced from a state of greater development, now remaining as a mere vestige (see *rudimentary*).

viscous. Of the consistency of oil or treacle.

viviparous. Bringing forth living young, instead of laying eggs; applied to insects in which the eggs hatch internally, and either young larvæ or fully fed ones are deposited.

REFERENCES

BASDEN, E. B. 1954. The Distribution and Biology of Drosophilidae (Diptera) in Scotland, including a new species of Drosophila. *Transactions of the Royal Society of Edinburgh.* Vol. **62,** pp. 603–654.

BASTIN, HAROLD. 1954. *Freaks and Marvels of Insect Life.* London: Hutchinson. 248 pp. Illus. 16/–.

BASTIN, HAROLD. 1956. *Insect Communities.* London: Hutchinson. 142 pp. XX plates. 15/–.

BECHYNE, JAN. 1956. *Open Air Guides: Beetles.* London: Thames and Hudson. 158 pp. 48 col. figs. 207 black and white. Translated and edited by C. M. F. von Hayek, from the German original *Welcher Käfer ist Das?*

BEIRNE, BRYAN P., and others. 1955. *Collecting, Preparing and Preserving Insects.* Science Service, Entomology Division, Canada Dept. of Agriculture. Publ. **932,** 133 pp. 93 figs.

BODENHEIMER, F. S. 1951. *Insects as Human Food: a Chapter of the Ecology of Man.* 8vo. The Hague (Junk). 352 pp. 46 figs. Price 10 Dutch guilders.

BORROR, D. J. and DELONG, D. M. 1954. *An Introduction to the Study of Insects.* New York. Rinehart & Co.

BRETHERTON, R. F. 1954. Moth traps and their lamps: an attempt at comparative analysis. *Entomologists' Gazette.* Vol. **5,** pp. 145–154.

BUCK, F. D. 1956. Black-and-white entomological drawings for reproduction. *Transactions of the South London Entomological and Natural History Society.* **1944–55,** pp. 160–179.

BUNTING, W. 1954 (on breeding Orthoptera). *Entomologists' Monthly Magazine.* Vol. **90,** pp. 214–215.

BURR, MALCOLM. *The Insect Legion: the Significance of the Insignificant.* London: James Nisbet. 2nd Edn. 1954. 336 pp. Illus. 21/–.

CANNON, H. GRAHAM. 1936. *A Method of Illustration for Zoological Papers.* London: Association of British Zoologists. Published price 3/6.

CHEESMAN, EVELYN. 1952. *Insects Indomitable.* London: G. Bell, 205 pp. 17 figs.

CLAUSEN, LUCY W. 1954. *Insect Fact and Folklore.* New York. Macmillan. 194 pp. 24/6.

COLAS, G. 1956. *Guide de l'entomologiste: l'entomologiste sur le terrain; preparation et conservation des insectes et des collections.* Paris: Boubée et Cie.

COPENHAGEN DECISIONS ON ZOOLOGICAL NOMENCLATURE: additions to, and modifications of the Règles Internationales de la Nomenclature Zoologique. Approved and adopted by the fourteenth International Congress of Zoology, Copenhagen, August, 1953. London: International Trust for Zoological Nomenclature, 41 Queen's Gate, London, S.W.7. 5/–.

CROWSON, R. A. 1956. Coleoptera: Introduction and Keys to Families. *Handbooks for the Identification of British Insects.* Vol. **IV.** (**1**), 59 pp. The Royal Entomological Society of London.

DAVID, W. A. L. and GARDINER, B. O. C. 1952. Laboratory breeding of *Pieris brassicae* L. and *Apanteles glomeratus* L. *Proceedings of the Royal Entomological Society of London.* Series A, Vol. **27,** pp. 54–56.

DAVIES, D. A. L. 1954. On the preservation of insects by drying *in vacuo* at low temperature. *Entomologist.* Vol. **87,** pp. 34–36.

DETHIER, V. G. 1955. Mode of Action of Sugar-baited Fly-traps. *Journal of Economic Entomology.* Vol. **48,** pp. 235–239.

DIRSCH, V. M. 1956. The phallic complex in Acridoidea (Orthoptera) in relation to taxonomy. *Transactions of the Royal Entomological Society of London.* Vol. **108,** pp. 223–356.

DUFFY, E. A. J. 1950. The preservation of beetle larvæ. *Proceedings of the South London Entomological and Natural History Society,* **1948-49,** pp. 146–7.

EASTON, N. T. 1954. (Note on use of cellotape for mounting insects). *Proceedings of the South London Entomological and Natural History Society,* **1952-53,** p. 28.

EDMUNDS, GEORGE F., JR. 1956. Exuviation of Subimaginal Ephemeroptera in Flight. *Entomological News.* Vol. **67,** pp. 91–93.

EMBERGER, M. R. and HALL, M. R. 1955. *Scientific Writing.* New York: Harcourt Brace & Co. 468 pp. Illus. $4.50.

VAN EMDEN, F. I. 1942. The Collection and Study of beetle larvæ. *Entomologists' Monthly Magazine.* Vol. **78,** pp. 73–79.

FERRIS, G. F. 1928. *The Principles of Systematic Entomology.* Stanford University publication on Biological Sciences. Vol. **3.** 169 pp. 11 figs.

FOLLETT, W. I. 1956. *An unofficial interpretation of the International Rules of Zoological Nomenclature as amended by the XIII International Congress on Zoology, Paris, 1948, and by the XIV International Congress on Zoology, Copenhagen, 1953.* Not published. Distributed by the Society of Systematic Zoology, Californian Academy of Sciences.

FORD, L. T. 1940. Notes on breeding and setting Lepidoptera. *Proceedings of the South London Entomological and Natural History Society.* **1939-40,** pp. 90–94.

FREEMAN, J. A. 1945. Studies in the distribution of insects by aerial currents: the insect population of the air from ground level to 300 ft. *Journal of Animal Ecology.* Vol. **14,** pp. 128–154.

GAY, F. J. Common Names of Insects and allied Forms occurring in Australia. 1955. *Bulletin of the Commonwealth Scientific and Industrial Research Organisation in Australia (Melbourne)*. Vol. **275.** 32 pp.

GREENBERG, B. 1954. A method for the sterile culture of house-fly larvæ, *Musca domestica* L. *Canadian Entomologist*. Vol. **86,** pp. 527–528.

HALLIBURTON, W. and FRIEND, W. G. 1956. A simple air-conditioning unit for insect cages. *Canadian Entomologist*. Vol. **88,** pp. 55–56.

HAMPTON, U. M. 1952. Reproduction in the house-fly (*Musca domestica* L. *Proceedings of the Royal Entomological Society of London*. Series A, Vol. **27,** pp. 29–32.

HATCH, MELVILLE H. 1954. Entomology in Search of a Soul. *Annals of the Entomological Society of America*. Vol. **47,** pp. 377–387.

HEDGES, A. V. 1949. Technique of breeding Lepidoptera. *Proceedings of the South London Entomological and Natural History Society*. **1947–48.** pp. 75–81.

HIESTAND, W. A. 1928. A new type of moth trap. *Entomological News*. Vol. **29,** pp. 158–160.

HINTON, H. E. 1946. A new classification of insect pupæ. *Proceedings of the Zoological Society of London*. Vol. **116,** pp. 282–328.

HUNGERFORD, H. B., SPANGLER, P. J. and WALKER, N. A. Subaquatic light traps for insects and other animal organisms. 1955. *Transactions of the Kansas Academy of Science*. Vol. **58,** pp. 387–407.

HUNTER-JONES, P. 1956. *Instructions for Rearing and Breeding Locusts in the Laboratory*. London: Anti-Locust Research Centre. 10 pp. 1 fig. Free on application.

HYDE, GEORGE E. 1949. *A Pocket-Book of British Insects*. London: A. C. Black. 7/6.

HYDE, GEORGE E. 1956. *All About Photographing Insects With Your Camera*. Photo Guide 73. Focal Press Ltd., London. 2/–.

IMMS, A. D. 1947. *Insect Natural History*. Collins: New Naturalist Series, pp. xviii+317. 72 plates (40 col.), maps, diagrams.

IMMS, A. D. 1957. *A General Text-book of Entomology*. 9th Edition revised by O. W. Richards and R. G. Davies. London: Methuen. 876 pp. 609 figs. 75/–.

JAQUES, H. E. 1947. *How to Know the Insects*, pp. 205. 411 figs. Wm. C. Brown Co., Dubuque, Iowa.

JARVIS, F. V. L. 1950. The Meteorological approach to Entomology. *Entomologists' Gazette*. Vol. **1,** pp. 201–216.

JEANNEL, R. *Introduction to Entomology* (in Press, 1958).

JOHNSON, C. G. and TAYLOR, L. R. 1955. The development of large suction traps for airborne insects. *Annals of Applied Biology*. Vol. **43,** pp. 51–62.

JORDAN, B. M. and BAKER, J. R. 1956. The House-cricket (*Acheta domestica*) as a Laboratory Animal. *Entomologist*. Vol. **89,** pp. 126–128.

KALOOSTIAN, G. H. 1955. A magnetically suspended insect cage. *Journal of Economic Entomology* (U.S.A.). Vol. **48,** p. 756.

KLOET, G. S. and HINCKS, W. D. 1945. *A Checklist of British Insects.* Stockport.

LAURENCE, B. R. 1954. The larval inhabitants of cow-pats. *Journal of Animal Ecology.* Vol. **23,** pp. 234–260.

LINSSEN, E. F. 1953. *Entomological Photography in Practice.* London: Fountain Press. 112 pp. 54 figs. 32/6.

MALAISE, RENE. 1937. A new insect-trap. *Entomologisk Tidskrift,* Stockholm. Vol. **58,** pp. 148–160.

MOORE, B. P. 1949. (Use of xylonite as a mounting base for insects.) *Entomologists' Monthly Magazine.* Vol. **85,** p. 102.

MOORE, B. P. 1951. On preserving the colours of dragon-flies and other insects. *Proceedings of the South London Entomological and Natural History Society.* **1949–50,** pp. 179–186.

MORELAND, C. R. 1955. A wind frame for trapping insects in flight. *Journal of Economic Entomology.* Vol. **47,** p. 944.

MORETON, B. D. 1950. *Guide to British Insects: An Aid to Identification.* London: Macmillan. pp. viii + 188. 96 figs.

LE MOULT, EUGENE. 1956. *Mes chasses aux Papillons.* Paris: Pierre Horay. 353 pp. XIX plates. 990 frs.

MUNDIE, J. H. 1956. Emergence traps for aquatic insects. *International Association for Theoretical and Applied Limnology (Mitt. Int. Ver. Limnol.).* Communication No. **7.** 13 pp. 3 figs.

NEWELL, I. M., VAN DEN BOSCH, R. and HARAMOTO, FRANK H. 1951. An improved method of rearing field-collected fruit fly-larvæ. *Proceedings of the Hawaiian Entomological Society.* Vol. **14,** pp. 297–299.

OMAN, P. W. and CUSHMAN, A. D. 1948. *Collection and Preservation of Insects.* U.S. Dept. of Agriculture Miscellaneous Publications No. **601.** 42 pp.

PARMENTER, L. 1951. *Collecting Flies (Diptera).* Amateur Entomologists' Society's Leaflet No. **5.** 2/6, post free. 8 pp. 7 plates. 6 text figs.

PETERSEN, ALVAL. 1953. *A Manual of Entomological Techniques.* 7th Edn. 367 pp. 182 plates. 17 tables. Edwards Bros., Ann Arbor, Michigan.

RICHARDS, O. W. 1956. *Hymenoptera: Introduction and Keys to Families.* Handbooks for the Identification of British Insects, **VI. (1).** 95 pp. Royal Entomological Society, London.

ROBINSON, H. S. and ROBINSON, P. J. M. 1950. Some notes on the observed behaviour of Lepidoptera in flight in the vicinity of light-sources, together with a description of a light-trap designed to take entomological samples. *Entomologists' Gazette.* Vol. **1,** pp. 3–20.

ROBINSON, H. S. 1951. The effects of light on night-flying insects. *Proceedings of the South London Entomological and Natural History Society.* **1951–51,** pp. 112–123.

ROBINSON, H. S. 1952. On the behaviour of night-flying insects in the neighbourhood of a bright source of light. *Proceedings of the Royal Entomological Society of London*, Series A. Vol. **27**, pp. 13–21.

ROSS, EDWARD S. 1953. *Insects Close Up: a Pictorial Guide for the Photographer and Collector.* University of California Press. 80 pp. Many figures, coloured and half-tone. 11/6.

SCHENK, E. T. and McMASTERS, J. H. 1956. *Procedure in Taxonomy: including a reprint of The International Rules of Zoological Nomenclature, with summaries of opinions rendered to the present date.* Completely indexed. 72 pp. Stanford, California and Oxford University Press. 8/6.

SPENCER, K. A. 1956. The British Agromyzidae (Diptera). *Proceedings of the South London Entomological and Natural History Society.* **1954–55**, pp. 98–108.

TORRE-BUENO, J. R. DE LA. 1950. *A Glossary of Entomology.* 336 pp. $5. Brooklyn Entomological Society, Brooklyn, New York.

TUXEN, S. L. (Editor). 1956. *A Taxonomist's Glossary of Genitalia in Insects.* Copenhagen. 284 pp.

USINGER, ROBERT L. 1956. The Stability of Scientific Names. In STEINHAUS, EDWARD A. and SMITH, RAY F., *Annual Review of Entomology.* Vol. **1**, pp. 59–70. Stanford, California: Annual Reviews, Inc.

USINGER, R. L., and others. 1956. *Aquatic Insects of California.* University of California Press. 508 pp. Many figures.

WAGSTAFFE, R. and FIDLER, J. HAVELOCK. 1955. *The Preservation of Natural History Specimens. I. Invertebrates.* London: H. F. & G. Witherby Ltd. pp. xiii + 205. 139 figs. Price 42/–.

WALLIS-NORTON, S. G. 1950. (Killing burnet-moths with lighter fluid.) *Proceedings of the South London Entomological and Natural History Society.* **1948–49.** p. 3.

WEST, LUTHER. 1951. *The House-fly.* 584 pp. New York: Comstock (London: Constable).

WIGGLESWORTH, V. B. 1956. *The Principles of Insect Physiology.* London: Methuen. 5th Ed. 546 pp.

WILLIAMS, C. B. 1948. The Rothhamsted light-trap. *Proceedings of the Royal Entomological Society of London*, Series A. Vol. **23**, pp. 80–85. 5th Ed. 564 pp

WILLIAMS, C. B. 1951. Comparing the efficiency of insect traps. *The Bulletin of Entomological Research.* Vol. **42**, pp. 513–517.

WILLIAMS, C. B., SINGH, B. P and EL ZIADY, S. 1956. An investigation into the possible effects of moonlight on the activity of insects in the field. *Proceedings of the Royal Entomological Society of London*, Series A. Vol. **31**, pp. 135–144.

WORLD LIST OF SCIENTIFIC PERIODICALS, published in the years 1900–1950. Edited by W. A. SMITH, F. L. KENT and G. B. STRATTON. 3rd Edn. 1952. London: Butterworth's Scientific Publications.

DE WORMS, C. G. M. 1939. Insects at light. *Proceedings of the South London Entomological and Natural History Society.* **1938–39,** pp. 80–84.

DE WORMS, C. G. M. 1950–56. The Butterflies and Moths of London and its surroundings. *London Naturalist.* Butterflies, **1950,** 35 pp. Moths, **1954,** 46 pp. and map. **1955,** 42 pp. **1956,** 44 pp.

WYKES, N. G. 1955. The technique of entomological drawing in water-colours. *Proceedings of the South London Entomological and Natural History Society.* **1953–54,** pp. 98–104.

USEFUL ADDRESSES

Materials:

T. GERRARD & CO., Biological Laboratories, 46a–48 Pentonville Road, London, N.1.

FLATTERS & GARNETT LTD., 309 Oxford Road, Manchester.

WATKINS & DONCASTER, 110 Parkview Road, Welling, Kent.

L. CHRISTIE, 127 Gleneldon Road, Streatham, London, S.W.16.

WARDS NATURAL SCIENCE ESTABLISHMENT, 3,000 Ridge Road East, Rochester 9, New York.

GENERAL BIOLOGICAL SUPPLY HOUSE, 761–763 East 69th Place, Chicago 37, Illinois.

ROBERT G. WIND, 827 Congress Avenue, Pacific Grove, California.

N. BOUBÉE & CIE, 3 Place Saint-André-des-Arts, Paris 6. For Specimens, illustrated books, models and apparatus.

EMIL ARLT, Specialnadelfabrik, P.O.B. 36, Salzburg 1, Pfeifergasse 18, Austria. For entomological pins, especially minuten pins.

Entomological Books:

E. W. CLASSEY, F.R.E.S., 22 Harlington Road East, Feltham, Middlesex.

Cabinets, new and second-hand

J. J. HILL & SON, Yewfield Road, London, N.W.10

INDEX

A

abdomen, 212
abdominal contents,
    removal of, 106
aberration, 199
absolute alcohol, 133
acetic acid, glacial, 140
Acrididae, 220
adhesives, 117
Agromyzidae, rearing, 72
alcohol, absolute, 133
alcohol, 80%, 82, 132
alderflies, 239
allotypes, 205
Ametabola, 215
ammonia, 80
amyl acetate, 117
Anisoptera, 227
Anoplura, 230, 273
Antarctica, insects of, 287
antennae, 211, 283
antlions, 20, 240
ants, 17, 259
ants, attacks of on collections, 91
aphids, 17, 236
Apocrita, 257
appendages, 210
Apterygota, 215
Arctic, insects of the, 287
Arthropoda, 209
artificial foods for larvae, 69
aspirator, 40
Australasian Region, 286

B

background, in photography, 178,
    193
bags, net, 29
bait animals, 23, 254
baits and bait-traps, 53, 56
balsa cement, 86, 117
bark, collecting insects under, 21

bathrooms, collecting in, 44
beating, 17, 27, 32
bees, 16, 259
beetles, 17, 241
benzene, 80, 132
Berlese funnel, 62
binomial system of naming animals,
    200
bird-lice, 230
bleaching preparations, 140, 144
bloodsucking insects, keeping alive,
    68, 254
blowing and stuffing, 105
boards, setting-, 102
book-lice, 229
bot-flies, 23, 254
boxes, store-, 123, 127
box-type light-traps, 45
breeding insects, 65
bristles, drawing of, 173
bristle-tails, 215
Bristol board, 115, 116, 142, 170
British Isles, insects of, 214, 287
British insects, works on, 287
bugs, 232
bull's-eye lens, 147, 155
butterflies, 248

C

cabinets, 125
caddisflies, 246
caddisfly larvae, cases of, 246
cages for insects, 38
camera, choice of, 179
    long-extension bellows for, 178
    lucida, 164
Canada balsam, 137, 141
carbon tetrachloride, 135
card, for staging insects, 114
carding insects, 115
carnivorous insects, 17, 68, 69
castes, 198

W   321

caterpillars, 248
   blowing and stuffing, 105
caustic potash, boiling in, 138
cedarwood oil, clearing in, 137, 140
cells of the wing, 280
celluloid stages, 114
cellulose wadding, 38, 90
cerci, 271
chaetotaxy, 255
chalk-pit, collecting at a, 20
chewing-lice, 230
chitin, 210
chloral hydrate, 132
chloroform, 80
cicadas, 17, 236
ciné-films of insects, 191
Classes of animals, 201
classification of insects, 198
cleaning specimens, 97
clearing agents, 140
clove oil, 137, 140
coccids, 17
Coccinellidae, 17
cockroaches, 219
Coleoptera, 241, 271, 275, 276
Coleoptera collecting-bottle, 243
collecting-bottles, 39
collection, arrangement of, 129
Collembola, 216, 273
colour-filters, 184
colour-photography, 186
combs (of fleas), 256
composite mouse food, for larvae, 69
Comstock-Needham system, 240, 277
condensation, avoidance of, 38, 67, 75, 88, 89, 97
Conservation, Principle of, 207
'Continental' pins, 111
cork linings of boxes, 124
corks, 37
cornicles, 237
Corrodentia, 229
costa, 278
cover-slips, 141
cow-dung, insects in, 22
creosote, 132
crickets, 221
crochets, 213, 248
crosshatching, 171

cuticle, 109, 209
cyanide, potassium, 76

D

damselflies, 84, 227
dancing of insects, 16, 65
debris, collecting insects in, 21, 61
dead animals, insects associated with, 23
de Faure's fluid, 143
dehydrating, 140
Dermaptera, 223, 271, 273, 275
destruction of killing-bottles, 80
diapause, 71
Dictyoptera, 217, 219, 275
Diptera, 252, 272, 273, 274
direct-mounting fluids, 143
direct pinning, 112
dissecting, 136
downs, insects of, 22
dragonflies, 22, 227
   preserving the colours of, 83, 84
drawers, glass-topped, 125
drawing insects, technique of, 169
drawing with the microscope, equipment for, 164
dredge, 32
drowning of insects, 81
dry preservation of adult insects, 95
dry preservation of larvae, 108
dung, insects breeding in, 23
duns, 226

E

earwigs, 223
ectoparasites, 23
egg-packing, use of in breeding-cages, 70, 75
electronic flash photography, 188
elytra, 241
embankments and cuttings, collecting from, 20
emergence cages, 61
endoparasites, 23
Endopterygota, 239, 272
'English pins', 110
enlarger, used as a projector, 186
Ephemeroptera, 226, 271, 272, 275
epipharynx, 280

ether, 99
Ethiopian Region, 286
ethyl acetate, 42, 79
Euparal, 144
Exopterygota, 217
exoskeleton, 209
eye-piece micrometer, 167

F

false legs, 212
Families of insects, 201
fells, insects of, 22
films, choosing and processing, 181
filters, colour-, 184
fixatives for preserving larvae, 82
flagellum, 284
flash bulbs, 188
flash photography, 188
fleas, 256
flies (Diptera), 252
fluid, relaxing, 96
food, for insects in captivity, 67
foreign literature, 291
forms of insects, 199
formalin, 132
frames for nets, 27
freeze-drying, 108
'frosting' of pupae, 71, 72
fuller's earth, 132
fungus, see mould

G

galls and gall-making insects, 18
gall-wasps, 259
garden, collecting in a, 19
genera, 200
generic names, 200, 206
genitalia, dissecting and mounting, 137
geographical races, 198
Geometridae, 18
glacial acetic acid, 140
glasses, use of with microscope, 150
glass tubes, bending, 41
glossae, 282
goat-moth larvae, 55
grasshoppers, 217, 220
grassland, insects of, 21
grease, removal of, 99, 132

greenfly, 17
gum chloral, 143
gums used in mounting insects, 117

H

halteres, 252
hand-lens, 145
handles for nets, 35
head, 211
heathland, collecting on, 22
hedgerow, insects of, 16
Hemimetabola, 217
Hemiptera, 232, 270, 273, 274, 275
Heterocera, 249
hibernation, 25
Hiestand's trap, 46
high altitudes, insects of, 22
Holarctic Region, 286
holding and manipulating specimens, 160
Holometabola, 239
Holophot, 186
holotypes, 204
homonyms, 206
Homoptera, 236, 270, 271, 274
honeydew, 237
hot water, killing insects by means of, 82
hover-flies, 253
hovering, 16
hydrofuge hairs, 234
Hymenoptera, 257, 271, 274
  aculeate, 259
hyperparasites, 259
hypodermic needle, for killing insects, 81
hypopharynx, 281

I

ichneumon flies, 18
identifying an insect, 263
illustrating entomological papers, 169, 298
index-cards, usefulness of, 268, 295
indoors, collecting, 25
information to be given on labels, 118
infra-red photography, 185
infra-specific categories, 199
injecting killing fluids, 81

ink, drawing in, 170
inquilines, 226
insects, numbers of (table), 214
  relationships with other animals, 209
  carriage of, 85
  keeping alive, 65
integument, 109, 209
International Rules of Zoological Nomenclature, 201
Isoptera, 225, 272, 275

J

jars, for spirit collections, 134

K

Key to the Orders of Insects, 270
keys for indentification, using, 264
  constructing and adapting, 268
killing-bottles, 76
  destruction of, 80
killing insects, methods of, 76, 81, 84

L

labella, 252, 282
labelling, recommended methods of 118, 142
  boxes and drawers, 129
  collections in the field, 89, 91
  each specimen, 89, 105, 118
label lists, 130
labels, making, 120
labium, 211, 280
labrum, 280
lacewings, 44, 239
ladybirds, 17
larvae, 69, 217, 282
laurel leaves, as killing agent, 77
layering, 90
leaf-insects, 219
leaf-miners, 18, 260
lectotypes, 205
legs, 212
lens, hand-, 146
lens-hood, 181
lenses of microscopes, 148
Lepidoptera, 248, 270, 274, 275
  mounting wings of, 144

lice, 230, 273
light, collecting at, 43
  attraction of insects by, 48
lighter-fluid, for killing moths, 85
lighting for microscopy, 154
  for cinematography, 192
  for still photography, 179, 184
light-traps, 25, 45
line shading, 171
Linnaean system, 200
liquid killing-agents, 78
locality labels, 118
locusts, 220
  rearing and breeding, 74

M

Malaise's method of packing small insects, 92
  insect-trap, 57
Mallophaga, 230, 273
mandibles, 211, 280
mantids, 17
manuscripts, preparation of, 298
mask, of dragonfly nymph, 228, 282
mating of insects, 16, 65
maxillae, 211, 280
mayflies, 22, 226
mechanical stage, 160
Mecoptera, 245, 272, 274, 275
Megaloptera, 239, 272, 276
mercury-vapour lamp, 52
methylated spirit, 133
Microlepidoptera, 249
  rearing of, 72
micrometer eyepiece, 167
Micropterygidae, 248
microscope, choosing and testing a, 147
  binocular, 147
  monocular, 152
  slides, 142
miniature cameras, 179
mines, 18
minuten pins, 111
moisture, control of in insect cages, 66
moll (lining material for boxes and drawers), 124
moniliform antennae, 230
moors, insects of, 22

moths, 248
killing in lighter-fluid, 85
motor-car, use of in collecting, 24
mould, avoiding, 91, 97, 99, 132
mountains, insects of, 22
mouthparts, 211
movement, recognising insects by
their, 18, 145

N

naming insects, 199
naphthalene, 97, 124, 131
Nearctic Region, 286
Neotropical Region, 286
neotypes, 205
nests of birds and small mammals,
20, 24
net-forceps, 30
net, general purpose, 27
getting the insect out of, 36
material for a, 29
small-framed, 21, 30
sweeping, 32
using a, 35
water-, 32
Neuroptera, 239, 272, 275
night, collecting at, 25, 43
Nomenclature, International Rules of,
201
notum, 210
nymphs, 217

O

ocelli, 248
Odonata, 227, 272, 276
oil-immersion lens, 153
Orders of Insects, 201, 213
Oriental Region, 286
Orthoptera, 217, 270, 275

P

Palaearctic Region, 285
palpi, 271, 281
papering, 88
paradichlorobenzene, 90, 97, 124, 131
parasitic insects, 23
Hymenoptera, 259
paratypes, 205
pasture land, insects of, 21

peat, lining material for boxes and
drawers, 124
pedicel, 283
periodicals, names of some entomological, 296
pests, protection against, 136
petiole, 225, 257
phase-contrast apparatus, 157
Phasmida, 217, 219, 275
phenol (carbolic acid), 97, 99, 132
phoresy, 24
photoflood lamps, 187
photographing insects directly, 175
through the microscope, 182
alive, 186
photography, making labels by, 122
Phthiraptera, 230
Phyla of animals, 201, 209
pill-boxes, 38
pinching, killing insects by, 81
pinning insects in the field, 85
pinning, methods of, 109
pins, choice of, 110
sizes of, 111
pitfalls, for trapping insects, 56
plankton-net, 33
Plecoptera, 223, 271, 276
pleuron, 210
pocket collecting-boxes, 86
points, mounting on, 116
pinning on, 111, 115
polyporus, for staging insects, 114
polyvinyl lactophenol, 143
ponds, collecting at, 32
potash, caustic, 137
potassium cyanide, 76
Priority, Rule of, 200, 207
projection apparatus, for drawing,
167
pronunciation of scientific names, 201
proofs, 299
Protura, 216
pseudopods, 212
Psocoptera, 229, 271, 275
Pterygota, 217
publication of scientific names, 204
publish, when and what to, 294
where and how to, 296
pupation under artificial conditions,
70, 72

Q

quarry, collecting at a, 20

R

races, 197, 198
raisins as food for insects, 68
rearing insects, 65, 69
relaxing, 96
reprints, 293, 299
re-staging, 115
reviews of new publications, 291
Rhopalocera, 249
ringing of mounts, 143
robber-flies, 17
Robinson's light-trap, 48
rot-holes in trees, 21, 55
rubbish, collecting insects from, 21, 61

S

Saltatoria, 217, 220, 275
sand-living insects, 20, 241
sand-pit, collecting at a, 20
sawflies, 18, 258
scale-insects, 236
scape, 283
scientific names, 200
sclerites, 210
sclerotin, 210
scorpionflies, 245
screens, 34
scrub-land, collecting in, 20
segments, 210
separata, 293, 299
separator, 62
setting-boards, 102
setting, instructions for, 100
    upside-down, 105
sheeting, 44
shellac gel, 117, 143
sieves, 34
silica gel, 90, 91
silk-production by caterpillars, 249
silver-fish, 215
Siphonaptera, 256, 272
Siphunculata, 230
sleeving of larvae, 72
slide-mounts, making, 136
slides, microscope, 142
species, definition of, 197, 201

specific name, 200, 206
specimens, bringing home, 85
speed of flight of insects, 25
spinners, 226
spiracles, 211
spirit (80% alcohol), 82, 132
spirit collections, labelling of, 121
    maintenance of, 132
spirit-jars, 134
spotlight, 135
spreading (setting), 100
spring-tails, 216
squared eye-piece, 165
staging, 113
stalking insects, 27
stem-boring insects, 18
sternum, 210
stick-insects, 219
stippling, 171
stoneflies, 22, 223
storage of collections, 123
store-boxes, 123, 127
stored-products, rearing insects in, 66, 68
streams, collecting insects at, 32
Strepsiptera, 244
stridulation, 221
strip-system of arranging collections, 126
stuffing, 105
stylets, 282
'stylopised' bees and wasps, 244
sub-family, 201
subimago, 226
sub-species, 198
sucking-lice, 230
suction-tubes (aspirator), 42
suction-traps, 61
sugaring, 54
sulphur dioxide, for killing dragon-flies, 84
super-family, 201
supplementary lens, 177
supra-specific categories, 199
swarms, 16, 65
sweeping, 17, 27
sweeping-net, 32
Symphyta, 257
synonyms, 206
syntypes, 205
Syrphidae, 253

T

temperature-control in breeding-
  cages, 67
Terebrantia, 231
terminalia, 137
termites, 225
testing a microscope, 150, 154
tetrachlorethane, 50
Tetrigidae, 220
textbooks of entomology, 288
thigmotactic reaction, 70
thorax, 211
thrips, 231
Thysanoptera, 231, 271, 274
Thysanura, 215, 274
tins, relaxing-, 96
trachea(e), 211
traps for insects, 24
trawl, 32
tray-system of arranging collections,
  127
tree-trunks, collecting from, 21
trees, wounded, 155
triangulin larvae, 244
tribes of insects, 201
Trichoptera, 246, 271, 275
tubes, getting insects in, and out of, 37
  killing-, 79
  selection of, 37
  for spirit collections, 133
Tubulifera, 231
Turkey Mill paper, 170
types, 204

U

under-water light-trap, 50
unit-trays, collections arranged in, 127

V

vacuum-drying, 108
varieties, 199
veins of wing, 276
  intercalary, 258

W

warbles, 23, 252, 254
wasps, 17
watchmaker's lens, 146
water-bath, 138
water, collecting in, 32
Williams' light-trap, 46
windows, finding insects on, 25
winged insects, key to Orders of, 270
wingless insects, key to Orders of,
  272
wings, 211, 276
  mounts of, 142
wings of Lepidoptera, mounting, 144
wing-venation, 240 (fig. 121), 276
wood-boring insects, 21
woods, collecting in, 20
World List of Scientific Periodicals,
  290

X

xylol, 137, 140

Z

Zoogeographical Regions, 285
Zoological Record, 290
Zoraptera, 229, 275
Zygoptera, 227